HEREDITY, EVOLUTION, and SOCIETY

HEREDITY
EVOLUTION
and SOCIETY

I. MICHAEL LERNER
University of California, Berkeley

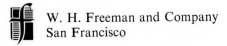

W. H. Freeman and Company
San Francisco

Printed in the United States of America. (K)
Library of Congress Catalog Card Number: 68-25409

To

TH. DOBZHANSKY

Biologist and Humanist
Mentor and Friend

PREFACE

This book has grown out of a course in genetics that I have been teaching for several years to students not majoring in biology. The course was designed to satisfy so-called breadth requirements like those in many universities and colleges which force students in the humanities and arts to suffer an exposure to natural sciences. All too often this exposure consists of fact-laden introductory courses in physics, chemistry, and biology more suited for students intending to pursue these subjects in greater detail later. In the past, biology majors and nonmajors alike have been, in effect, "marched through the phyla." With the development of molecular biology the subject matter has been changed but the method remains much the same: the students are now marched through the Krebs cycle.

In my view a different approach to the biological education of a nonscientist is required. It is not simply the presentation of facts that is objectionable; it is difficult (sometimes impossible) to explain principles without resort to facts because abstractions without illustrations have no substance. The difficulty lies more in the selection of facts to be presented. For the student who must live through the last third of the twentieth century, the most important facts are those that have social implications; those bits of information that demonstrate the involvement of every human being in the ethical, social, and political problems of this age of science, problems that are multiplying in geometrical progression in the wake of scientific and technological advances.

Essential details of biology that have daily import in a person's life (what do kidneys do?) should be imparted in high school or earlier. Compulsory laboratory exercises in which nonscientists perform experiments with fore-knowledge of outcome do nothing but give wrong ideas of the methods and purposes of scientific endeavor. There is no need for an educated layman to know or to remember the sequence of the stages of mitosis, the order of the geologic eras, or the wavelengths of different kinds of radiation (although such information does appear in this book). Similarly, although much technical language and, on occasion, scientific jargon, is unavoidable in presenting technical ideas, both facts and vocabulary must be servants of ideas and principles and not their masters.

There can be a great deal of disagreement over what emphasis a single-term course on the social implications of biology should take. Problems of ecology, including conservation and pollution, or problems centering on food supply could, no doubt, claim high priority. Allowing for a personal bias stemming from my education and research activity, it seems to me, however, that genetics and evolutionary thought may call for a higher one.

First of all, organic evolution through natural selection is the most important biological generalization of the century preceding ours. The shift that it generated from a typological mode of thought to a statistical one has over-whelming social significance, for example, in connection with stereotype images of racial differences.

Second, the discovery or deduction of the formal mechanism of hereditary transmission, Mendelism, formed a cornerstone of modern biology. Last, the deciphering of the language of biochemical communication within the cell and its relation to biological communication between generations was the most important experimental breakthrough of the biology of our day.

It would be protesting too much to insist at length that the interweaving of these three scientific advances and others accruing from them is having ever-growing effects on the individual, the family, and society. They are the advances that can supply the answers to the kind of questions that Francis Crick suggests intellectuals should be concerned with: "What are we?" "Why are we here?" "Why does the world work in this particular way?" They are the advances that pose novel questions calling for decisions from all levels of existence from that of an individual to that of a world-wide society. Genetics and evolution seem to me therefore to be the main biological areas of concern to the informed layman. Within these fields the choice of topics for a single course is so vast that it has to be made in a rather arbitrary fashion. In part, it is simply dictated by the writer's interests and knowledge. But the choices of particular topics may be defended on other grounds. For example, although I have referred to the molecular revolution in biology as most important, it appears to me that the details of molecular genetics, or of the growing field of biochemical developmental genetics, or, in general, the biology of lower organisms are less pertinent to the purposes of this book than, let us say, the peripheral subject of population explosion. I see no need to defend the particular subjects chosen for discussion, except, perhaps, for the biographical vignettes. Haldane, Galton, and Chetverikov have been singled out in this manner not because they are more important than Darwin and Mendel, but because of the socially significant overtones in their life or work.

The sequence of topics may need an explanation. It was chosen by trial and error to engage the attention and stimulate personal involvement of majors in psychology, economics, history, linguistics, and forty other departments. The progression of subjects is designed to feed tidbits of information of special concern to each of the diverse groups in turn, without losing the interests of any. The book then is structured with this intent in mind.

A word is also necessary about the handling of references. I believe that the names or identities of the architects of modern genetics and evolutionary theory should form part of the cultural equipment of a university graduate (a conviction that I find in my teaching experience shared only by history majors). But it is clearly impractical in a text of this kind to give more than a handful of names or to list all the sources drawn upon. This, in spite of the fact that many of the ideas presented, some of the expressions used, and most of the data included are derivative. I have therefore cited by name in the body of the text only a relatively small number of direct or indirect contributors to its contents. At the end of the book, however, is a list of scientists and others scholars whose work has been referred to without citation, and the Teacher's Manual accompanying this book contains a bibliography.

As a further prefatory word to both students and instructors, I want to comment on the problem of up-to-dateness. We are currently living in an era of tremendous scientific explosion. While the human population is doubling once every 35 years, the number of scientists and engineers in the United States is doubling once every ten years, although this does not give grounds to belief that scientists will soon outnumber people. The rates at which costs of research and development are doubling vary from once every two years in China and Japan to about once every five years in the United States, Great Britain, and Canada. Over 90 percent of all scientists who ever lived are alive today. The number of scientific journals has risen in the last two centuries from ten to 100,000. Now, while such statistics may not reflect completely the actual growth of knowledge, they do impose severe limitations on the possibility of any one single person staying up-to-date in any but a very narrow area of information. In some fields it is even difficult for a teacher to keep up with reviews, if he is also to continue with his own research. Because of this and because it takes time to produce a book, some material to be found within these covers is not the latest and may have been superseded. But it is my hope that the students, after using this book, will be sufficiently acquainted with the principles and prospects discussed to appraise the validity and import of new discoveries that may come to their attention.

Just as the beginning of this century was the age of physics and the middle of it seems to be the era of biology, the concluding years of the century may be expected to be the age of the behavioral sciences. And as knowledge advances along the hierarchy of organzation from subatomic particles, atoms, molecules, macromolecules, cells, organs, individuals, to socially organized groups, increasingly complex decisions have to be faced by members of society. In many areas, conflicts between individual and social values have already arisen. Many of us find such developments as conditioning of the mind or social control over the human gene pool or even predetermination of sex of unborn children repugnant. Yet these developments are technically possible and have to be considered. Our biology, our psychology, and our values have evolved over a long period of time to serve in stable or in very slowly changing physical and cultural environments, rather than the swiftly transforming ones of today. As the late Robert Oppenheimer, among others, has pointed out, in traditional society, culture, including ethics and religion, acted as a homeostatic stabilizing force. Now culture has become an instrument of rapid change. Reasoned decisions have become much more difficult in the absence of historical guidelines. Indeed, there are pessimists, such as Max Born, who think that science and technology have already destroyed the ethical basis of civilization. Scientific attitude, he maintains, creates doubt and skepticism towards both unscientific knowledge and the natural unsophisticated actions on which human society depends and without which keeping society together is impossible. This, I submit, is an unwarranted voice of desperation. There cannot be too much knowledge. But decision-making machinery in the atomic age should not ignore information about human beings and the world around them. Even if ethical principles are not deducible by the rational methods of science, it seems obvious that, wherever possible, consequences of alternatives must be considered before choices are made. It is impossible to foresee all the decisions related to genetics that the users of this book will be called upon to make in their lifetimes. But at least one of the purposes of education is to prepare students to make the more or less obvious ones. This is the aim of the course that I have been teaching, and this is the main goal of the present book.

Finally, a note on the boxes and the use of boldface type: Descriptive material and most of the tabular material has been segregated into inserts called boxes, some of which include illustrations. Subject matter of peripheral relevance to the central topics has also been so treated. The most important technical terms and names usually make their first appearance in **boldface type**. These are the terms and names that the student is expected to remember. In the index the numbers of pages on which they appear are also **boldface type**, for ready reference to their definitions. *Italics* are used for specific names, for the introduction of technical terms of transient significance, and for emphasis.

Berkeley and Stanford   I. MICHAEL LERNER
May 1968

ACKNOWLEDGMENTS

I am grateful to Ralph W. Tyler and to O. Meredith Wilson, who succeeded him as Director of the Center for Advanced Study in the Behavioral Sciences, Stanford, California, for the opportunity to write most of the book in the relaxed and intellectually stimulating atmosphere of the Center. Many members of the Center's staff contributed to making my stay there profitable and enjoyable. In particular, I want to thank Mrs. Irene Bickenbach who won against odds the battle with my handwriting.

I am grateful for many suggestions from colleagues and friends who have read and commented on all or parts of the manuscript. Much that may be good in the book is due to them, but they should not be held responsible for what is not: I am afraid I did not accept all of their suggestions. It is a particular pleasure to express my appreciation for the help received from Th. Dobzhansky, B. A. Hamburg, and D. O. Woodward, who read all of the first version of the manuscript.

Acknowledgment of sources of illustrations are given in the captions. I am grateful to all who supplied me with pictures. I also want to thank the University of British Columbia for permission to include several paragraphs in Chapter 21 that first appeared in a publication under its imprint.

I.M.L.

CONTENTS

HEREDITY, EVOLUTION, and SOCIETY

1

INTRODUCTORY

1.1 ORGANIC EVOLUTION

The concept of **organic evolution** is the most important biological generalization in the intellectual history of man. It is highly relevant to man's personal
well-being, his psychology, his social organization, and his future as a species
—not to mention his world outlook or his curiosity about himself and his
immediate and cosmic environments.

A one-term course of lectures, discussions, and intensive readings can cover
only in broadest outline what such a potent generalization is based on and
what its implications may be, especially if the assumption is made that many of
the students are starting with little knowledge of biology. The best that can be
done is to view such a course as one about evolutionary thinking rather than
one on details of evolution.

This book, then, is designed for a course on evolution appreciation, following a format often used in courses on the fine arts. The details of the evolutionary process and the intricacies of hereditary transmission on which it is based
will, at best, be only sketched in. What will be emphasized is what evolution is,
what its mechanisms are likely to have been, what its future course may be.
Above all, the significance of evolution to human thought, human experience,
and human affairs will be demonstrated.

It may be asked why a book entitled *Heredity, Evolution, and Society* begins with a reference to evolution rather than to heredity. Now, all biologists agree that organic evolution is a reality, and that the currently dominant species on this planet (man) and all other existing kinds of life were not always the way they are now, but descended with modification from preexisting forms. The concept of evolution stresses the idea that the world itself was not always as it is, but has a historical past and evolved from simpler origins. And one of the features of the process of evolution is that it embraces a historical continuum in which there are no sharp borders. Thus, it is possible to distinguish nonliving material from living organisms in a general way although the exact point at which one turned into another is a matter of somewhat arbitrary opinion. Similarly, the precise point in history at which creatures that can be described as human beings first appeared on earth is a matter of definition.

To many, evolution is self-evident. Yet it should not be forgotten that there are still states in which the law is equivocal about evolution (Arkansas and Mississippi, and until recently, Tennessee). There are still many people in the Western world who share the belief of the Irish theologian Bishop James Ussher (1581–1656) and a later English divine Bishop Lightfoot (1828–1889), arrived at by adding the ages of Bibilical patriarchs, that the world was created just as it is in six consecutive 24-hour days, starting precisely at 9 A.M. on the twenty-third of October of the year 4004 B.C.

The evolutionary outlook denies that the origins of today's world were as simple and straightforward as that. It is based on the evidence that the earth as we know it today and all its kinds of inhabitants were not the result of **Special Creation** but were produced by a complex, tortuous, and enormously long historical sequence of events.

Knowledge of the past and of the processes that have led from the beginnings of life on earth has not yet been apprehended in full detail. Our understanding of even some of the major aspects of the evolutionary process is vague and speculative. Indeed, all we have as yet are a few islands in a vast sea of ignorance. But the evidence that the process has occurred is overwhelming. In part it is based on the historical record deducible by observation; in part it stems from actual experiments. And evolution is also, given the basic facts of genetics, a logical necessity, which is where genetics enters into the picture.

1.2 GENETICS

For organic evolution to have occurred three attributes of matter are essential, and given the three it is an inevitable process: capacity for **reproduction** exceeding the numbers required for maintenance of population size, capacity for change, which leads to **variation** producing diversity between individuals, and capacity for continuity between generations, or **heredity**. In other words, what is needed for evolution to proceed is the conservative force of heredity and the radical force of variation, and **genetics** is precisely defined as the study of these two forces. It is also said to be the science of *biological communication* between generations, dealing with the problem of how information of a biological kind is transmitted from parent to offspring. Thus a single microscopic cell, depending on the recipe or information it contains, may give rise to a redwood tree or to a human being with a particular color of hair and, subject to the environment in which he develops, with a particular kind of intelligence and temperament. This information comes from the previous generation, which in turn obtained it from its ancestors, although parts of the recipe may have been changed in the course of transmission.

In the organisms that reproduce sexually, the parents convey the necessary instructions through **germ cells** or **gametes**, which unite to produce the **zygote**, or the initial cell of the offspring. The details of the mechanism of information transmission have been worked out only recently and represent a marvel of compactness and precision. The volume of material in a human zygote carrying all of the instructions by which a single cell will develop into a particular human being occupies eight cubic microns, weighing no more than 6×10^{-12} grams (a micron is approximately 1/25,000 of an inch, while a gram is about 1/28 of an ounce). To make this clearer, if one assumes that there are about three billion people on earth, the total **coding** material for all of their hereditary composition, resemblances, and differences, weighs about 18 milligrams and would fit into a drop of water. We shall review in due course the general features of the transmission mechanism. Meanwhile we shall be directing ourselves to the somewhat broader aspects of evolution, in order to place the significance of genetic processes into its proper perspective.

Genetics, then, deals with the fundamental aspects of evolutionary change, with the reasons and the machinery behind it that cause men to differ from elephants and men and elephants to differ among themselves.

Some of the facts about genetics and evolution seem, at present, valuable only for the satisfaction of intellectual curiosity. Others have intensely practical values for medicine, public health, agriculture, law, industry, and social relations. Recent scientific advances have enormously magnified our ability to direct the course of organic evolution of the flora and fauna around us, and, at least potentially, of man himself. As Garrett Hardin has put it, "Believe what you will of evolution in the past: but you had better jolly well believe it will take place in the future if you hope to make political decisions that will give your descendants a reasonable chance to exist. The principles of evolution are inescapably relevant to the analysis of man's predicament."

1.3 ORGANIZATION OF THE BOOK

This book consists of six unequal parts that, on occasion, are not sharply separated but merge one into another. The first part, containing the next four chapters, basically deals with the broad panorama of organic evolution. It considers the contribution of the most important figure in the history of evolution, **Charles Darwin** (1809–1882), whose *Origin of Species*, published in 1859, led to a major revolution in human thought. Also, some elementary principles of biology are surveyed, properties of living matter examined, and the process by which life originated on earth and gradually transformed itself into the complex web of organisms existing today, is broadly examined. Darwin's place in history, the impact of Darwinism on mankind, and the evidence that he adduced for evolution, as well as some more recently discovered facts, are presented in general outline.

The actual procession of evolutionary events is dealt with very summarily. Description of the specific changes that have occurred in the many billions of years of the existence of our universe, the five or more billion years of the earth's existence, or the more than three billion years during which there has been life on earth, are given only the briefest consideration. In general, throughout the book more emphasis is given to processes and factors operating on the microevolutionary level (that is, within a single species, as we shall define the term) than to those on the macroevolutionary one (that is, between such classes as mammals and birds or such higher categories as vertebrates and invertebrates). The last chapter in this part deals with man, his biological history, his special properties, and some possible aspects of his future.

The second part covers the informational machinery of the cell and the methods of intergenerational communication. The questions discussed relate to the language in which this information is transmitted, what happens to the directions received, how they are copied in successive generations of cells and organisms, and how the language of transmittal is translated into production of substances determining resemblances and differences between individuals. This part merges, in Chapter 7, into the third part, which is devoted to the phenomena of Mendelism, the formal mechanics of heredity, named after the founder of the science of genetics, the Augustinian monk, **Johann Gregor Mendel** (1822–1884).

In Chapters 8 through 11, the discussion centers on the laws of inheritance established by Mendel and extended by many others since. The hereditary determination of sex in man is considered as a model Mendelian trait in a somewhat extended discussion of various genetic aspects of sex in humans and other organisms. More complicated features of inheritance are taken up next, involving the action of and interaction between the units of inheritance first described by Mendel. A discussion of the inheritance of rather more complex traits than he studied and the general problem of interaction between heredity and environment follows. Particular emphasis here is laid on the interaction of nature and nurture in the determination of complicated characters that enter intelligence and behavior.

The fourth part is introduced by Chapter 12 on the genetics of populations and continues with the consideration of evolutionary forces determining the structure of populations. The subject of selection, introduced in the section on Darwinism, is returned to at a more formal level and its interaction with mutation, the important force producing variation, is considered. This part concludes with Chapter 15 which deals with man-made sources of genetic variation, such as radiation and fallout.

The fifth part is devoted primarily to human inheritance. The bases of human diversity are examined with particular weight given to genetic problems of race, including some attention paid to the biology of the American Negro. A sampling of a variety of inherited human traits is given, containing examples from medical genetics, following which the inheritance of blood groups is discussed. The last chapter in this section deals with the genetic consequences of various human mating systems.

The final part is devoted to social, ethical, and political issues in genetics, methods of possible and potential manipulation of human genetic resources, with the penultimate chapter given to a description of how genetics and politics have become intertwined in a contemporary society.

1.4 PURPOSE OF THE BOOK

Before turning to the specific material just outlined, an additional word on the general pedagogical attitude from which this book has been written may not be amiss. In science there are basically two kinds of instruction: (1) giving information, and (2) teaching how to obtain and evaluate information. As a rule the second kind is the more important, if it can be used. One reason for this is that the first kind can only provide knowledge of what is currently thought to be correct. The example of Simon Newcomb, an astronomer, considered during his time as one of the greatest living American scientists is an instructive one. In October, 1903, shortly before the memorable date of December 17 of that year on which the Wright brothers made their first flight, he published an article proving, on the basis of all known physical facts, that heavier-than-air devices cannot fly.

In general, the history of science is a history of errors corrected. While we can assert that knowledge today is closer to some kind of reality than it was 100, twenty, or ten years ago, it shall be much closer to reality ten, twenty, or 100 years from now, provided we choose to use our tools and our mental equipment wisely. In an introductory survey course it is not feasible to use exclusively the second, and better, kind of instruction. The sources of information are too vast and too widely scattered, and many of them are in highly technical language. Some remedy is provided by suggestions for additional reading. But essentially the best that can be done is to present what is known today, perhaps indicating along the way what appears to be fact and what is speculation. In addition, an attempt should be made to engender an outlook combining curiosity with skepticism. Persons who are now students will be deluged for the rest of their lives with a cataract of information about further scientific advances. Hence, a background for judging new information must also be provided.

Ideally, then, absorption of the material covered in this book should be accompanied by development of the capacity to be informed and to act intelligently on new information. In our age mankind is facing a very dangerous part of his long journey. In the past we often traveled blindly, but the development of science and technology has imposed on us an increasing necessity for careful choice. As we strip the veils from what were previously considered the mysteries of God or Nature over which we had no control, decisions are bound to weigh heavier on us. Not too long ago in most societies, whether a given couple would have ten, three, or no children was not up to them but to divine will. It may be fully expected that in a few years a couple will not only be able to decide on the number, but also on the sex, and perhaps other characteristics of each child. And this is an example of only one of the more trivial powers that we are to have. The graver ones, including decisions of whether mankind is to continue at all, need to be wielded on the basis of an approach involving rational thinking, sensing, feeling, and believing, and a most scrupulous evaluation of the consequences of our actions. It is in the spirit of developing such an outlook as well as to provide reliable information, that the following chapters are written.

2

LIFE

2.1 PROPERTIES OF LIVING MATTER

Many criteria have been suggested to distinguish living from nonliving matter. It is likely that there is a point on the scale of organization where a clear-cut distinction cannot be made. This is essentially a matter of import only to linguistic purists, philosophers, or theologians. For our purposes we can list a set of properties that will define life. The first is *capacity for self-reproduction*. This refers to the production of reasonable replicates, of like, but not, generally speaking, identical offspring.

The second is the *capacity to respond to environmental stimuli*. It can vary from simple irritability, such as an amoeba's movement when touched by a foreign body, to man's conscious change from light summer clothes to winter flannels (of course, machines can also react to external stimuli).

The third is the *capacity for metabolism*, for the binding or releasing of energy. Inflow may involve the use of energy that the organism itself obtains from inorganic sources (such organisms are **autotrophs**, or "self-feeders") or energy made available by other beings, as when animals eat plants (animals are **heterotrophs**, or "other feeders").

On the one hand, *photosynthesis* is a process in which energy is bound or stored by plants synthesizing sugars from water and carbon dioxide using energy from light sources:

$$H_2O + CO_2 + light \longrightarrow sugar + O_2, \text{ containing potential energy.}$$

Respiration, on the other hand, involves a release of stored energy:

$$sugar + O_2 \longrightarrow H_2O + CO_2 + \text{kinetic energy.}$$

Both of these processes are mediated by **enzymes**, protein molecules which act as catalysts, that is, which promote a chemical reaction without being themselves consumed.

The fourth property is the *capacity to grow*. This is the capacity to differentiate, as well as to increase in size; that is, to use energy to transform materials into appropriate heterogeneous structures, following the instructions provided by the informational machinery of the cells.

Finally, there is the *capacity for change and perpetuation of change*, which is very important from the evolutionary standpoint. This is essentially the capacity for variation and its transmission to succeeding generations. More strictly, it is called the capacity for **mutation**, of which two kinds must be distinguished. Essentially a mutation is a change in the instructions to cells. When such a change—perhaps by error of transmission—takes place in a cell that will eventually give rise to gametes, the mutation is said to be **germinal** and is transmitted to the next generation. The "memory" of the change is *intergenerational*.

Somatic mutations are changes in cells that do not give rise to gametes (say, liver cells or leaf cells). Cells carrying somatic mutations will pass on the changed instructions to cells descended from them, but these changes will disappear with the death of the individual, at least in sexually reproducing organisms. The memory of the change here is *intragenerational*.

It should be obvious that in sexually reproducing organisms only germinal mutations are of significance to evolutionary processes, although somatic mutations may be important to an individual. For instance, if a change in instructions should render a liver cell unable to manufacture an essential enzyme, the individual concerned may not survive but no evolutionary change will occur.

One further property is sometimes erroneously ascribed to living matter: some kind of directedness or urge of organisms to convert part of their environment into their own likeness. The now largely extinct group of "objective vitalists" assumed that life involves some sort of "élan vital" or "entelechy," forever impossible to analyze by reduction, that is, in terms of lower levels of organization. Samuel Butler, a better novelist than evolutionist, described this property as the tendency for all living beings to live beyond their income. There is no evidence whatsoever that supports vitalistic views. At best, we can describe this "urge" as an empirically discovered analogue to the first law of motion: living matter left alone and given the building materials will tend to increase itself indefinitely. As Bertrand Russell said: "every living thing is a sort of imperialist seeking to transform as much as possible of its environment into itself and its seed." There are, however, also now "subjective vitalists" who believe that awareness and consciousness are phenomena of personal experience: we can postulate their existence in others but cannot observe them in anyone but our own selves.

Organic evolution refers to changes in the living world. To tell a complete story, we would have to begin with a discussion of inorganic evolution, that is, the evolution of nonliving matter, or the historical changes in our universe before the appearance of life. We would also have to speak of social or cultural evolution, which treats of changes in social organisms determined by information transmitted either between members of the same generation or between generations by means of instruction and learning. Some social information may be transmitted in biological ways, as for instance, among various social

---

BOX 2.A HIERARCHY OF ORGANIZATION

This table outlines the levels of organization of matter and the scientific disciplines devoted to them. In reality these disciplines may overlap to a greater extent than shown. This is particularly true of the various branches of genetics.

Level of organization	Field of study	Branch of genetics
Subatomic particles	Physics	
Atoms	Chemistry	
Molecules	Biochemistry	
Macromolecules[1]	Biology	Molecular and biochemical
Cell organs and organelles[2] nucleus chromosomes ribosomes mitochondria endoplasmic reticulum plastids and other organelles		Cytogenetics
Cell	Cytology	
Tissue	Histology	
Organ	Anatomy	
Organism	Physiology[5]	Formal[12]
	Morphology[6]	Special[13]
	Embryology[7]	Developmental
Deme	Ecology[8]	Population
Species	Paleontology[9]	
	Behavioral Sciences[10]	
Higher taxa[3]		
Local biota[4]		
World biota		
Universe biota	Exobiology[11]	

[1]Giant molecules of the order of 100 Angstroms in diameter (see Box 2.B).
[2]See Box 2.C.
[3]Taxa (sing. taxon) are classifications that range in inclusiveness from species through genera, families, orders, classes, phyla, and kingdoms.
[4]The totality of various organisms living in the same region.
[5]Study of function.
[6]Study of form.
[7]Study of development.
[8]Interrelation of organisms and their environment.
[9]Study of extinct forms.
[10]For the study of man these include anthropology, psychology, and sociology.
[11]As yet a speculative endeavor (see Section 2.7).
[12]Classified by the organism studied: human, mammalian, plant.
[13]Such as radiation genetics, agricultural genetics.

BOX 2.B SCALE OF SIZES

This illustration (redrawn with modification from Simpson *et al.*) shows the relative sizes of objects from single atoms to the largest living organisms. Note that the scale used is an exponential one: each successive subdivision represents a tenfold decrease. Thus, in the illustration shown, the distance between one meter and ten meters is as great as that between ten meters and one hundred meters. As may be seen, one micron is a thousandth of a millimeter, and an angstrom is one ten-thousandth of a micron.

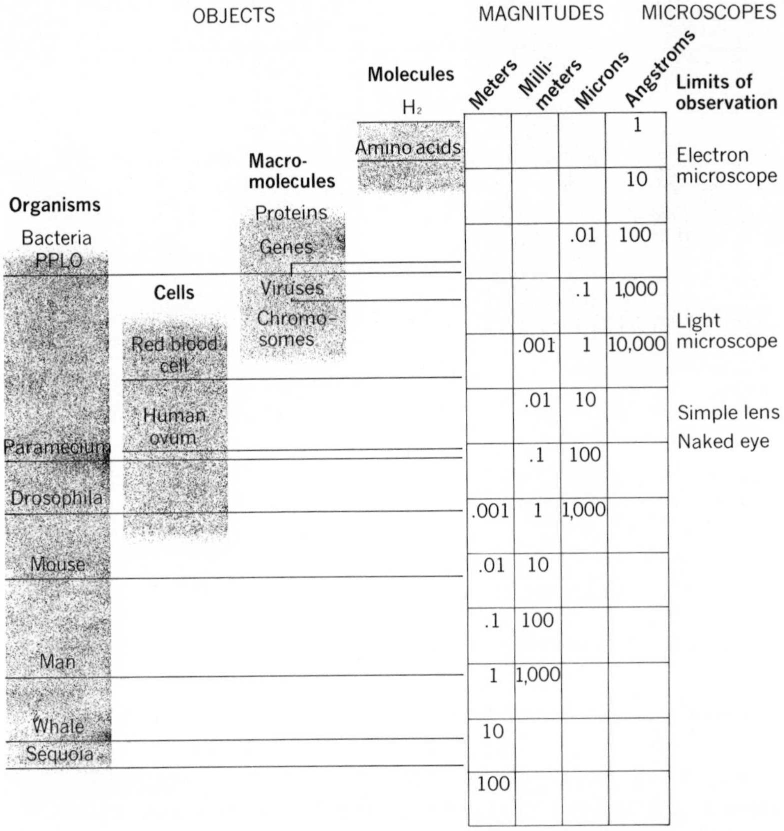

OBJECTS   MAGNITUDES   MICROSCOPES

Molecules
H₂

Macro-molecules

Organisms
Bacteria
PPLO

Cells

Proteins
Genes
Amino acids

Red blood cell

Viruses
Chromo-somes

Human ovum

Paramecium

Drosophila

Mouse

Man

Whale
Sequoia

Meters	Milli-meters	Microns	Angstroms	Limits of observation
			1	
			10	Electron microscope
		.01	100	
		.1	1,000	
	.001	1	10,000	Light microscope
	.01	10		
	.1	100		Simple lens
.001	1	1,000		Naked eye
.01	10			
.1	100			
1	1,000			
10				
100				

insects. Within the framework of this book we shall allude to inorganic evolution only very briefly and to social evolution primarily with reference to humans. Our major emphasis will be on organic evolution since our concern here is primarily with life processes.

Before turning to evolution we should consider the hierarchical fashion in which the universe is organized. This is illustrated in Box 2.A, which shows the levels of organization of matter from particles to the total cosmos of living things. Box 2.B may be helpful for visualizing the range of physical sizes at the various levels through the organismal one. Of particular significance in our discussion will be the cell and its composition and the species.

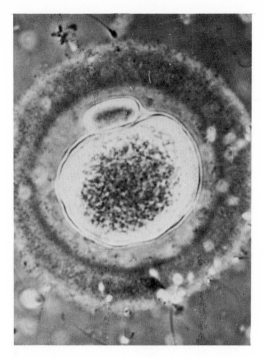

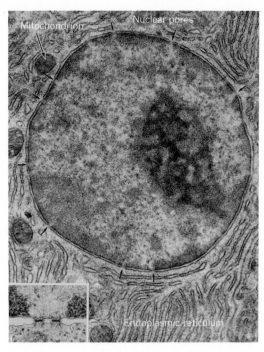

Figure 2.1.

A photomicrograph of a human egg. Note the spermatozoa surrounding it and the first polar body just extruded (see Section 7.1). (Reproduced, with permission, from L. B. Shettles, *Ovum Humanum*. Hafner Publishing Co., New York.)

Figure 2.2.

Electron micrograph of a nucleus surrounded by the cytoplasm. Arrows point to the pores in the nucleus, which permit passage of material to the cytoplasm. Note the dots, which are the ribosomes, lining the endoplasmic reticulum. (Courtesy Don W. Fawcett.)

2.3 THE CELL AND ITS COMPOSITION

The **cell** may be viewed as the basic unit of life and the lowest one, with the possible exception of **viruses** (see Box 2.E). Box 2.C gives an enormously oversimplified diagram of a cell. Figure 2.1 is a photograph of human cells and Figure 2.2 an electron micrograph of a cell's nucleus. Cells are exceedingly complex aggregates of subunits even as they can be seen through a microscope. Chemically, their intricacy is awesome. Of the various kinds of materials in cells the most abundant is water. Others include lipids (fats and related substances), carbohydrates, and ash, but the most important from our standpoint are **proteins** and **nucleic acids**.

There are two kinds of nucleic acids: **deoxyribonucleic acid,** usually referred to as **DNA**, and **ribonucleic acid**, designated **RNA**. Their significance lies in the fact that they are the vehicles for transmission of genetic information. They are the carriers of hereditary instructions for the manufacture of the proteins that give any particular organism its distinguishing characteristics. Indeed, the specificity of each and every living being is determined by the particular combinations of the various proteins that its cells can manufacture. We shall return to a more detailed consideration of nucleic acids in Chapter 6.

Proteins are large molecules consisting of folded chains of **amino acids**, which contain an amino group (NH$_2$) and a carboxyl group

There are twenty common ones that will primarily concern us. They are built on the model:

where R stands for an atom or group of atoms. Thus when R is merely a hydrogen atom, we have the simplest amino acid, glycine:

BOX 2.C THE CELL

This illustration provides a generalized schematic representation of a plant cell. There are certain differences between plant and animal cells (for example, the latter do not have cell walls or plastids), which, however, are not relevant to our purposes here. Only some of the structures are shown and labeled.

Chromosomes are cell organs containing protein and nucleic acids, which are the bearers of hereditary information (see Chapter 7).

The *endoplasmic reticulum* is a network of membranes connected to other cell inclusions and is involved in lipid formation.

Mitochondria are self-reproducing energy powerhouses that have the capacity to change shape.

The **nucleus** is the cell organ that contains the chromosomes, carriers of genetic messages. The material outside the nucleus is referred to as the **cytoplasm**.

Plastids are self-reproducing bodies, some of which are concerned with photosynthesis.

Ribosomes are the sites of protein synthesis.

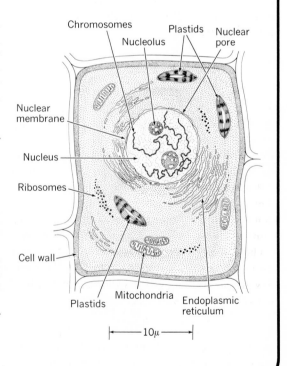

containing ten atoms. Others, for example, tryptophan, have more complex structural formulas:

Series of linked amino acids connected through peptide bonds

are known as **polypeptides**. They become linked in chains by dehydration synthesis:

The so-called primary structure of proteins depends on the particular sequence of amino acids in the polypeptide chains composing a given protein and on the number of chains. In addition there may be other differences among proteins, differences in how the chains are held together by bonds, differences in the orientation of the amino acids, and differences in the manner in which the chains are folded in space.

Proteins may also be found in compounds with other substances, such as nucleic acids, forming, in this example, *nucleoproteins*. They may combine with other small molecules, as for instance in **hemoglobin**, the coloring matter found in blood, whose function is the transport of oxygen.

The potential differences among proteins are thus enormous and their structural complexity is exceedingly great. Human hemoglobin happens to be a very simple protein, but it would be impractical to give its structural formula here, since it contains 9,512 atoms:

$$C_{3032}H_{4816}O_{872}N_{780}S_8Fe_4.$$

The very simplest organism known, again excluding viruses, is the so-called pleuro-pneumonia-like organism (PPLO) with a diameter of 0.1 micron and a weight of 5×10^{-6} grams (one-billionth that of an amoeba). It contains some

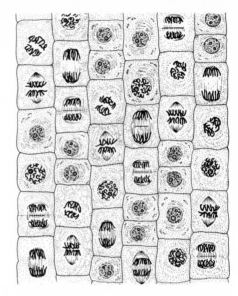

Figure 2.3.

A schematic representation of a tissue showing various steps in the process of nuclear division.

1,200 molecules, while ordinary cells visible under the light microscope may have around a quarter of a million protein molecules alone, each averaging, perhaps, 20,000 atoms. It is easily seen how far from each other are the levels of complexity between atom and cell in Box 2.A.

More complex organisms have cells organized in tissues, one kind of which is schematically illustrated in Figure 2.3. Cells in each type of tissue show characteristic differences of shape and appearance, which are the result of differentiation in the course of development.

2.4 THE SPECIES

Above the level of single individual organisms lie aggregates or groups of individuals. Of major biological significance is the smallest of these, the **deme**, or an interbreeding population. It should not be confused with race, a term to be considered in Chapter 16. The next more inclusive group is the **species**, a word which has been used in a variety of meanings and which stands for an exceedingly important concept in evolution. It has been used and misused in a variety of senses. Whatever its original meaning in Latin was, medieval philosophers (for example, St. Thomas Aquinas) considered it to be as real, discrete and immutable a unit as the nineteenth-century atom. Even now neo-Thomist theologians talk of animal, vegetable, and mineral as being the three species.

In the eighteenth century, the Swedish botanist Carolus Linnaeus (1707–1778) devised the currently used system of classification (see Box 2.E) of living things. The term species was applied by him to groups of plants or animals that were assumed to be similar to each other, to have descended from common ancestors of special creation, not to interbreed with other such distinct groups, and to be constant in all but insignificant characteristics. The Linnaean system calls for identification of each such group by the name of the genus (the taxon above species) and the species. Thus, for example, the human species is called *Homo sapiens*, the fruit fly used extensively in genetic experiments, *Drosophila melanogaster*, and cultivated rice, *Oryza sativa*. The name of a genus is often abbreviated to a single letter (*Gallus gallus*, the domestic chicken may be written *G. gallus*).

Implicit in the taxonomic usage of the term species is the Platonic notion that there is for every species a prototype and that the variations observed among individual men, fruit flies, or rice plants are due to imperfections and deviations from the ideal. This **typological** approach is completely inconsistent with evolutionary thinking, although it may be necessary for purposes of classification. It may provoke repercussions in social attitudes because it gives rise to stereotypes, often in caricature form, for subspecific groups, such as the Jew in Nazi mythology or the American Negro in that of reactionaries of the southern United States.

Students of genetics and evolution must reject this approach, replacing it by a more dynamic, populational view of living systems. There is no prototype for an evolutionary species. The variation, not only the average or mean, is the important aspect of such a group. Species do change because of the hereditary transmission of the deviations from the mean of various properties that may exist at any given time. A single species may split into several under the influence of a number of evolutionary forces; the formation of a new species by splitting or transformation is called **speciation**. The various species in existence today originated by such processes from common ancestors. Although some individuals seem to be in marginal areas, where they cannot be clearly assigned to one species or another, generally speaking the **populational** or **statistical** viewpoint can be used not only in discussing evolution, but also for classification.

There are three provisions in the evolutionary meaning of species. If a **gene** is defined as a unit of inheritance, or a unit of information transmission from

BOX 2.D THE ESTIMATED NUMBERS OF LIVING SPECIES

Mammals	3,200
Birds	8,600
Reptiles and Amphibians	6,000
Fish	20,000
Total Chordates[1]	39,500
Invertebrates[2]	1,050,000
Total animals	1,100,000
Plants[3]	325,000
Protists[4]	75,000
Total species	1,500,000

[1] See Box 2.F.
[2] Including 850,000 insects.
[3] Probably an underestimate.
[4] See Box 2.E; species classification of protists that reproduce entirely by fission is a moot point, since they do not form a reproductive community.

generation to generation, these provisions are, according to **George Gaylord Simpson**: (1) community of inheritance among the members, (2) capacity of the genes to spread throughout the group, and (3) inhibition of the gene spread to other groups.

Perhaps a fuller comprehension of the concept of species is provided by the definition proposed by **Theodosius Dobzhansky**, and particularly appropriate to biparental organisms. Dobzhansky views a species as *the most inclusive population in time and space representing a discrete reproductive community*.

The reference to time simply means that the unit maintains its form from generation to generation even if its components change. This is analogous to the life of a given organism, in the course of which the cells of its body will be continuously replaced, though its identity remains the same. Or to take another example, a country, such as the United States of America, is referred to as a particular geographical and political unit, although its inhabitants, its social institutions, and even its landscape, change continuously over the course of history.

The notion of reproductive community refers to the fact that members of a given species share common descent and interbreed. "Discrete" relates to the idea that different species do not share the same gene pool (see Section 4.3), nor are they able to exchange genes. Thus, horses and asses are separate species. Although they will mate with each other, the offspring, mules and hinnies, are sterile and therefore do not pass their genes into either of the parental populations. Finally, the term "most inclusive" denotes that a species contains all potential interbreeding populations, which in fact may not really interbreed. Thus, St. Bernards are not likely to cross with Chihuahuas, but they belong to the same species, *Canis familiaris*, because the two breeds may exchange genes through intermediate breeds.

The number of living species described to date is shown in Box 2.D. There are many more species that have become extinct in the course of the history of life on earth than there are living ones. Indeed, it has been estimated that more than 99 percent of all species that ever evolved are no longer in existence.

2.5 PROPERTIES OF MAN

We are not concerned here with the detailed characteristics of various kinds of living beings. Box 2.E will suffice to indicate the major differences between the three different kingdoms. Having an anthropocentric outlook, we may, however, want to have a look at man's position in the animal kingdom. Box 2.F gives a simplified taxonomic classification. But there are numerous attributes of man that not only place him on the uppermost rung on the evolutionary ladder, but that make him what we think of as a human being. There are many articles and books on this subject and it is impossible to give here a comprehensive list of unique and near-unique characteristics of *H. sapiens*. However, an incomplete listing is still worthwhile.

One must remember that at present man is the endpoint of a continuous evolutionary process. Competition in occupying similar ecological **niches** (that is, exploiting similar environments) is strongest between similar species. Hence

BOX 2.E CHARACTERISTICS OF LIVING KINGDOMS

The kingdom is the highest taxon used in biological classification (see Box 2.F). Currently many biologists recognize three kingdoms: protists, plants, and animals.

Protists are mainly unicellular (or, perhaps, acellular, in the sense that they are not further divided) organisms that are simple in structure, although they may live in conjoined colonies. They may be either autotrophs or heterotrophs. Some biologists still adhere to the classification in which the various types were viewed either as plants (for example, algae) or animals (for example, amoebae), but resemblances among the various protists are greater than between them and any members of the other kingdoms. Some biologists consider the protists to constitute three separate kingdoms: protists proper, fungi, and a group including blue-green algae, bacteria, and viruses. Whether viruses are, indeed, living organisms is debatable. Although they reproduce and mutate, they do not grow or metabolize. It seems unlikely because of this that they originated before living cells. They are, perhaps, either degenerate descendants of bacteria, or they may have originated from cells as detached pieces of nucleoprotein (see Figure 2.4). The kingdom of protists comprises twelve phyla.

Plants are autotrophic multicellular organisms. Many of them capture energy by photosynthesis. They are usually immobile. Their cells have walls and their reproductive cycle differs in certain ways from that of animals. The importance of plants in the biota is shown by the fact that about two-thirds of the energy they bind is taken up by heterotrophic animals. There are two phyla of plants.

Animals are multicellular heterotrophs. None of them have the apparatus for photosynthesis. They are usually mobile and, except for the sponges, have nerve cells coordinating different parts of the body. Their cells do not have walls. They have two very important attributes that plants by and large lack: (1) a fixed developmental pattern, so that each individual's life history goes through a set of stages characteristic for its species, and (2) possession, in a high degree, of the property of **homeostasis**, or the capacity for self-regulation, adjustment, and balance of function. For example, sweating in response to high temperature is a homeostatic property of warm-blooded animals. The animal kingdom is subdivided into nine phyla.

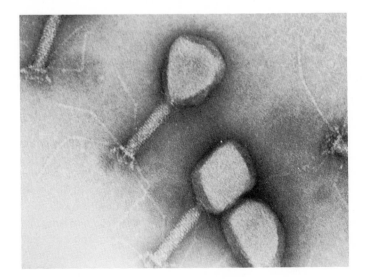

Figure 2.4.

An electron micrograph of one of the larger and more complex viruses, T4 bacteriophage, enlarged about 125,000 diameters.

(Courtesy of Michael F. Moody.)

BOX 2.F CLASSIFICATION OF *Homo sapiens*

If visitors from outer space were instructed to bring back to their home specimens of the species *Homo sapiens*, they might well be provided with the following key to enable them to identify the creatures desired. The classification given is very incomplete; for instance, the infra-order is not given, and only a few of the characteristics appropriate to the given taxa are listed.

This classification is based primarily on anatomical features. With the development of biochemical genetics, it will become possible to develop a similar taxonomic table based on differences in protein structure. Similarly, it should eventually be possible to establish as precise a scheme on the basis of behavioral traits.

Kingdom	Animalia	From this point on the hunter would neglect all creatures that do not have the properties of animals (Box 2.E).
Phylum	Chordata	Have an embryonic elastic rod of cells as part of the internal skeleton.
Subphylum	Vertebrata	The adults have a vertebral column.
Superclass	Tetrapoda	Four-limbed.
Class	Mammalia	The young are suckled.
Subclass	Theria	Young are liveborn.
Infraclass	Eutheria	Do not have pouches like kangaroos.
Order	Primates	Among many other special traits have flat nails.
Suborder	Anthropoidea	Tailless and either semierect or erect.
Family	Hominidae	Erect and have large brains.
Genus	Homo	Modern brain structure and largest relative brain size.
Species	Homo sapiens	Only living species of the genus.

modern man has displaced forms with properties closest to his, so that some of his attributes are unique. Yet he shares many others with his existing relatives. For instance, man used to be defined as a tool-making ape, until it was found that other apes are capable, to some slight extent, of this feat. Similarly, the statement that man's distinct characteristic is educability by his own species is no longer valid. And when it is said that "the animal knows, of course; but certainly it does not know that it knows," there is no firm assurance of such certitude since awareness is a subjective phenomenon. Hence, the following discussion must be viewed in relative, not absolute, terms.

In his morphology, anatomy, and physiology, man has many striking properties: he is the only running mammalian biped (the kangaroo, for example, is a leaping mammalian biped); man's legs are longer than his arms; the size of his brain is both absolutely and relatively greater than that of any other primate, and its structure is more complex; the females are sexually receptive continuously after a period of prolonged immaturity; he is generally not as hairy as his living close relatives. There are even more interesting psychological and behavioral differences, many of which Darwin recognized. We may list some under five headings:

Control of the physical environment. The invention of clothes, the ability to refine metals, and the use of a variety of artifacts provide man with a non-physiologically controlled ability to maintain a steady state. He can therefore exploit environments for which his biological makeup is not suitable. Indeed, this is probably the reason that man is the dominant species on earth and can utilize nearly all available niches. He can also manufacture objects not found in the natural world and maintain them against dissolution. Thus man makes vertical, walled, and hollow structures from reduced metals, while most non-living natural objects are sloping and metals in nature are mostly in the oxidized state.

Educability. Whereas chimpanzees and even mice can learn by observing others of their species perform invented novel acts, modern man has a very advanced ability for deutero-learning, that is, learning how to learn. This is, in part, one cause of his rapid cultural evolution and clearly it has an important effect on mankind.

Capacity of communication across space and time. The ability to communicate nonbiological information not only to contemporaries, but to remote descendants (though, alas, not to remote ancestors) is known as **time-binding**. It is an exceedingly important and complex ability and it makes rapid cultural evolution possible: acquired cultural characters are transmissable to succeeding generations, whereas acquired biological ones, such as somatic mutations, are not. This general ability is connected, as cause or effect, with a great many features of man: the development of symbolic spoken and written language; the use of words for things instead of sounds and actions, and the use of words for ideas; the ability to abstract; the possibilities of lasting influence of single individuals on the species; the so-called property of *displacement*, that is, speaking of things in the past or future or of things imagined.

Consciousness of self. Man is also very likely the only living being who knows he has a history as a species and recognizes its historical dimension. He is probably the only creature that knows that he as an individual is mortal, which may be why he has developed a sense of the sacred (as well as a sense of the scared).

Capacity for conscious direction of evolution. Man already uses this ability in many ways. For instance, in agriculture he produces new kinds of crops and modifies many economically useful animals; in medicine, new forms of antibiotic-producing protists; for his pleasure, new kinds of ornamental plants, new breeds of dogs, and fast-running race horses. His capacity for directing his own evolution will be discussed in the last part of this book.

2.6 THE ORIGIN OF LIFE

Having briefly considered the most complex organism that has developed in the course of evolution, let us now turn to the beginnings of the process, **biopoiesis**, or the origin of life on earth. There have been numerous speculations on this subject. They may be summarized under five headings.

Divine creation. This hypothesis involves a supernatural agency, and hence is outside the realm of science. It is neither provable nor disprovable by experiment, but there is nothing to prevent anyone who so chooses from believing that all other theories are included in this one. However, the special creation theory must be considered as highly improbable, if not outright false.

Life always existed. The geological and chemical record provides grounds for rejecting this hypothesis.

Cosmic dust. This is the theory that primitive life forms arrived on earth from outer space. Material resembling nucleoproteins has been found in meteorites, but there remains the question whether unprotected living matter could have survived passage through the radiation belts surrounding earth. The theory is difficult to disprove; its acceptance would still leave the question of how life originated elsewhere.

Unique and repeated spontaneous generation. These are the most likely hypotheses and there is much evidence for them. Nearly every step in the process can be accounted for.

Continuous spontaneous generation. This hypothesis, widely held in the nineteenth century, was experimentally disproven by the French chemist **Louis Pasteur** in 1859–1861. No spontaneous generation occurs now: all living matter today must come from preexisting life.

That this was always true was accepted until the nineteen-twenties, when the British polymath **J. B. S. Haldane** (Box 2.G) logically pointed out that unless either the second or third hypothesis is correct, spontaneous generation must have occurred at least once in the past. A few years earlier, the Russian biochemist **A. I. Oparin** had formulated an explicit theory of how spontaneous generation might have happened and why it is no longer happening.

Much experimental work has been done since. At present it is generally considered that given (1) a certain range of temperatures, (2) the presence of a number of primitive compounds, (3) a reducing atmosphere (one lacking oxygen, which has now accumulated in the earth's atmosphere from organic processes such as photosynthesis), and (4) protection from already present heterotrophs, then successful biopoeisis is highly likely.

According to one hypothesis, the process is presumed to have taken place in the following sequence. After the earth was formed, either by evolution from a nebula, or by capture by the sun of a gaseous dust cloud, or in some other way, simple compounds of hydrogen, oxygen, carbon, and nitrogen began to be formed. These included

$$H—O—H \qquad O{=}C{=}O$$
water · carbon dioxide

$$H—N—H \qquad H—\overset{\overset{H}{|}}{\underset{\underset{H}{|}}{C}}—H$$
ammonia · methane

In a reducing atmosphere and with energy available from ultraviolet radiation, these could start forming slightly more complex compounds, such as

$$H—\overset{\overset{O}{\|}}{C}—O—H \quad \text{and} \quad H—\overset{\overset{H}{|}}{\underset{\underset{H}{|}}{C}}—\overset{\overset{O}{\|}}{C}—O—H$$
formic acid · acetic acid

These substances have, in fact, been synthesized by using high energy from a cyclotron.

Further inorganic synthesis under similar conditions could lead to increasingly complex precursors of organic compounds such as the amino acids, although it has recently been suggested that polypeptides could have arisen

BOX 2.G J. B. S. HALDANE [1892–1964]

Haldane was one of the most stimulating and erudite men of modern science. His many books and articles dealt with cosmology, genetics, biochemistry, evolution, animal behavior, politics, religion, the social order, and an infinity of other topics. He was one of the last of men of universal culture—a polymath—equally at home with Dante's *Divina Commedia* and Sanskrit epics on the one hand, and mathematics, astronomy, biology and behaviorial sciences on the other (music was the one blank area among his interests, since he was tone-deaf). His father, J. S. Haldane, was a foremost physiologist of his day, and his uncle, Lord Haldane, a philosopher who served as Minister of War in a Liberal government and later as a Labor party Lord Chancellor. Haldane was educated at Eton and Oxford, receiving degrees in classics and mathematics simultaneously.

After serving in World War I, he turned to evolution, genetics, and biochemistry. For over forty years he continued at Cambridge and London to produce an astonishing output of books and theoretical papers in a variety of disciplines. He was much preoccupied with problems of social justice, was an excellent popularizer and journalist, and served for some ten years as chariman of the editorial board of the British communist *Daily Worker*. Between the time of the Spanish Civil War and his retirement from the chair of biometry at University College in London, he was a brilliant apologist for Marxist thought. This philosophy was gradually displaced in his writings by Hinduism, some aspects of which he accepted and others of which he criticized severely. In 1957 he immigrated to India, where, while continuing his teaching and research in genetics, he adopted the Indian form of dress and vegetarian diet, and became an Indian citizen. The photograph reproduced here by courtesy of Dr. Krishna Dronamraju, one of his students, was taken in this last period of his life.

There were elements of eccentricity, hot temper, and bohemianism in his personality, and he could willingly be unbelievably rude. But essentially he was an abstemious, courteous, kind man in whom, at times, perhaps, the ratio of wisdom to intelligence fell below the point considered desirable by many who admired him, and who was always in conflict with his environment. As a scientist he was essentially a theoretician, most of his actual experimental work being done with himself as a subject (he suffered severe spinal injuries while studying escape systems in submerged submarines). The all too few references to his work scattered throughout this book do but very little justice to the fertility of his ideas in the human quest to understand nature.

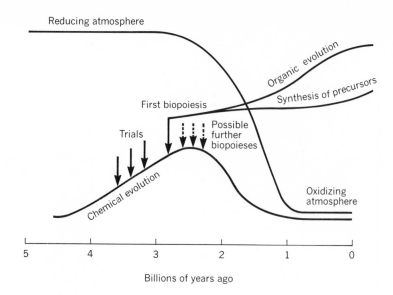

Figure 2.5
Probable origin of
life and course of
evolutionary events.
(Redrawn with
modification from
J. Keosian.)

directly from condensation products of such gases as ammonia and hydrogen cyanide. Indeed, in 1953, the American chemist Stanley Miller subjected a mixture of methane, ammonia, water, and hydrogen to an electric discharge (simulating lightning) and obtained glycine (see Section 2.3) and alanine, which is another amino acid, as well as other materials.

Little by little, a sort of soup of these various materials came into being. From what is known of chemistry, it is not difficult to see how nucleotides (see Chapter 6), which are the building blocks of nucleic acids, would arise. Today amino acids, polypeptides, carbohydrates, plus energy-transporting substances

---

BOX 2.H THE ORIGIN OF SECONDARY HETEROTROPHS

The first living organism, X, was heterotrophic and to survive needed *C*, a substance that X could not manufacture itself. *C* was produced by inorganic synthesis from *A* and *B*:

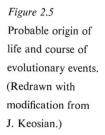

X lives on *C*.

Organism Y descended from X, but a genetic change gave Y the capacity to produce the enzyme needed for manufacturing *C*:

Y lives on *A* and *B*.

As supplies of *C* became scarce, the autotroph Y had an advantage over X and could completely replace it, an example of natural selection, which is a fundamental of current evolutionary theory (see Chapter 3). Further mutation involving loss of the relevant enzyme could occur in Y, and produce the secondary heterotroph Z:

Z lives on *C* from Y.

Both forms will continue to exist, because an equilibrium between the numbers of·Z and Y will be established.

essential for the operation of a cell, and nucleic acid have all been synthesized in the laboratory.

Once nucleic acids combined with proteins, the instructional apparatus for organisms became available in the form of DNA. The incompletely understood step is how an organic shell was formed, resulting in a cell-like organism. However, it is known that complex molecules can develop surface layers and boundaries like soap bubbles by concentration in droplets in water solution. These can increase in size, split, and perhaps eventually acquire a complex self-duplicating apparatus. Thus the origin of organic molecules, their aggregation into droplets, and evolution of unit-replicating machinery appear able to account for the original spontaneous generation. Whether this happened only once or several times we shall probably never know. Perhaps a number of biopoieses occurred in close succession (Figure 2.5). But once living matter became established on earth, the atmosphere began to contain oxygen and the reduced conditions for the reactions necessary for further spontaneous generation no longer existed. Furthermore, as heterotrophs appeared and increased in number, further biopoieses were less likely to establish viable lines: the newly arising forms would likely have been quickly consumed.

Indeed, the first life on earth was probably heterotrophic, feeding on precursors of organic matter. From it photosynthetic autotrophs could arise, in turn giving rise to secondary heterotrophs. One suggestion that has been made about this process is illustrated in Box 2.H.

It is not possible to date precisely the events described, but it is likely that they occurred somewhat more than 3 billion years ago, since fossil bacteria of that age are known to exist (see Chapter 4 for dating methods). The length of time it took for human beings to evolve from primordial living matter is illustrated in Box 2.I.

It is not very likely that we shall ever know for certain how life did originate here. All that experiments will permit us is to infer how it might have originated. It is also possible that information on the existence of life elsewhere than on earth will throw some light on the question. This is the subject matter of the still highly speculative new science of **exobiology**.

2.7 EXOBIOLOGY

Much effort and time is being spent in preparation for seeking and investigating life outside our own planet. There is considerable debate whether this work can yield useful results. As will be shown presently, there is a very high probability that life exists elsewhere in our universe, but there is no certainty that meaningful communication with any sentient extra-terrestrial beings can be established soon—or ever—by any means within our command. It is not very probable that there are humans or humanoids elsewhere, except in the view of extreme determinists. They claim that, given conditions similar to those that existed on earth, similar forms of life, including man, would inevitably have evolved.

Life, as we know it, depends on the development of self-replicating machinery of information such as is provided by nucleoproteins. As we have seen, this development can proceed only under certain conditions. These include a reducing atmosphere, a certain degree of humidity (life is impossible without water), and a restricted range of temperature, perhaps averaging from 0°C to 80°C, and in general not dropping below −100°C. Under temperature that is too low reaction rates proceed too slowly; with temperature too high, precursors of organic molecules would break down.

Looking first at our own solar system, we can eliminate all but one of the heavenly bodies as possible places, in addition to earth, for life to develop. The moon, Mercury, and the asteroids have no atmosphere and no surface liquid. Jupiter, the Jovian moons, Saturn, Uranus, and Neptune have reducing atmospheres, but they are too cold, judging from their atmospheric temperatures, for their surface temperatures are not known. Venus has a surface temperature of over 400°C, but a cooler upper atmosphere, and polar caps that cannot be excluded as possibilities, although they seem highly unlikely ones. Mars is left as the only serious candidate.

The atmosphere of Mars has no detectable oxygen, much ultraviolet radiation to supply energy, and a temperature range from about 30°C in the summer daytime to −40°C in the winter. Whether enough water vapor is present for life is still debated. Seasonal changes in color that could be interpreted as polar-cap melting have been observed. All evidence, however, suggests that if life is present on Mars, it is represented only by microscopic forms. Among various kinds of evidence on this point, there is the astronomic one on particle size. Some astronomers, while believing that present conditions may be too harsh, do not exclude the possibility that life once existed on Mars.

United States' space program recommendations are for a Mars landing mission in a few years, and various kinds of exploration probes are being developed. One plan calls for landing a microscope with a moving strip of nutrient materials, which could signal changes in color when certain essential energy-transport substances indicated a metabolic reaction. Another probe involves the labeling of nutrients with radioactive carbon. If radioactive carbon dioxide were then released into the atmosphere it would be an indication of the presence of living matter. One important requirement of the project is seeing that the probes do not carry with them terrestrial microorganisms that could establish themselves on Mars and hopelessly becloud the inquiry regarding existence of native Martian life. Similarly, if any material were returned from Mars, precautions against contamination here would have to be taken. It is not out of the question that Martian life is completely different from ours (for instance, silicon-based instead of carbon-based) and, if brought to earth, might be impossible to control.

The probability of life outside the solar system has also been seriously examined. Only a little is known about exact conditions prevailing beyond our system, but some deductions may be made. One essential for life to develop on a planet is that the planet have an orbit that is not excessively eccentric, since an eccentric orbit would produce a range of temperatures greater than that under which life can exist. The likelihood of finding planets with appropriate orbits in any particular solar systems depends on the origin of that system: if by collision, the right kind of orbit is unlikely; if by gaseous condensation, highly probable.

From what we know of nearby systems, they are not promising habitats for living matter. Within five parsecs (approximately one hundred trillion miles, or about 16 light years) of our solar system, there are 41 stars. Our nearest neighbor, Alpha Centauri (4.25 light years distant), does not have suitable planets. Indeed, among our close neighbors, only Epsilon Eridani (10.8 light years away) and Tau Ceti (11.8 light years distant) have.

Altogether, in the Milky Way alone, there are at least 100 billion planetary systems like ours, and claims have even been made that within the 10,000 cubic parsecs proximal to earth some 200 billion inhabitable planets exist. This leads many astronomers and biologists to the view that it is almost certain that life has developed on many of these. Yet, the distances are so great that we may never be able to detect such life or communicate with any sentient beings that may have evolved on such planets. A short term attempt has already, however, been made to search with medium-short radio waves for signals from outer space. It is not improbable that living beings on some planets have a technology that would permit them to contact us, but the whole matter is beset by innumerable uncertainties. We do not know, for instance, how long civilizations last. It may be possible that the luminous outbursts called supernovae, which could be exploding stars, record the destructions of civilizations, or that we ourselves, by triggering thermonuclear reactions, shall become a self-destroying civilization before we learn if life is to be found elsewhere.

3
DARWINISM

3.1 PRE-DARWINIAN VIEWS

The outstanding landmark in the history of evolutionary thought was the publication in 1859 of Charles Darwin's *On the Origin of Species by Means of Natural Selection and the Preservation of Favoured Races in the Struggle for Life*. As is often the case with important generalizations, his central thesis, natural selection (see Box 2.A), was not entirely new. But his work appeared when the intellectual time was ripe, and as he marshalled overwhelming amounts of convincing evidence, the idea caught fire. It spread and made numerous converts. Little by little, with setbacks and organized opposition in many places (some as near to us geographically and chronologically as the court tests in Tennessee in the twenties, and Arkansas in the sixties, of laws, since repealed, against teaching evolution), Darwinism became an important and central part of human thought. Indeed, it is difficult to find any informed person unbiased by Fundamentalist considerations who does not consider that, with or without Divine Design, evolution is the way man arrived on earth.

Four periods may be distinguished in the history of Darwinism:

1. The pre-Darwinian period was essentially speculative, with primary consideration being given to the question whether evolution occurred at all.

Figure 3.1.

Charles Robert Darwin in his later
years of life. (From the collection
of George Eastman House in
Rochester, New York.)

2. Darwin and his immediate followers lived in the observational period, that is, when observations were gathered as evidence.

3. The early part of the present century was devoted to continued accumulation of observations but with greater emphasis on experiments and model building and with a more rigorous examination of objections to the notion of natural selection.

4. The neo-Darwinian and current period is one in which the synthesis between his ideas and the newly established laws of hereditary transmission was attained. The rediscovery of Mendel's laws erased the main difficulties of Darwin's own scheme of evolution. The more recent and profound investigations of molecular biology and biochemistry have not only removed any equivocation about evolution having happened, but made this process a compelling idea. They also gave us a highly probable account as to how life could have originated in the first place. Of course, there is a great deal yet to be learned about details, some of which may forever remain speculative.

The first of these periods goes back to the beginnings of the human search for understanding of man and the world, which to Western culture means back to the classical Greek philosophers. The Greeks proceeded in their rationale from *a priori* philosophical grounds, from observation by the unaided eye, and from logical arguments and so-called common sense. Hence many things that we know to be false were reasonable to them: for example, continuous spontaneous generation and the transmission of somatic changes from generation to generation (**inheritance of acquired characters**). In general, there is a tendency to read more science into the views of the Greeks than is really there and to credit them with pre-vision. For instance, Democritus, who lived in the fifth and fourth centuries B.C., is sometimes called the father of atomic theory, although there is hardly any resemblance between the atom he talked about and that of current nuclear physics.

Among Greek philosophical writings, from the sixth century B.C. on, speculations are found about life originating from the sea. They also include mythical ideas about the adaptive changes involved in the transition from the

BOX 3.A SOME PREDECESSORS OF DARWIN

In addition to Linnaeus (Section 2.3), who was the father of modern classification of living creatures but a believer in special creation, the following may be mentioned among pre-Darwinian students of natural science.

Francis Bacon (British, 1561–1626) was a firm Aristotelian and thought that species were immutable. He is generally credited with the revival of scientific inquiry, but many philosophers and biologists now believe that deduction rather than the inductive Baconian method is the appropriate way towards scientific discovery.

William Harvey (British, 1578–1657) is often credited with the first biological experimentation and the discovery of the circulation of blood, although he had some forerunners in these investigations.

Georges L. L. Buffon (French, 1707–1778) was, perhaps, the first true evolutionist, suggesting, with reservation, an evolutionary process based on the inheritance of acquired characters.

Erasmus Darwin (British, 1731–1802) was the grandfather of Charles Darwin and a speculative evolutionist. His main theses were that earth's history was longer than specified by Ussher's chronology and that all life came from a common source. By the end of the eighteenth century the general idea of evolution was becoming relatively popular.

At least three different men wrote of natural selection without, however, arriving at a firm statement of its role in evolution. Two of them were British. They were Edward Blyth, who thought that natural selection, by discriminating against variation, would lead to immutability of species, and Patrick Mathew, whose discussion of the phenomenon was hidden by an appendix to a treatise dealing with naval timber and architecture. The third was Charles Wells, a South Carolina physician, who wrote of the idea as a commonplace fact in a paper on a white female, part of whose skin resembled that of a Negro.

Jean Baptiste de Lamarck (French, 1744–1829) advanced the first comprehensive theory of evolution. One of the mechanisms he invoked for the process was the inheritance of acquired characters, which is now referred to as **Lamarckism**, although he was not the first believer in it. The usual example of Lamarckism given is that of the giraffe, whose ancestor was assumed to have acquired his long neck by stretching to reach upper leaves on a tree and to have transmitted the acquired length to his progeny. We now know that it is more likely that giraffes who happened to have longer necks could obtain more food and thereby had an advantage over others, enabling them to leave more offspring. If their long necks were even in part due to a difference in their hereditary endowment, their offspring, more numerous than that of the others, would receive genetic instructions for the formation of longer necks through the gametes. Thus, the average neck length of the next generation would be increased. This cumulative process is **natural selection**.

Thomas R. Malthus (British, 1766–1834) suggested in his "Essay on the Principle of Population" that mankind multiplies geometrically while the means of subsistence do not. Although Darwin credited his reading of this essay with generating in his mind the notion that an average individual produces more offspring than can survive, thus permitting selection to occur, there appears to be evidence that Darwin discovered the principle of natural selection before reading Malthus. He had also read Blyth, Mathew, and Wells.

Georges Cuvier (French, 1769–1832) was a defender of special creation and Lamarck's opponent in the evolutionary debate of the day. He recognized that fossils were extinct forms of life, following the discovery in 1791 by an English surveyor, William Smith, that different layers of rock contain different kinds of fossils. But his explanation was the theory of **catastrophism**, that is, that in the past, life on earth was destroyed several times, as in the Biblical account of the flood, and then created anew.

Charles Lyell (British, 1797–1875) countered catastrophism with the theory of **uniformitarianism**, which held that historical changes on earth were not due to a series of catastrophes but to the same gradual changes as may be observed today, an important cornerstone of evolutionary thought.

aquatic to the terrestrial form of existence. Fossils were recognized by at least one Greek philosopher as being animal remains. Views on the nature of change, the basic tenet of evolution, ranged from the idea that all change is merely an illusion of the senses to the idea that everything is always in flux. The first vague notion of organic evolution appeared in the fifth century B.C. It held that the various living beings arose by a fortuitous combination of parts, and that those which were badly put together did not survive. It thus contained the germ of the principle of natural selection.

The most important scientific influence was that of Aristotle (384–322 B.C.), the creator of natural history and of the logical method exclusively used in science until recent years. He was a teleologist, that is, a believer in intelligent design and in the idea that processes in nature were directed towards certain ends. Teleology was rejected by modern scientists until the recent discoveries that, contrary to the situation in physical science, many biological processes are based on feedback and are, indeed, end-determined; for example, production of enzymes by cells, which will be described in Chapter 6. Aristotle's views and his classification of plants and animals were basically nonevolutionary, and, in many ways, his authority inhibited development of evolutionary ideas for a millenium and a half or more.

There is little to be said about the post-Aristotelians, the medieval scholastic philosophers, because they contributed mostly to metaphysics and to moral, rather than natural, philosophy. Some of them established the notion that conditions of life were immutable. The view was taken that the world was always as it is now and that both biologic and social relations and structures were static. Interpretation by previous authorities, which Dobzhansky calls the "comfortable certainties of the traditional medieval world," was replaced only over a long period of time by scientific questioning.

A thorough history of pre-Darwinian thinking is, of course, impossible here. Box 3.A provides some guidelines. The details of how Darwin (1809–1882) and, independently of him, **Alfred Russel Wallace** (1823–1913) came upon the ideas of natural selection will not be given here.

As a young naturalist, Darwin made a trip around the world on H.M.S. *Beagle*, in the course of which he accumulated a vast store of observations. Combined with his reading and deductive cogitation, they led him to the formulation of his theory. Wallace, who studied the natural history of Malaya, apparently had an intuitive flash about the role of natural selection in the evolutionary process, and, in 1858, wrote to Darwin about the idea. This led to the reading of papers by the two men, although they were not themselves present, at a historical session of the Linnean Society of London, followed by the publication in the next year of *Origin of Species*. The 1,250 copies of the first printing of the book were sold immediately. It is a curious fact that the annual report of the Linnean Society records that "nothing of significance happened in 1858."

Darwin had a large number of immediate followers who popularized his ideas and added to his observations. There were many critics, and various objections were raised, some reasonable and some based on lack of comprehension. We shall omit the history of post-Darwinian developments, but, before discussing the essence of Darwinism, shall consider the nature of the revolution produced by Darwin and its relation to other scientific revolutions.

3.2 SCIENTIFIC REVOLUTIONS

Historians of science differ about how science develops. Traditionally, it has been assumed that scientific progress is always gradual and slow, and that in a historical continuum there are no critical points or revolutions. Recently, the view has been advanced that there are, indeed, revolutionary discrete moments in the history of ideas, such as are exemplified in the works of Aristotle, Descartes, Newton, Maxwell, and Einstein. It is possible to find examples both of advances that took a long time to come to fruition and of sudden advances, of which it may be said that they shook the world. We may look at some of these sudden advances, choosing them from different disciplines in order to place in perspective the magnitude of the Darwinian one, which, it may be argued, eclipsed all others in significance.

The Keplerian revolution was in the realm of astronomy. A number of contributors to it are listed in Box 3.B. It was the beginning of the discovery that man is not the center of the universe, and it substituted the **heliocentric** for the **geocentric** view of our solar system. No one now questions the idea that earth, far from being the center of the universe, is one of innumerable planets and no more distinguished than billions of others.

Though this revolution affected both science and general intellectual activities, it was probably less significant to human society than Darwinism. It

---

BOX 3.B THE COSMOLOGICAL REVOLUTION

Although it may be necessary to choose only one of these names to provide an eponym for this revolution, all of these men made important contributions to it. The list illustrates the fundamentally international character of scientific progress.

Nicholas Copernicus (1473–1543), a Pole, first suggested that the earth is merely a planet revolving around the sun, rather than the center of the sun's orbit.

Tycho Brahe (1546–1601), a Dane, observed what are presumably exploding stars, or novae, a phenomenon suggesting that the universe is not a static but a changing place.

Giordano Bruno (1548–1600), an Italian, proposed that the universe always existed and was not created as in Genesis. The Inquisition could not agree less and burned him at the stake.

Galileo Galilei (1564–1642), another Italian, brought experiment to natural philosophy, helped establish the view of Copernicus, and changed the basis of our questions about nature from "why" to "how."

Johannes Kepler (1571–1630), a German, proved that Copernicus was right, and worked out the laws of planetary motion.

Isaac Newton (1642–1727), an Englishman, generalized the laws of motion that prevailed in cosmology for over two hundred years. Curiously enough, he was a believer in special creation and in Ussher's calculations.

is a defensible view that the latter had even more important social effects than the revolution dealing directly with society initiated by Karl Marx (1818–1883) roughly at the same time. Marx and his associates in the field of political and economic thought introduced momentous notions about the nature of motivation in human history and about the historicity of social change. They believed they had discovered the fundamental laws of the development of societies. The political effects of Marxism were eventually exceedingly far-reaching. Yet it is arguable that they were at the practical level and not really a matter of scientific or intellectual principles in the way Darwinism was. Communist philosophers would, no doubt, disagree with this evaluation.

The outlook of Darwinism is that man was not created the lord of all he sees; that he was not at the time of his arrival the center of activities on this planet; that he has become the dominant species by a blind process and not by design; that his antecedents were just as humble as those of the rest of living beings. In brief, it led to the rejection of **anthropocentrism**.

Today it may be fashionable to say that Darwinism and the religious outlook, in particular the Judeo-Christian and Moslem traditions, are not in conflict with each other. This is probably correct, but only because most religions retreated from literal scriptural interpretations of the world's origin and of man's historical position in the face of the overwhelming impact and evidence of Darwinism. But it would be correct to say that in Darwin's time organic evolution through natural selection and the Established Church were in opposition.

In general, there is no compelling reason for science and religion (in the sense of ultimate concern for values and ethical systems rather than revelation of the historical past) to be at odds. One enlightened view is that religion, dealing with absolutes, cannot deny verifiable facts, and must adjust itself to scientific progress. And the process of reappraisal has to go on continuously. If contraception has proved a bit of a stumbling block, it is easy to imagine the theological problems that discovery of life on other planets, replacement of organs, including the brain, or creation of human beings in a test tube would provoke (see Chapters 20 and 22).

The Darwinian theory also produced Social Darwinism. This was an outlook wherein "struggle for existence" and the unfortunate term "survival of the fittest," were used to justify social inequalities and unethical commercial practices, aggression, colonialism, imperialism, racism, and military expansion. This was a misuse of Darwinian notions of organic evolution, and it can only be deplored that evolutionary thought did not always work on the side of the angels. The point is brought up merely to illustrate the widespread effects of the Darwinian revolution.

Since Darwin, some other revolutions have occurred. Whether Sigmund Freud (1856–1939) was right or wrong, his approach to man as a not entirely rational animal had great repercussions on our behavior, views of personal interrelationships, and social structure. It is, perhaps, too early to evaluate the ultimate consequences of the psychological revolution, which is, no doubt, incomplete. The same is true of the revolution in physics. Thus, the demonstration by Albert Einstein (1879–1955) that observation is a function of the observer's position and of matter-energy equivalence, as well as the other aspects of the new physics, such as the complementarity principle (mutually exclusive ways of seeing phenomena) may possibly take us to the stars. This revolution may also enable us to blow ourselves up, making evolutionary thought somewhat irrelevant. But the effects of Darwinism in all our intellectual activity and in all our understanding (incomplete as it is) of ourselves and our world, are with us every day.

3.3 THE ESSENTIALS OF DARWIN'S REASONING

Darwin's idea holds that all modern living forms descended with modification from preexisting forms, which, in turn, had ancestral forms. The modifications were undirected. That is to say, contrary to a teleological view, they arose without reference to the needs of the plants and animals bearing them. Because those organisms that were better adapted to their environment left more offspring than those that were not, modified forms might replace, over a period of generations, the nonmodified ones. This process of natural selection led to the origin of more and more complex forms capable of exploiting diverse ecological niches. If it is possible to speak of progress in evolution (there are differences of opinion on this point), the progress consisted of increasing individual adaptability, so that increased homeostatic (Box 2.E) powers developed.

Darwin's definition of natural selection started out with the premise that there are checks on an indefinite increase in the number of surviving offspring an individual produces. They include predation, limitations of food supply, such physical factors as climate and disease. Today we know a variety of other population-regulating mechanisms, which themselves evolved as a matter of natural selection.

On the basis of this premise Darwin said: "As many more individuals of each species are born than can possibly survive, and as, consequently, there is a frequently recurring struggle for existence, it follows that any being, if it vary however slightly in any manner profitable to itself, under the complex and somewhat varying conditions of life, will have a better chance of surviving, and thus be naturally selected. From the strong principle of inheritance, any selected variety will tend to propagate its new and modified form."

Elsewhere he continued: "This preservation of favorable individual differences and variations, and the destruction of those which are injurious, I have called Natural Selection, or the Survival of the Fittest." Actually, the term "selection" was, as Darwin made explicit, a metaphorical term, and did not imply a conscious choice either by the organism or by an external agency, except for **artificial selection**, in which man exerts control over the development of plants or animals by choosing certain individuals for breeding.

An important part of Darwin's definition of survival was success in leaving progeny. Obviously, to have offspring an organism must survive for a certain length of time, but the significance of survival lies essentially in giving the organism an opportunity to have progeny. In the past, the factor of survival in natural selection operated to a considerable extent in human life, as many individuals died before reaching the reproductive stage. As it happens now, survival plays only a minor part in human natural selection: it is, rather, based on differential reproduction. Thus, for example, in the Marshall Islands 25 percent of the women produce 75 percent of the babies.

It is the terms "fittest" and "fitness" that have caused most difficulty in interpreting Darwin's ideas. Many early evolutionists and others today have, because of this term, attached anthropomorphic value judgments to the process of selection. Yet Darwin did not have this in mind at all. Neither strength of character, nor moral goodness, nor any attributes of physique or size, nor high intelligence, nor even long life *per se* cause an individual to produce more than the average number of offspring, or to be fit in Darwin's sense. Indeed, often organisms that are totally undistinguished by any physical or mental standards, organisms that exhibit average dimensions for various properties, are the ones most successful in propagating themselves. In a group adapted to its environment, more often than not, it is the mediocre that survive and reproduce and not the exceptional. The Darwinian fitness of George Washington, of Beethoven, of Lenin, of Albert Schweitzer, or of Leonardo da Vinci, none of whom had children of record, is zero, whereas that of a half-witted and crippled hillbilly, who has fourteen grown children, is very high.

It is incorrect to explain evolution by saying that the fittest have the most offspring, since this would be a logically circular statement. If capacity for reproduction is the criterion of fitness, the only connecting proposition between "reproduction" and "fitness" that avoids tautology is that individuals having the most offspring are the fittest ones. This is neither an assumption nor a hypothesis, but merely a definition.

Darwin's description of natural selection may now be paraphrased:

1. in nature individuals differ among themselves;
2. their differences are, in part, determined by hereditarily transmissible factors;
3. whenever these differences involve fitness, that is, success in leaving offspring surviving to reproductive age, the characteristics of the more fit individuals will be represented in succeeding generations to an increased extent.

Thus, changes in characteristics of successive generations are determined in a measure by the inequalities between reproductive rates of individuals differing in hereditary endowment. This endowment is referred to as the **genotype**: the instructions that the different individuals are capable of transmitting to their descendants. The carriers of the various genotypes may be selected or rejected on the basis of their **phenotypes**, that is to say, their somatic properties that make them more or less able to leave surviving progeny in any particular environment. *Natural selection, then, is essentially the differential reproduction of the different genotypes.*

Natural selection by itself cannot account for evolution. As Darwin realized, some apparatus of hereditary transmission and some variation are necessary. The first property is now understood very clearly, due to Mendel and his successors, and to workers in molecular genetics. The second property in large part is due to the phenomenon of mutation, which will be fully discussed in Chapters 14 and 15, and to a number of other processes, including occasional hybridization between species. Some of the other evolutionary forces are **isolation**, which prevents interbreeding between species, and population size, to which we shall return in Section 4.3.

34

Figure 3.2.
The 14 species of Galapagos and Cocos Island finches. **A** is a woodpecker-like finch that uses a twig or cactus spine instead of his tongue to dislodge insects from tree bark crevices; **C, D,** and **E** are insect-eaters; **F** and **G** are vegetarians; **H** is the Cocos Island finch. The birds on the ground eat mostly seeds. Note the powerful beak of **I** which lives on hard seeds. The birds are shown about one-third size. (From David Lack, "Darwin's Finches." Copyright © 1953 by Scientific American, Inc. All rights reserved.)

In the more than a century since the publication of Darwin's book, a tremendous amount of evidence on evolution has accumulated, including experimental observations on a level of refinement not even dreamt of by him. Let us consider a few examples of the data Darwin gathered. In the next section, a few examples from the post-Darwinian age will be given.

The first type of evidence Darwin used was that from the geographical distribution of organisms, which he observed on his *Beagle* voyage. If one considers the flora and fauna of oceanic islands that have arisen from the sea a comparatively short time ago, he may expect, whether he prefers the hypothesis of special creation or of evolution, that the inhabitants of such islands

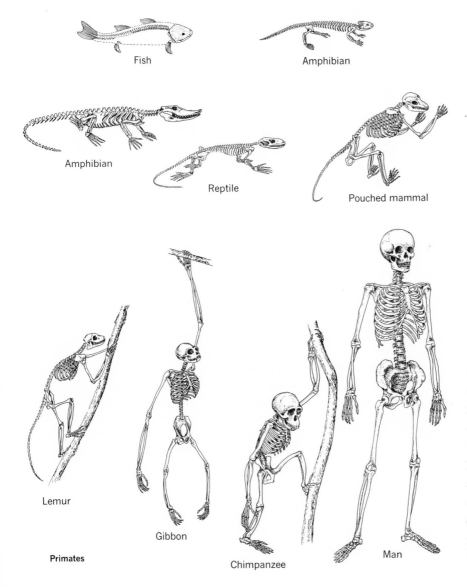

Figure 3.3
Comparative features of skeletons on different rungs of the evolutionary ladder. Both fossil and living forms are represented. (Redrawn, with modification, from W. K. Gregory.)

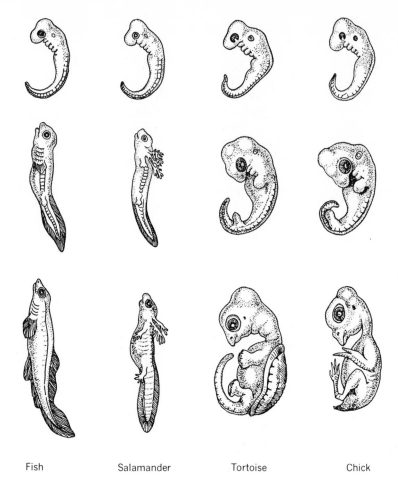

Figure 3.4.
Comparative stages
in the embryology
of vertebrate forms.
(From Garrett
Hardin, *Biology:
Its Human
Implications.*
W. H. Freeman
and Company.
San Francisco,
Copyright 1949.)

| Fish | Salamander | Tortoise | Chick |

have descended from individuals that arrived there from the mainland. From the first hypothesis, the expectation is that they would remain the same as their ancestors. From the second, it is predicted that many lines of such inhabitants, because of their isolation and the mechanism of mutation followed by selection, would change into forms unique to that locality. Indeed, this is what happens. Even rats on many islands develop into varieties distinct from mainland ones. On the Azores, a group of volcanic islands some 900 miles off Portugal, of 74 species of insects, 14 are not known elsewhere; of the 69 species of landshells, 32 are peculiar to these islands; and of the 480 species of plants, there are 40 species related to but different from any on the mainland.

Of the various localities visited by Darwin, the most important to him was the Galapagos Islands. This is a group of twenty small islands that arose off the coast of Ecuador by volcanic eruption some million years ago. Two species of sea lions, five species of reptiles, and several kinds of birds live there, of which all but one are land birds of common ancestry. The 13 species of finches (another species is found on the neighboring Cocos Island) are apparently of common origin, but have developed remarkable differences suiting

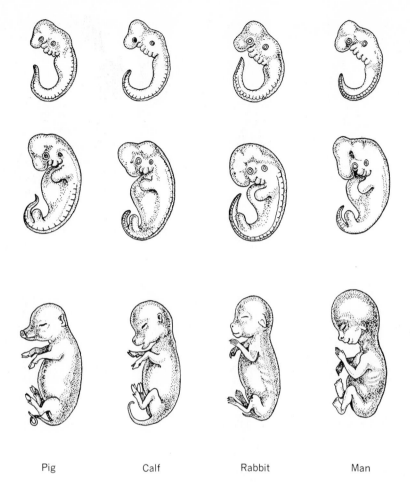

Pig   Calf   Rabbit   Man

them for a variety of niches at their disposal. In particular they differ in size and in beak structure, depending on whether they are ground or tree dwellers and on what they eat. Figure 3.2 illustrates these differences. Examples of adaptations of this sort are very numerous in a great variety of plants and animals.

The second kind of evidence Darwin relied upon came from comparative anatomy. From the hypothesis of special creation there is no reason to expect anatomical resemblances between various forms of life. If we, however, postulate an evolutionary process, transitional types are to be expected. Figure 3.3 presents an example of anatomical changes in structure in the course of evotionary diversification.

Another type of evidence for evolution is found in comparative embryology. Similarities between young forms related to each other are greater than those between adults. This is also to be expected. All animals arise from single cells that resemble each other very closely. As each individual develops, it assumes little by little the form characteristic of its own species and thus diverges from individuals of other species. Figure 3.4 illustrates this process.

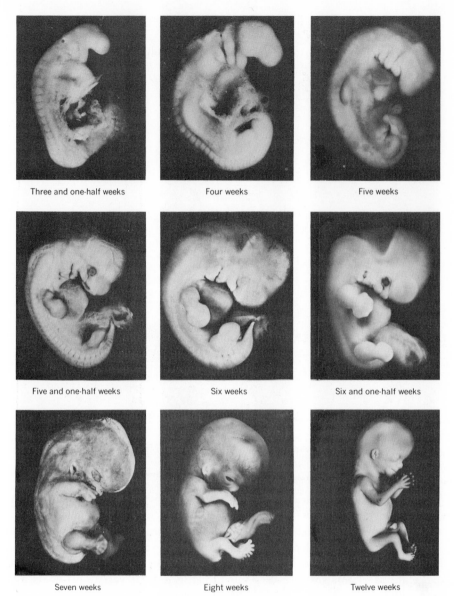

Three and one-half weeks

Four weeks

Five weeks

Five and one-half weeks

Six weeks

Six and one-half weeks

Seven weeks

Eight weeks

Twelve weeks

Figure 3.5.
Photographs of
human embryos.
(By G. W. Bartelmez,
courtesy of
A. S. Romer.)

Figure 3.5 pictures the stages of development of human embryos, which show a remarkable likeness in the early stages to embryos of other vertebrates.

The most massive testimony to evolutionary theory is found in the fossil record studied by paleontologists, which supplies a very clear picture of evolution. Until the birth of genetics, paleontology was the source of the most convincing evidence for the principle of evolutionary change. Fossils in rock layers of different ages show a distinct progression of change from the simplest to the most complex forms of life. An incomplete but consistent history of life on earth has become available through the use of a variety of geologic and chemical methods for dating the remains of extinct forms. We shall discuss the fossil record in the next chapter.

Finally, Darwin drew very heavily on analogy between natural and artificial selection. He was not aware of the real dynamics of these processes, knowledge of which today lends some more weight and precision to the case for evolution. We shall discuss in Chapter 13 examples of artificial selection. Suffice it to say here that the experimental evidence available supports and strengthens Darwin's general views on the matter.

3.5 POST-DARWINIAN EVIDENCE

Since Darwin's time much new information has accumulated to bear witness to his notions of evolution, to amplify them, and to make his generalizations precise. Some of it falls into the categories described in the previous section; other evidence is based on our understanding of cytology, biochemistry, molecular biology, and comparative behavior, fields of study in which most research has been done since Darwin's time.

One of the most spectacular and convincing observational and experimental examples is from the study of the **industrial melanism** of certain insects. About 70 species of moths have light and dark (melanic) variants. Until the middle of the nineteenth century, the former were the common kind, with only an occasional melanic or dark moth found. Since then, however, it has been noted that in areas close to factories, the dark forms have tended to replace the light ones, while in the countryside far from industrial pollution by smoke particles, the light forms are still more prevalent.

A group of British biologists has carefully studied this phenomenon in nature, as well as in the laboratory. They found that the rate of survival of the two forms depended on their visibility to the birds who live on these insects. In unpolluted areas, light moths sitting on tree trunks are practically invisible, while the dark forms are conspicuous. As a consequence, predation by birds tends to eliminate the dark forms. In industrially polluted areas, where tree trunks are covered with soot, the reverse is true. Figure 3.6 illustrates the camouflage in the two environments. The phenomenon has been not only observed and recorded on photographs and films, but quantitative experiments involving release and recapture of the two types of moth in the two environments were conducted. The hypothesis that natural selection was responsible for the spread of the melanic forms was fully substantiated.

Another type of evidence unavailable to Darwin is found in the study of chromosomes. It may be recalled from Box 2.C that chromosomes are the bearers of hereditary information. Their number and structure are characteristic of each species Just as the anatomical features of related organisms bear a resemblance to each other, so it might be expected that chromosome number and details of their internal organization in closely related species would be similar. Indeed, this is found to be the case in many groups of living beings studied.

The chromosome numbers of various kinds of wheat are in multiples of seven (14, 28, 42). Those of chrysanthemums are in multiples of nine (18, 36,

Figure 3.6.
Left: Peppered moths on a tree trunk in an unpolluted area. The almost invisible light form is
below and to the right of the melanic form. *Right:* The visible and invisible forms are reversed in a
polluted area. (From the experiments of H. B. Kettlewell, University of Oxford.)

54, 72, 90). Man has 46 chromosomes, and among his closest living relatives,
the chimpanzee and the gorilla have 48 and the gibbon has 44. A number of
related species of Drosophila, the fruit fly, have from six to twelve chromosomes. Their characteristic shapes and sizes are such that it is possible to reconstruct from their number and appearance their **phylogeny** (the evolutionary
history of a species).

In the salivary glands of the larvae of Drosophila and some other insects
there are giant chromosomes whose fine structure can be readily studied. It
has been found that each chromosome is characterized by an orderly succession of cross bands and knobs (Figure 3.7). In some species the order of bands
can become reversed in sections of certain chromosomes, and the study of such
inversions permits the reconstruction not only of species phylogeny, but also
of the history of a species. Figure 3.8 shows a reconstruction of the evolutionary history of three Drosophila species. In the middle of the figure, two
arrangements of portions of the third chromosome are designated Standard
and Arrowhead. Arrows from them lead to other arrangements with different
names. The phylogenetic relations within and between the three species of
Drosophila (*D. persimilis*, *D. pseudoobscura*, and *D. miranda*) can be thus

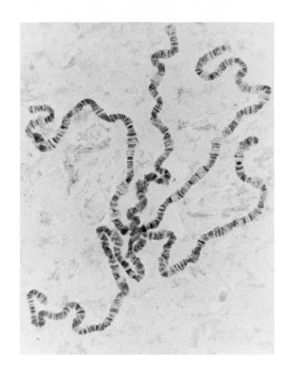

Figure 3.7.
Salivary-gland chromosomes
of *Drosophila melanogaster*.
(Courtesy of Berwind P.
Kaufmann.)

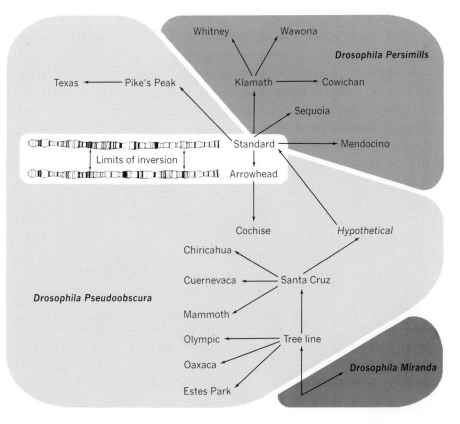

Figure 3.8.
Phylogeny of
third-chromosome
arrangements in
three species of
Drosophila. See
text for
explanation.
(Redrawn from
Th. Dobzhansky
and B. Wallace.)

reconstructed. Many studies of this type with a variety of plants and animals have shed much light on the evolutionary record and the mechanisms underlying it.

Even more spectacular support for evolution has come from more recent studies in immunology, biochemistry, and molecular biology. **Immunology** is the study of behavior of tissues and organisms towards foreign proteins. It

---

BOX 3.C IMMUNOGENETICS OF DOVE ANTIGENS

To determine the community of antigens between two species of doves, blood cells from the Pearlneck dove, containing particular antigens, are injected into rabbits. These antigens then produce specific antibodies. Blood cells from the Ring dove are then added to the serum from the immunized rabbits. Antigens common to the two species combine with (agglutinate) the Pearlneck-induced rabbit antibodies and can be precipitated. The antibodies for antigens that the Pearlneck dove has and the Ring dove lacks, however, remain in suspension. This can be verified by adding again Pearlneck blood cells to the rabbit serum from which the first precipitate has been removed and obtaining a second precipitate after centrifugation. The amount of precipitation observed gives estimates of the community of antigens in these two species. The method can, of course, be extended to any number of species. (Based on the work of R. W. Cumley and M. R. Irwin.)

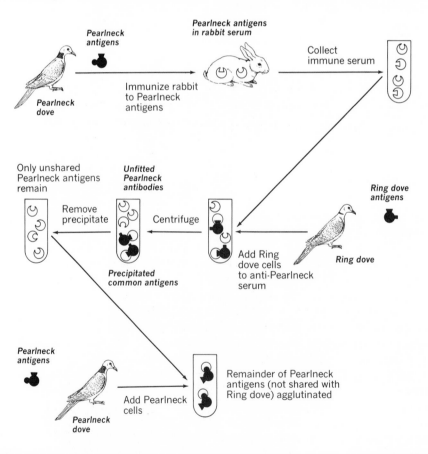

may be recalled that each organism is characterized as possessing a specific combination of proteins determined by the genetic message received from its parents. Some of these proteins may be found in all members of the species (or higher taxa). Others are peculiar to the particular individual.

Normally, the body of an organism recognizes its own proteins and distinguishes them from those foreign to it. When foreign proteins, known as **antigens**, are introduced into the body, it reacts in defense against these invaders by producing **antibodies** that inactivate the invaders. This is the mechanism by which an organism combats infectious disease, that is, invasion by the foreign proteins of viruses, bacteria, and other protists.

The important point is that the antibodies, which are found in the **serum** of animals (blood consists of plasma and blood cells; the fluid left after clotting agents are removed from the plasma is the serum), are highly specific for each kind of antigen. In other words, every antigen is inactivated by a particular antibody. Blood-group substances (discussed in greater detail in Chapter 18) can act as antigens. Thus if blood cells of type A are introduced into the bloodstream of an individual whose genotype is B, the A-antibodies will destroy them by clumping (**agglutination**). Other antigens, under similar conditions, are subject to dissolution (*lysis*), precipitation, or other forms of destruction. Incidentally, on occasion, because of failure of recognition, a body may start manufacturing antibodies against its own proteins, giving rise to such severe *autoimmune* diseases as lupus. Treatment of this disease by *immunosuppressive* drugs, like cortisone, or by X-rays lowers the capacity of the organism to produce any kind of antibodies, thus rendering it defenseless against infection.

Now the closer two individuals are related, the more proteins they will have in common. By a variety of techniques, one of which is illustrated in Box 3.C, it is possible to establish the relative amounts of protein kinds shared by related species and to establish phylogenetic connections between them. Further consideration of phenomena of this type within the human species will be given in Section 16.2. Here it only need be said that confirmation of the facts of evolution is provided once more by this type of investigation.

It is also possible to study the variety of proteins found in the blood serum of various animals by biochemical techniques. Many proteins are characterized by a particular net electrical charge that makes them travel at different rates in an electrical field. When, for instance, the serum of primates is given such **electrophoretic** treatment, it separates into some 19–25 different components (Box 3.D). Here again, relationships among species can be established by noticing resemblances and differences in the pattern of protein movement. Other techniques for separating proteins, or specific enzymes, have also been used, giving clues for the reconstruction of evolutionary history.

Methods of studying variation in proteins are continually being refined. It is now possible to analyze the polypeptide chains of many proteins and to establish exactly what their amino acid sequences are. For instance, cytochrome c is an important enzyme involved in transporting electrons in the cell. Different species have different kinds of cytochrome c, each with its own particular sequence of amino acids. For example in the horse this enzyme consists of a chain of 104 amino acids, in yeast it has 108, and in wheat germ 112. The order of the acids has been established for at least seven different species.

The process of mutation involves a change in the genetic message, ordering a

BOX 3.D ELECTROPHORESIS PATTERNS OF HOMINOIDS

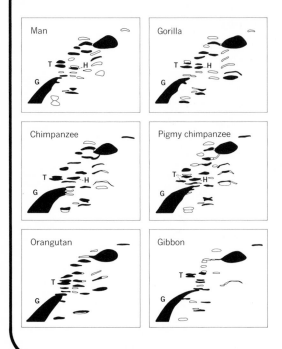

The illustration represents the patterns observed in the study of electrophoretic behavior of some primate sera. Each spot or blob represents a particular kind of protein. The ones labeled T are *transferrins* (used in iron transport), those labeled H are *haptoglobins* (proteins that bind hemoglobin of old and broken down red blood cells), and those labeled G are *gamma globulins* (proteins of the antibodies). Note the strong resemblances between man and his near relatives. Note also the occasional differences (for example, in gamma globulins). While a single analysis of this type is not sufficient to establish relationships among species, the variety of biochemical techniques combined with anatomical information about living and extinct forms should eventually enable us to make fair reconstructions of the history of life on earth. (The illustration is based on the work of M. Goodman.)

cell to place, in a specific position in a given sequence, an amino acid different from that found in the analogous position among the ancestral forms. If many such changes become established in the population by natural selection, they can give rise to gradual differentiation among individuals, and ultimately to the development of new species. Now, by comparing the sequence of the amino acids along the polypeptide chain of one species with that in the analogous chain of another, it is possible to estimate how many mutational steps were taken from the point of divergence from a common ancestor. Even the number of years since the division into two species can be estimated, if we make certain assumptions about the rate of substitution. For cytochrome c the number of differences in amino acids between several different species have been established as follows:

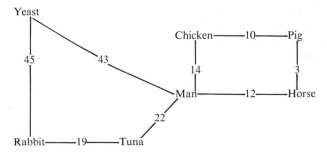

The chronology to be reconstructed can be only an approximate one, since it is possible that different proteins have different rates of substitution. Even the same protein may show variation in this respect. Thus, although there is only one amino acid difference between the cytochrome c of man and that of apes, in yeast there are two forms of this enzyme that differ in 21 amino acids positions.

Another example of evolutionary relationships based on biochemical relationships between different species is illustrated in Box 3.E. As may be seen, there is a general correspondence between the number of differences in amino acids of the proteins examined and the estimates of chronological separation of the various species, although it is not perfect. If the two sets of figures are to be taken as true, then some variation in the rate of amino acid substitution must be conceded. An average rate of one substitution per million years has been suggested in the evolution of cytochrome c and of hemoglobin.

BOX 3.E BIOCHEMICAL EVOLUTION

An example of determination of the evolutionary relationships of a number of mammalian species is given in a study by R. F. Doolittle and B. Blömback. They investigated the amino acid sequences in portions of the molecules of fibrinogen, a protein involved in blood clotting. The two portions, fibrinopeptide A and fibrinopeptide B, contain chains of 17 to 19 and 13 to 21 amino acids in the species studied. In the diagram the numbers in italic type give the percentage of correspondence between the different species with respect to the kind of amino acid found in each position of the chains (data for the two fibrinopeptides are combined here). The bold face numbers give the estimated time since the divergence of the species in millions of years.

If we now tabulate the estimated number of years (in millions) since any pair had a common ancestor against the percentage of amino acids common to the same position in their fibrinopeptide molecular chains, we find a close but not a perfect correlation.

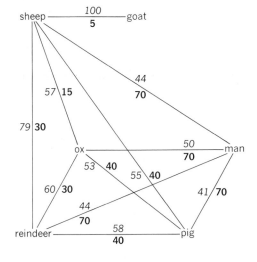

Time of divergence in millions of years	Percent correspondence in amino acids
5	100
15	57
30	60
30	79
40	53
40	55
40	58
70	41
70	44
70	44
70	50

Molecular methods of studying evolutionary relationships are being developed, including attempts to distinguish the DNA of different taxonomic groups. These various techniques are exceedingly powerful tools for the study of evolution and permit the accumulation of extremely significant evidence on the Darwinian process.

3.6 SOME OBJECTIONS TO DARWINISM

Many objections to Darwinism have been raised in the course of more than a century of its history. Most of them carry little conviction in the face of the growing body of data and the increasing comprehension of evolutionary mechanisms. Some objections arose from a lack of understanding of the principles involved; others from traditional religious conviction. For instance, the English naturalist, Philip Gosse (father of the writer, Edmund Gosse), admitted all of the evidence adduced by Darwin. Then he proceeded to say that it proved that the Creator had made the earth six thousand years ago as a going business, giving it the appearance of having evolved in order to test man's faith in his Creator. In fairness to Gosse, this view was expressed long before the mechanism of heredity was discovered, but one may nevertheless ask why an omnipotent Creator should play such childish games.

Because evolution is the only consistent explanation of our accumulated observations on current and extinct life on earth, it may be said that evolution has been demonstrated beyond all reasonable doubt—although dissipation of unreasonable doubt, such as expressed by Gosse or the Mississippi Fundamentalists, has by no means been accomplished.

We shall not take time to examine the varieties of objection to evolution except for two; one, somewhat trivial, the other (to which Darwin had no answer, but which was dismissed after Mendel's laws were established), somewhat more serious.

The first one suggests that life is such a complex phenomenon that it is improbable that it arose on earth. This argument is not a very convincing one, because, first, evolution is indeed a mechanism of generating the highly improbable. Second, it is becoming increasingly clear that life is the potential property of matter, so that given (1) enough time, (2) the presence of conditions already specified, and (3) the nonrandom sequence of events during biopoeisis, life was bound to have originated on earth. But even if this were not so and there was much randomness in the process of evolution from inorganic matter to man, the improbability argument still does not hold.

Consider an event which is so improbable that it can happen only once in a thousand times. The probability of it not happening on a single trial is then 999/1000. But if it is attempted 1000 times, the laws of chance tell us that the probability of not happening drops to $(999/1000)^{1000}$ or 0.37. The probability of its occurrence in 10,000 tries, by a similar method, works out to be 19,999/20,000, that is to say, it is practically inevitable.

Despite assertions to the contrary, it seems highly unlikely that a regiment of monkeys provided with typewriters would along with much gibberish produce all of the books in the British Museum. But we must distinguish probability before the fact and probability after the fact. For instance, the probability of a person being dealt a bridge hand consisting of 13 spades is roughly one in 54 quadrillion, a highly improbable occurrence that few bridge palyers ever witness. This probability, however, is no less or no more than any other hand specified *a priori*. Yet no one raises an eyebrow over hands containing a miscellaneous assortment of cards of all suits that have no greater probability of being dealt. It is not proper to compare, let us say, *Homo sapiens* to the one-suit hand (or any that is designated *a priori*), as is often done by disbelievers in his origin by evolution. Man and all other species are more appropriately represented by the ordinary hands whose specifications are not known until they are dealt.

An evolutionary precept that was recognized after Darwin's time and that reduces the claims of the improbability argument is that selection, far from being blind—operating entirely by chance, and begetting successful kinds of organisms as a result of improbable accidents—may be correctly described as a *creative* process. The meaning of this term, in reference to natural selection, is well illustrated by quoting Michelangelo on the process of creation. The opening lines of one of his best known sonnets says, in a somewhat free translation:

> The best of artists has that thought alone
> Which is contained within the marble shell;
> The sculptor's hand can only break the spell
> To free the figures slumbering in the stone.

In the same way, natural selection does not originate its own building blocks in the form of mutations. From such blocks selection does create complexes; it solves in a diversity of ways the great variety of problems that individuals and populations face. Step by step, it builds entities of infinite complexity, ingenuity, and perhaps, beauty. It needs appropriate raw materials; it may not be able to make a silk purse out of a sow's ear; yet, interacting with other evolutionary mechanisms, it has created the human species out of stuff that in its primordial stage may not have looked very promising.

The second objection weighed heavily on Darwin. He, like most of his contemporaries, believed that the mechanism of inheritance was of a **blending** type. That is to say, that the carriers of hereditary information from the two parents blended in the offspring, just as a glass of water mixed with a glass of red wine will produce a pink liquid. The difficulty with this scheme of inheritance lies in the fact that half of the variation in a population would be lost in every generation by the blending process. Very soon, therefore, complete uniformity would be produced and natural selection would run out of material on which it could operate.

Observation showed that the rate of occurrence of mutations is not sufficiently high to maintain the level of variation seen in nature. Darwin's need to overcome this objection led him to adopt a hypothesis whereby different organs of the body send through the blood particles as messengers to the **gonads**, the organs of reproduction. As the body organs change under environmental influences so would the messenger particles, thereby producing new variation. Essentially, this is a form of Lamarckism.

Darwin's remarkable cousin, **Sir Francis Galton** (1822–1911), some of whose contributions are sketched in Box 10.B, tested this hypothesis by injecting blood of rabbits of one color into females of another. According to Darwin's theory the offspring of the recipients having the new kind of message with respect to color should have shown the fur coat color of the donor. The results were completely negative, although, as we shall see in Chapter 21, this issue was revived again many years later.

The solution of the problem of how variation is maintained came when the Mendelian laws of inheritance were established, proving that inheritance was **particulate**. The units of hereditary information received by the zygote from one gamete do not blend with the units received from the other but retain their identity. They are reassorted in the following generation and, with minor exceptions in some lower organisms, are not contaminated by having been present in a zygote containing the mixture. The details of this process are considered in Chapter 7.

Under this scheme of inheritance, instead of one-half, only $1/2N$ (where N is the number of effectively interbreeding individuals in a population) of initial variation is lost, and this figure is compatible with observed facts. The removal of this objection to Darwin's theory was of great importance in the development of current concepts of organic evolution.

At this point, we are ready to examine in broad terms the evolutionary process as revealed by the paleontological record and the forces which shape evolutionary change.

4

THE EVOLUTIONARY RECORD

4.1 THE FOSSIL STORY

Fossils are remains or impressions of living forms found in the layers of the earth's crust. They provide a clear, but fragmentary, record of the past. The more recent the period under investigation, the more precise is the information available. This is not only because of the proximity of recent fossils to the surface of the earth, but also because the parts of organisms that may best be preserved are such hard ones as skeletons, which are of relatively late origin in history of life on earth. Nonetheless, bacteria, pollen, seeds, and imprints of soft parts are also found.

Paleontologists have learned to make complete reconstructions of many forms, though some biases and a certain amount of guesswork enter into them. Behavior, as well as the anatomical features of extinct forms of life, may be deduced from the fossil record; for example, certain animals have left tracks that indicate burrowing. Other details about the life of a particular organism may be inferred from fossils, such as the kind of food an animal ate (inferred from the structure of its teeth and from coprolites, or fossilized excrements). Recently, it has been proposed that it is even possible to reconstruct the body temperatures of extinct organisms by studying the chemical structure of pre-served fossil proteins, which vary depending on the temperature at which they were synthesized.

Mistakes, disputations, and even hoaxes have been entered in the paleonto-logical record. For example, an amateur English paleontologist, for motives unknown, reported an anomalous find, the "Piltdown man." Many years later it was discovered that a human skull had been combined with an ape jaw. To their credit, professional paleontologists did not accept the find as authentic even before the hoax was proven.

The oldest fossils of protists are from some three billion years ago. Fossils found in Canada are more than two billion years old, and have been inter-preted as remains of multicellular animals, although their real nature has not been conclusively demonstrated. But only a limited fossil record before the Cambrian Period (some 500–600 million years ago) is available (Figure 4.1.)

In early attempts to reconstruct the past, paleontologists dated fossils by assigning an age to them corresponding to the age of the rocks in which they were found. On the assumption of uniformitarianism, with allowances for earth movements and other geologic phenomena, the age of the rocks was cal-culated from known or inferred rates of sedimentation. In recent years, chem-ical methods have become available to obtain the dates not only of the rocks but of the fossils themselves.

It is known that C^{14}, the radioactive isotope of carbon, originates by bom-bardment of nitrogen in the upper atmosphere by cosmic rays and decays at a known rate. In the atmosphere, an equilibrium between C^{14} and ordinary carbon, C^{12} exists. Hence, the ratio of C^{14} to C^{12} is a constant and is known, let us say, for carbon dioxide. A living animal will take up the two kinds of carbon in CO_2 in this particular ratio. When the organism dies, the decay continues but no new carbon is incorporated into its body, and, therefore, the ratio of C^{14} to C^{12} drops at a constant rate. Thus, by determining the carbon

Figure 4.1.

Fossil worm from Australia, about 600 million years old, shown approximately twice the actual size. (Courtesy of M. F. Glaessner.)

South America	North America	Old World

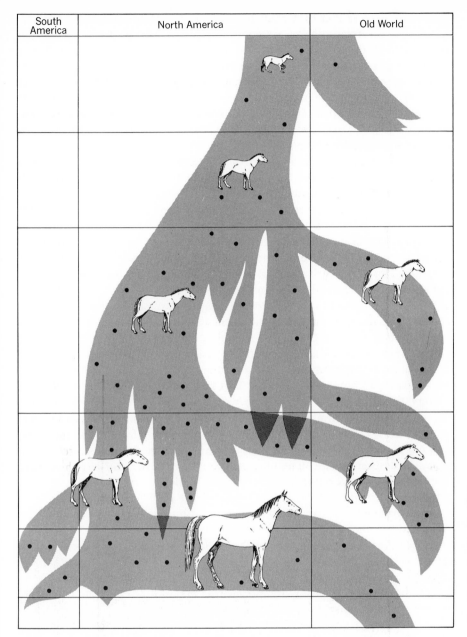

Figure 4.2.
Simplified family
history of the
modern horse,
extending back 60
million years.
Each dot stands for
a species.

ratio in the fossil, it is possible to establish when the animal or plant died. The rate of C^{14} disintegration is expressed by saying that it has a half-life of 5,760 years, that is, one half of its radioactivity disappears in that period of time. Carbon dating is generally acknowledged to be accurate for material up to 30 thousand years old, although some paleontologists set the figure at 70 thousand.

Other elements have similar properties, making them useful for dating. The half-life of radioactive potassium is a billion and a third years; that of radioactive uranium is four and a half billion years. The decay of potassium to argon is useful for dating of material from 230 thousand to 26 million years old, that of thorium and uranium to lead for 10 million years, and that of rubidium to strontium for 20 million years.

There are many general principles that have become established on the basis of the paleontological record. We may list some of them:

1. Animals and plants in the available fossil sequences belong to the same major phyla as do organisms living today, but, in general, they differ from the living species in many features.

2. Fossils found in a given layer of the earth's crust differ from those in other layers.

3. The most advanced phyla, such as the chordates, are represented in the oldest layers not by the specialized forms alive today, but by more generalized ones. Indeed, at least one evolutionist suggests that of the nearly 40 thousand vertebrate species currently on earth, 98 percent derive from eight species of earlier periods. These gave rise to: sharks and rays; advanced bony fish; most amphibia; turtles; lizards and snakes; birds and, perhaps crocodiles; all mammals but the pouched ones; and all pouched animals.

4. The more recent the layer of rock, the more resemblance there is between the fossils found in it and the living forms.

5. The number of extinct types is enormously greater than the number of living ones (Section 2.3).

6. It is common to find at the end of one geologic period many new forms that become dominant in the next. This fact illustrates an important evolutionary principle. Since the periods were essentially a consequence of vast climatic changes, their ends coincided with drastic environmental changes and the appearance of new niches. These produced new selection pressures and new adaptations by the surviving species to the changed external world.

7. The descent of many lines of related forms can be reconstructed very fully. For instance, the evolutionary history of the modern horse is exceedingly well documented for the last 60 million years (Figure 4.2).

8. According to the fossil record, rates of evolutionary change seem to vary. That is to say, there are bursts of species formation and long periods of species stability. However, many biochemists (see Section 3.5) interpret their data on amino acid substitution in the genetic message on the basis of a constant rate of change. This is not necessarily a contradiction, because the sample of chemical traits available for study by biochemists may not be representative of all properties of organisms.

The time scale of the evolutionary process is such that paleontologists consider a rate of change in quantitative characters (for example, changes in tooth length or shape) of about one percent every million years as a rapid one. Evolutionary changes in brain size even more rapid than this occurred among the ancestral forms shortly before the appearance of *Homo sapiens*. They are computed to be approximately 0.1 percent, or one gram, per thousand years.

On the one hand, mammals, which appeared only 120–150 million years ago, have undergone their rapid expansion within the last 70 million years. On the other, there are many forms, the so-called living fossils, that appear not to have changed over very long periods of time. In New Zealand, a living lizard-like creature, the *Sphenodon*, looks exactly like a fossil in rocks 175 million years old. The opossum has a fossil counterpart 75 million years old.

Live specimens of the ocean fish, *Coelacanth*, known as a fossil 100 million years old, were first found a quarter of a century ago. There is also an animal, *Lingula*, which looks somewhat like a clam, but is unrelated to it, whose genus may be 400 million years old; some paleontologists, however, place the fossil into a different genus from that of the living form. Recently, a freshwater protist fossil, apparently morphologically identical with living forms, was dated at 900 million years.

4.2 GEOLOGIC ERAS

An exceedingly condensed summary of the paleontological record is given in Box 4.A. There are a great many finer subdivisions used by geologists than are indicated in the box, but these need not concern us here. The oldest good fossil

---

BOX 4.A THE GEOLOGIC TIME SCALE

Geologists usually arrange time scales from bottom to top to correspond to the layers of rocks. It is, however, more customary for human beings to read from top to bottom. Hence this latter arrangement has been adopted in the various tables and figures of this book, excepting those directly reproduced from other sources.

The customary time classification corresponding to rock layers is into eras, which are subdivided into periods, and, further, into epochs. The units are named either descriptively (for example, Pleistocene Epoch from *pleisto* = most, indicating that this layer contains the most fossils), or by the location at which the typical rock layers were originally found (for example, Cambrian Period,

from Cambria, the ancient name for Wales). For our purposes the details of the kinds of life found in different layers are not important, and only a few names of the different subdivisions are given in the text.

Estimates of the age of the different subdivisions are undergoing constant revision as more information is being accumulated. Hence there are discrepancies among the various ages published; but differences of several millions or tens of millions of years are not significant for us in the context of the five or more billion years of the earth's history. The arrangement shown is not to scale.

Geological era	Millions of years ago	Dominant forms	Ranges of living forms
Origin of earth's crust	4500		
Archeozoic or Azoic (archaios = old; a = without; zoon = animal)	3000	protists	
Proterozoic (proteros = early)	1000	aquatic forms	
Paleozoic (palaios = old)	500–600	fish, land plants	
Mesozoic (mesos = middle)	200–220	reptiles	
Cenozoic (kainos = new)	60 – 75	mammals	
Origin of man	1–2	man	

Ranges of living forms: protists, marine plants, invertebrates, land plants, fishes, amphibia, reptiles, mammals, birds, man

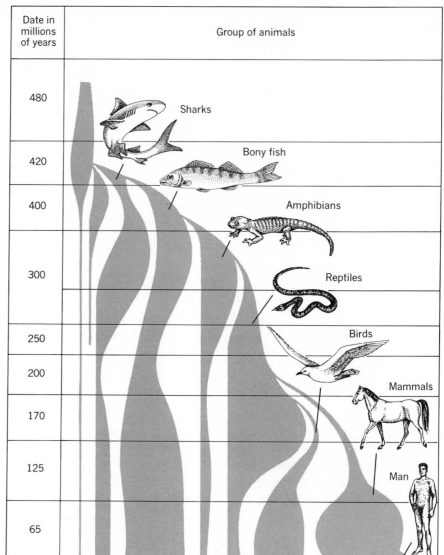

Figure 4.3.
Relative importance
of various vertebrates
since the Cambrian
period. (Redrawn
from Garrett Hardin,
*Biology: Its Human
Implications.*
San Francisco,
W. H. Freeman and
Company. Copyright
1949.)

material is from the Cambrian Period of the Paleozoic Era, when invertebrates, marine flora, and many protists became abundant. In the course of the next 300 million years, crustaceans, spiders, insects, and vertebrates made their appearances (Figure 4.3). The plants invaded land, the first trees established themselves, sharks, amphibia, and, eventually, the first reptiles appeared. The end of the era saw the beginning of dominance by the reptiles and a series of glaciations or ice ages.

There have been three important glaciations since the Cambrian: one possibly in the early stages of the Paleozoic Era, one in the Permian Period at the end of that era some 250 million years ago, and one only some thousands of years ago in the Recent Epoch of the Cenozoic Era. Their causes are not known, but it has been computed that a general reduction of only 3.0–4.5°C.

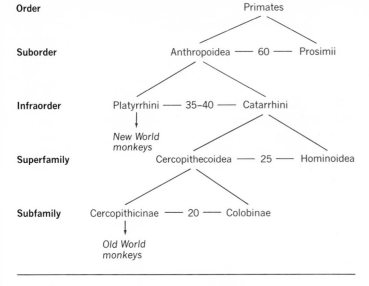

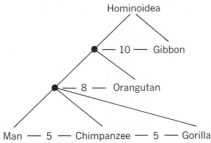

Figure 4.4.

A biochemical pedigree of primates based on resemblances between
serum albumens of living forms. The numbers represent millions of years,
going back to the last common ancestor. The lower part of the figure
differs from morphological reconstructions of lines of descent.
(Data from V. M. Sarich.)

in the earth's temperature would be enough to produce them. The environmental changes would have had a profound evolutionary effect, spreading plants and animals widely in retreat from the encroachment of the earth's
ice cap and affecting the kind of natural selection pressures to which they
were exposed.

The Mesozoic Era was the age of reptiles. The first dinosaurs appeared at
its beginning. Mammals and birds originated during the middle of it, and by
the time the Cenozoic Era started, the dinosaurs were gone. After this, flower-
ing plants, deciduous trees, and mammals dominated.

The Cenozoic Era has two divisions, the Tertiary, which lasted about 70
million years, and the Quaternary, barely a million years long. During the
Tertiary, the differentiation between monkeys, apes, and man occurred (Figure
4.4). This, like much of the evolutionary process, involved radiation, which

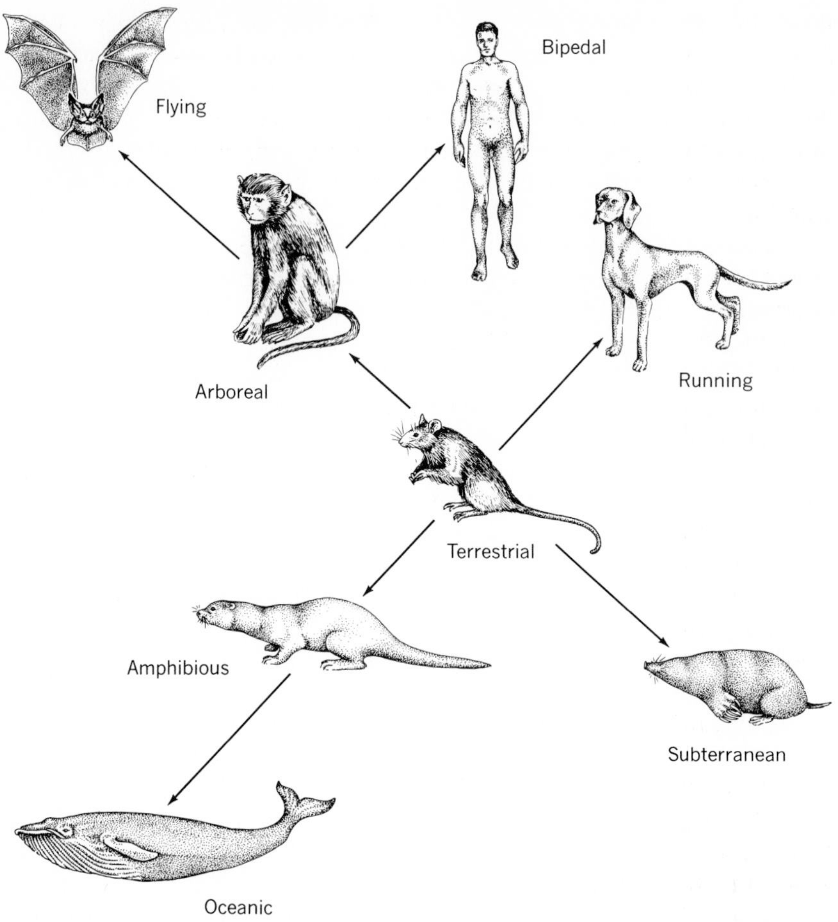

Figure 4.5.
Adaptive radiation
with respect to
locomotion and
habit life (precise
relationships between
the various forms
are not intended
to be shown).

means, in evolutionary thinking, adaptive diversification of form and function. It is schematically represented for mammals in Figure 4.5.

Man appeared in the Pleistocene Epoch of the Quaternary. Use of tools goes back, probably, one and three-quarter million years, *Homo sapiens* appeared on earth some 20-50 thousand years ago and arrived in America shortly thereafter.

4.3 EVOLUTIONARY FORCES

We have noted the conditions necessary for organic evolution to occur: the presence of variation, machinery to transmit to its descendants the revised instructions that produce a variant individual and a differential reproduction or fitness of such variants.

One of the fundamental sources of genetic variability is the process of germinal mutation, which acts on the transmission of hereditary instructions to succeeding generations. It is possible that unique mutational events have occurred. Yet, what has happened once is thus generally possible, so that it is likely that what happened once could happen many times. Given the long evolutionary history of the living species, most mutations are probably **recurrent**. Every time a given mutation arises it is subject to selection, and may be rejected or incorporated into the totality of the population's genes, its **gene pool**.

A second source of variability, which depends upon former mutations, is **recombination**. In the apparatus of particulate inheritance, units of genetic information can be reshuffled (Chapter 7), giving rise to a great number of different genotypes among which selection operates.

Still further sources of genetic variation derive from **immigration**, the introduction of genes from other populations into a gene pool. Many populations are **reproductively isolated** from others. Through mutation and recombination followed by selection they may attain genetic compositions that make them well adapted to their particular localities. On occasion, members of such a population may mate with individuals that belong to a different population. This process either introduces into the gene pool some genes not previously present or changes frequencies of other genes (see Section 7.4) in the gene pool. Sometimes even genes of different species may be introduced, a process known as **hybridization**. Like mutations, the new genes brought in by immigration and hybridization must go through the sieve of natural selection.

The evolutionary force of selection can be of several different types. If a population is highly adapted, most of its recurrent mutations have already been tried out and incorporated into the gene pool if favorable, or discarded if disadvantageous, in the given environment. Similarly, with respect to such quantitative characters as stature, it is likely that in adapted species variation between individuals falls within a range optimal for the success of the species. Any recurrent mutations that produce phenotypes outside this range will be discriminated against by selection. The form of selection that operates against mutations producing relatively unfit phenotypes is known as **stabilizing selection**. It works towards the maintenance and persistence of the species as is.

However, if an environment so changes that the properties of the population are no longer at an optimum, or if mutations previously untested under the particular conditions arise, selection becomes **directional**. It causes the composition of the gene pool or the ranges of phenotypic expressions (stature, disease resistance, etc.) to shift in some direction. It may involve what a leading American evolutionist, **Ernst Mayr**, has called a **switch** type of evolutionary change, which enables the species to spread and occupy new niches.

A third form of selection is **diversifying**, which simultaneously favors two or more phenotypes and is possible in an environment that has multiple niches. This form of selection can lead to formation of subspecies characterized by different phenotypic ranges. If gene interchange between them ceases, that is to say, if reproductive isolation is established, they form separate species. This splitting of a species into more than one, as illustrated by *Drosophila persimilis* and *Drosophila pseudoobscura* in Figure 3.8, is one method of speciation. The other is replacement or transformation, which happened, for example, when *Homo sapiens* replaced his ancestral form.

The last type of evolutionary force we need consider is **drift**, or the chance effects of a small number of parents on the gene pool of their descendants. It is best illustrated by the **founder principle**, so named by Mayr. Suppose a mainland human population consisted of a certain proportion of brown- and blue-eyed individuals. In the absence of any evolutionary disturbances, this proportion would be expected to remain constant from generation to generation. Suppose, further, a group of individuals from this population decided to colonize a previously uninhabited island. If this group were large, the proportion of blue-eyed individuals in it might be expected to be close to that in the whole population. But if it were small, it is possible that, by chance alone, all the founders of the island community might be blue-eyed. In this case, if the islanders became reproductively isolated from the parent population, all their descendants would be blue-eyed. An evolutionary difference between the two populations would have thus arisen. A number of examples of founder effects in man are given in Section 17.3.

Now, many populations have great fluctuations in population size, and may pass through genetic bottlenecks, such as represented by the founder principle. The tighter the bottleneck, or the smaller the population, the greater are the effects of chance on the composition of the succeeding gene pool.

Perhaps a brief interim summary of what we have learned so far about the genetic basis of the evolutionary process is appropriate at this point. Nuclei of cells contain certain instructions for the manufacture of the different proteins which characterize species and individuals, coded in the form of nucleic acids. These instructions also include machinery for duplicating themselves, since the adult form is arrived at through a series of cell divisions, starting with the single-cell zygote. Errors, or mutations, in the coded genetic message, may occur. If they arise in cell lines that do not produce gametes, these mutations may affect the phenotype of the individual, but will have no evolutionary consequences, because they will not be transmitted to the next generation. Such mutations are called somatic.

If, however, the mutations are in germ cells, they will be passed on to the next generation, provided that the individual carrying them survives and produces offspring. Such germinal mutations are the raw material of evolution. They furnish the variability on which selection can operate. Favorable mutations are those that increase the fitness of their carriers in the environment in which they live. As natural selection takes its course, they will tend to displace the original gentic messages.

Other evolutionary forces that may change the composition of the gene pool include introduction of genes from other populations (immigration) or even from other species (hybridization). A further effect can be produced by reduction in the size of the reproducing population, so that a genetic bottleneck occurs. The composition of the gene pool of the generation following the bottleneck will depend to a degree on chance.

Changes in environment can be responsible for changing the magnitude or the direction of selection. Indeed, if the environment were completely stable, evolution would cease after the various species had reached their optimal adaptation levels. An exception might be found if mutations permitted a species to enter a previously unexploited niche or a niche occupied by species with which the mutant forms could now compete. The latter case, however, is tantamount to a change in environment, because environment comprises not only the inorganic world in which a species exists, but the total biota surrounding it as well.

The results of the various evolutionary pressures operating on the population can lead either to the maintenance of the species as is (by stabilizing selection), to its gradual transformation into a different species (by directed selection), or to its splitting into two or more species (by a variety of mechanisms including diversifying selection). Reproductive isolation that prevents gene interchange between groups is generally a requirement for the process of speciation to go to completion.

The evolutionary forces discussed are the ones that operated in the past. They are still operating today, subject in many instances to man's intervention, which, of course, is part of the environment. They are expected to continue in the future, although their effects may be modified or attenuated.

Views have been expressed that the levels of adaptation reached by most species existing today have approached their optima. Further major evolutionary changes seem unlikely to those who hold this opinion. But the fact is that the environment is constantly changing, and is likely to continue to change—if for no other reason than that man is steadily introducing into it new factors of evolutionary significance. Industrialization leading to melanism, discussed in Section 3.5, is but a single example. Pollution, urbanization, man-made radiation, pest control, public health and medical practices, and increased human mobility, which carries in its wake increased mobility of plants and animals, are but a few others.

If man were wiped off the earth completely, he might not evolve again from the lower forms that survived. Major specialized adaptations are generally irreversible. The other species may no longer have the genetic variability that would permit them to begin the evolutionary sequence which culminates in the production of man. But a new dominant form would very likely arise. Meanwhile, evolution in man himself most certainly is going on at the microevolutionary level, as will be shown in Section 7.4. It is even possible that microevolutionary changes leading, let us say, to *Homo superior* or *Homo continuus* (see Section 8.6) will occur.

Evolution as a discipline represents a historical outlook. It *explains* the past, but is not necessarily capable of *predicting* the future. Just because we understand how evolutionary changes could have taken place, we cannot necessarily forecast the future. We have no way of foreseeing what the dominant species on earth will be 150 million years hence, should the world last that long, although we can describe the dinosaurs that dominated life 150 million years ago. But we must realize that because of the cultural advances, and because of the accelerated rate of human cultural evolution, a new factor has entered the picture: our species has the potential capabilities of putting evolution under intelligent management. This has already been done with crops and domestic animals, and the possibility that this power can be extended to control even the evolution of man himself may be at hand. We shall return to this idea in later chapters. Meanwhile, to conclude the part of the book specifically dealing with the evolutionary process, we may take a look at man's immediate past and some of the prospects for his future.

5
MAN

5.1 MAN'S ANTECEDENTS

Figure 4.4 showed some relationships among primates based on biochemical resemblances. Figure 5.1 shows, in a schematic way, relationships among man's antecedents and living relatives. In general, the branching pattern of descent (or ascent, as portrayed in the illustration) with many branches terminating because of extinction, is characteristic of evolutionary trees. The details of the exact stages in man's origin are not entirely worked out but a general picture is beginning to emerge as a result of numerous fossil finds.

When Darwin, some dozen years after publication of *Origin of Species*, speculated on the descent of man, he had no fossil remains as evidence. Since then, numerous finds of hominoid and anthropoid fossils in Africa, Asia, and Europe have permitted the reconstruction of the sequence shown and of the illustrations to follow.

Paleontologists and anthropologists dispute the proper classification of fossil remains. There are splitters, who assign nearly every find to a separate species, and lumpers, who group many apparently divergent forms into a single species. Although a layman, reading about modern man's predecessors, may be confused because of such variance in treatment of fossil material, some

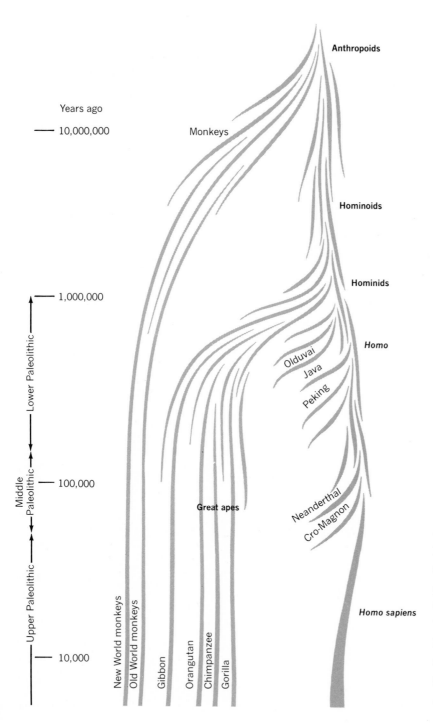

Years ago

—— 10,000,000

—— 1,000,000

—— 100,000

—— 10,000

Upper Paleolithic — Middle Paleolithic — Lower Paleolithic

Anthropoids

Monkeys

Hominoids

Hominids

Homo

Olduvai

Java

Peking

Neanderthal

Cro-Magnon

Great apes

Homo sapiens

New World monkeys

Old World monkeys

Gibbon

Orangutan

Chimpanzee

Gorilla

Figure 5.1.
Pedigree of *Homo sapiens*
and his living relatives
on an exponential time
scale. (From Sherwood L.
Washburn, "Tools and
Human Evolution."
Copyright © 1960 by
Scientific American, Inc.
All rights reserved.)

Figure 5.2.
Reconstruction of *Proconsul*, made from a 1948
find in the Olduvai Gorge in Tanzania. (Reproduced
by permission of the Trustees of the British
Museum, Natural History.)

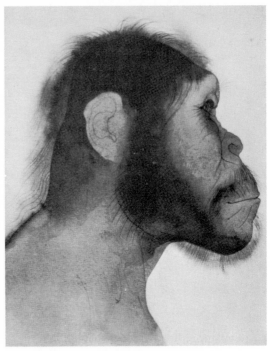

Figure 5.3.
Reconstruction of *Australopithecus robustus*
(formerly known as *Zinjanthropus*). Note
resemblance to *Proconsul* and increased size of
forehead. (Reproduced by permission of the
Trustees of the British Museum, Natural History.)

areas of agreement are being reached, and much of the confusion is disappearing. For our purposes, it will simplify the picture to side with the lumpers.

The form that existed in what is now Tanzania some twenty million years ago at the point of separation between monkeys on the one hand, and man and the apes on the other is known as *Proconsul* (Figure 5.2), and is represented in the fossil record by several hundred specimens. In the line leading to man, two species of apes appeared. *Australopithecus robustus* (Figure 5.3) became extinct and the smaller *Australopithecus africanus* evolved into the genus *Homo*. The great apes and man diverged from each other perhaps five million years ago. The apes differentiated into the groups shown at the top of Figure 5.1. From the evolutionary viewpoint they were not as successful as the monkeys. It is possible that the number of living species of apes and the sizes of their populations are small because they had to compete with their more successful rival, *Homo*.

The numerous finds of early man, formerly considered separate species and labeled the Peking man, the Heidelburg man, the Java man, and so on, are now considered by many to be subspecies of *Homo erectus*. One such subspecies gave rise to forms of *Homo sapiens*, such as the Rhodesian, the Solo,

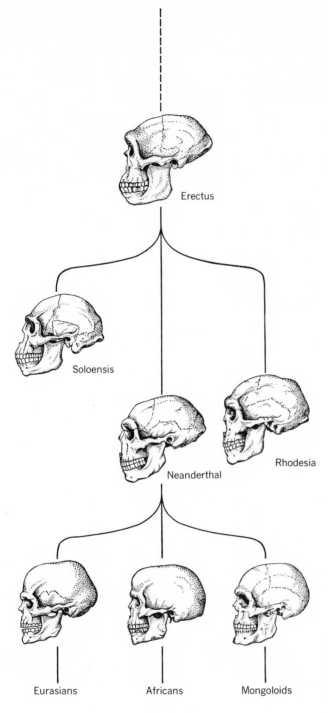

Erectus

Soloensis

Neanderthal

Rhodesia

Eurasians

Africans

Mongoloids

Figure 5.4.
Skull reconstructions of the genus *Homo*.
(From William W. Howells, "The
Distribution of Man." Copyright
© 1960 by Scientific American, Inc.
All rights reserved.)

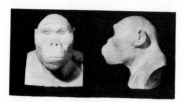

Australopithecus

African ape-man

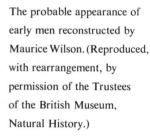

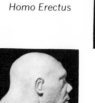
Homo Erectus

Java man

Peking Man

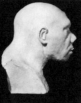

Neanderthal man

Homo Sapiens

Cro-Magnon man

Figure 5.5.

The probable appearance of early men reconstructed by Maurice Wilson. (Reproduced, with rearrangement, by permission of the Trustees of the British Museum, Natural History.)

BOX 5.A CRANIAL CAPACITY OF MAN AND HIS RELATIVES

Species	Chronological range of existence in thousands of years	Average brain size in cubic centimeters
Australopithecus	2,000–600	300–600
Homo erectus habilis	1,000–500	700–900
Homo erectus pekinensis		900–1,200
Homo sapiens neanderthalensis	150–40	1,200–1,500
Homo sapiens sapiens	50–0	1,350

The size of the brain of modern apes is comparable to that of *Australopithecus*. Chimpanzees average 350–450 cc; gorillas average about 500 cc, with 750 cc the maximum. In the microevolution of man, the correlation between brain size and intelligence may be tenuous, the variation in both being enormous (see Section 20.2). Thus, while the size of Turgenev's brain (the largest verified) was 2,102 cc, that of Thackeray, 1,664 cc, and that of Schubert, 1,420 cc, that of Anatole France, hardly the least intelligent of men, was only 1,017 cc. In macroevolution, however, a larger brain permits a more complex neurophysiological organization and certainly is responsible for the development of human intelligence.

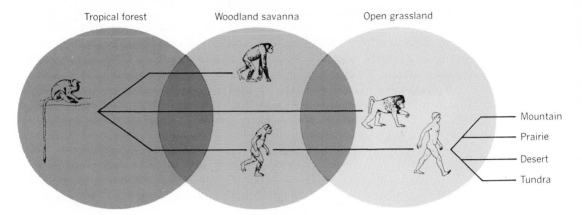

Tropical forest   Woodland savanna   Open grassland

Mountain
Prairie
Desert
Tundra

Figure 5.6.
Evolution of bipedal locomotion in man. (From John Napier, "The Antiquity of Human Walking."
Copyright © 1967 by Scientific American, Inc. All rights reserved.)

and the Neanderthal man (Figure 5.4). The changes in facial appearance from
African ape-man to modern man are illustrated in Figure 5.5.

The specific details of the transformation into *Homo sapiens* are too numerous to be listed. They include various anatomical, physiological, and
behavioral changes, of which the three important ones are descent from the
trees, invention of tools, and increase in size and complexity of the brain. Box
5.A gives some information on the cranial capacity of man and a number of
his relatives.

The origin of tools dates back to prehuman history. Indeed, chimpanzees
are known to make simple tools for obtaining food and water. They have been
observed to fashion sticks to dislodge insects, which they eat, from crevices in
trees, and to make sponges out of leaves to soak up water for drinking. When
more sophisticated tools appeared among the man-apes, they profoundly
influenced the course of future evolution.

To start with, a completely new dimension was added to natural selection
for brain development. The evolution of brain achievements in living forms
can be traced, according to the German evolutionist, **Bernhard Rensch**, along
the following lines. There is some protopsychic property in all matter that permitted the eventual development of mind. There are isolated sensations in
protists and, perhaps, mental images or recollections in the lowest invertebrates. They can become more complex in various associations in such animals
as worms, leading to more lasting coherent awareness in higher forms. Insects
and fishes are capable of memory storage, as judged from delayed reactions to
visual stimuli. Still higher forms are capable of some generalizations and of
transfer of information learned in one situation to another. The ability to
form abstract concepts, to understand symbolic gestures and the idea of numbers and values, is found in many mammals. Comprehension of causal relations appears next on the evolutionary ladder. Finally, the use of reason,
foresight, and displacement (see Section 2.5) developed. These last achievements place a selective advantage on complexity of brain structure, especially
of the cerebral hemispheres.

Bipedal locomotion (Figure 5.6) freed the arms and hands for fashioning and using tools in gathering food and in hunting. This, in turn, led to a reform in social organization, because hunting large and dangerous game was likely to require cooperation with others. Bipedal walking also freed the mouth and teeth, formerly much used for carrying things, for the development of human speech. These and many other significant changes in various structures, functions, and behavior allowed a great acceleration in the progress of man.

5.2 CULTURAL EVOLUTION

To enter the history of man's culture would not be appropriate here. Only the outline in Box 5.B and some general statements about the interaction between organic and cultural evolution need be made.

Cultural evolution, as already noted, is Lamarckian (see Box 3.A). It interacts with organic evolution, activating a mutual feedback between them (see Section 7.4). Natural selection pressures are changed because of changes in culture, and cultural changes are, in turn, affected by the biological and psychological changes due to organic evolution. This interchange led to the impressive speed-up in the transformation of an australopithecine into twentieth-century man. Time intervals between events representing changes contracted from millions, to thousands, to dozens of years. Whereas it took millions of years of organic evolution before birds could fly, man learned the same trick within a few years of his discovery of appropriate power sources. The cultural evolution of our ability to fly is such that we are now preparing to land on Mars.

The same interaction of cultural and organic evolution that has produced the great advances in our understanding of physical and biological phenomena is responsible for endowing man with tremendous control over nature. His mastery of the earth is not complete by any means: the polar cap may melt, another ice age may make its appearance, contaminants from outer space may be uncontrollable, and human folly, exploding enough megatons of thermonuclear weapons, may end it all for *Homo sapiens*. Barring such disasters, our species is in command and it is not likely to allow any other, which might evolve from existing lower forms of life, to displace it as the master of this planet.

Before long, the question of controlling further human biological evolution will face us. One of the favorite subjects of science fiction is the emergence of *Homo superior*. Whether this species has powers of clairvoyance or wings, whether it can defy the laws of gravity or has the powers to become invisible at will, or whether a member of it with an I.Q. of 250 will be considered an imbecile, such a species cannot replace us through natural selection, unless its members have a higher Darwinian fitness than we do.

Pressures for conformity would very likely place the potential founders of a breed of supermen at a disadvantage in a world controlled by our species. Artificial selection is, of course, technically as applicable to human beings as to chickens or corn. But the exercise of such selection is outside the realm of biology. Religious, ethical, political, psychological, and social considerations are paramount in the possibility of man's directing his own evolution with or without the consent of the selected (see Chapter 20).

BOX 5.B LANDMARKS IN HUMAN CULTURAL EVOLUTION

The Neanderthal men were succeeded by Cro-Magnon cave-dwellers, who resembled present-day humans. Figure 5.5 shows what they probably looked like. They inhabited the earth in the old Stone (Paleolithic) age and developed a culture that included notable art work. Their cave paintings, found in central and southern France and in Spain, were remarkable in their sophistication. Most of their subjects were the animals that they hunted. The pictures were probably painted as a part of compulsive or sympathetic magic practiced to secure success in hunting. Since these men lived in an interglacial period, it is not surprising that one of the animals depicted is the reindeer, which still roamed Spain some 15–20 thousand years ago. The illustrations below are reproductions (losing much by not being in color) of paintings from the so-called Magdalenian culture towards the end of the Paleolithic age, found in Altamira in northern Spain. They represent a reindeer, a bison, and a wild boar.

The old Stone age, or Paleolithic period, lasted from some million years ago until it was replaced successively by the middle (Mesolithic) and new (Neolithic) Stone ages, during which man's development extended as given in the table below.

The transitions from a social organization of dispersed hunters successively through those of larger hunting groups, agriculturists, pre-industrial cities, and the feudal system, to the current industrial society were accompanied by a steady growth of population, discussed in Section 5.3.

Age	Years ago	Control of the environment
Paleolithic	1,000,000	From tools to cave drawing
Mesolithic	10,000–15,000	Domestication of first animals (dogs); development of water transport
Neolithic	7,000	Change from hunting and gathering to agriculture
Bronze	5,000	Use of copper and tin, origin of urbanization
Iron	3,500	Beginnings of recorded history
Industrial	150	Industrial revolution
Atomic	20	Mastery of nuclear forces

CAVE PAINTING
REPRODUCTIONS
COURTESY OF
THE AMERICAN MUSEUM
OF NATURAL HISTORY

Meanwhile there is a much more pressing problem regarding man's future: the problem of uncontrolled population growth, which if it does not threaten our species with extinction, as do thermonuclear weapons, at least confronts it with untold misery.

5.3 POPULATION EXPLOSION

In spite of a great deal of publicity on the subject, most of the earth's people are not aware of its significance and urgency. Even in the presumably well-informed United States, a Gallup poll taken in the mid-1960's indicated that two-fifths of Americans did not view uncontrolled population increase as a major world problem.

Most animals have built-in regulatory mechanisms to limit population size. These by no means would be acceptable to humans: release, when there is crowding, of noxious substances that keep down mating frequency; hormonal inhibition of reproduction induced by the social stresses of crowding; spread of genes causing death or sterility; and so forth. Although a human female normally can produce no more than 10 or 12 offspring, which seem remarkably few when we learn that the tapeworm can lay 120,000 fertile eggs a day, man is increasing his numbers at a rate that is probably greater than that of any other organism. Diseases and famine, pestilence and war, infanticide and human sacrifice, unpleasant as it may be to admit it, have regulated population growth hitherto. They no longer do so.

A look at some statistics may help us see the problem, but a word of caution is necessary. All the demographic data to be cited are only coarse approximations. Census figures are notoriously unreliable, and estimates of population size and growth are subject to gross errors. For instance, figures given for the population of Communist China vary at their extremes by 100 percent. The population of Mauretania in Africa is estimated by its government as being threefold the figure given by the United Nations. During the partition of Pakistan and India, the number of migrants from one country to another was computed by dividing the amount of salt issued to them by the average salt requirement. The 1960 census of the United States in which the data were analyzed by the latest computerized techniques, showed that there were in the United States, 1,670 fourteen-year-old widowers, a figure of doubtful validity.

But no matter how much we allow for such inaccuracies, the picture is clear. The history of population growth in this world is shown in Figure 5.7. Put in another way, the tremendous acceleration in the increase of the human population is illustrated by the following figures: it took 4.5 billion years for the population to reach one billion people (1830); it took 100 years for it to reach two billion (1930); it took 30 years to reach three billion (1960); at the present rate of increase it will take 15 years to reach four billion (1975). About 5 percent of all *Homo sapiens* that ever lived roam the earth today.

We can calculate, as an average, that over the whole period of human history, the population doubled every 70,000 years. As recently as 1650 the rate of population growth required 200 years to increase the number of people on earth twofold. Today, the doubling time is about 35 years, varying from 23

Years ago	Cultural stage	Area populated	Assumed density per square kilometer	Total population (millions)
1,000,000	Old Paleolithic		.00425	.125
300,000	Middle Paleolithic		.012	1
25,000	New Paleolithic		.04	3.34
10,000	Mesolithic		.04	5.32
6,000	Village farming and early urban		1.0 .04	86.5
2,000	Village farming and urban		1.0	133
310	Farming and industrial		3.7	545
210	Farming and industrial		4.9	728
160	Farming and industrial		6.2	906
60	Farming and industrial		11.0	1,610
10	Farming and industrial		16.4	2,400
A.D. 2000	Farming and industrial		46.0	6,270

Figure 5.7.
Estimated population size and density from the Paleolithic Age to the end of this century.
(From Edward S. Deevey, Jr., "The Human Population." Copyright © 1960 by
Scientific American, Inc. All rights reserved.)

years in Brazil to 44 in the U.S., to 76 in Japan. According to these statistics, the 15 million people killed in the battles of World War II were replaced in something like three and a half months. The earth's population today stands at over 3.2 billion; the annual rate of increase is 2.5 percent or 80 million people. Every day the population rises by 220 thousand; every hour by more than 9,000.

How are these people to be fed? Today there are 1.2 acres of cultivated land per person, and yet 60 percent of the people have less than the average requirement of 2,200 calories a day. By the year 2000, through alienation of land and population growth, six billion people will have less than half of this amount per person available to them. In the next third of a century, we shall have to triple our food output, increase our production of lumber threefold and our output of energy, iron ore, and aluminum fivefold, just to permit the growing number of human beings to reach a decent living standard.

Technological advances in food production might alleviate the problem of feeding the growing world population. Some authorities think that the earth is potentially capable of supporting 50–100 billion people. But at present our food production is growing too slowly. Just to keep pace with the present population growth, without attempting to relieve widespread undernourishment, an increase of 2.5 percent a year in food production is needed. Our recent increases have been on the order of one percent a year. Thus, while North Americans produce more calories than they need, the average food supply available in India and elsewhere is lower than it was before World War II.

Many ways of resolving the situation have been suggested. The lack of fresh water for irrigation is one of the limitations on food production. Increased use of rational and intensive methods of farming, making fresh water from the sea, heating lakes to encourage cloud formation, and fish and game farming are all possible techniques for augmenting food sources now available. New forms of food may be produced. Man is a heterotroph, relying on the photosynthetic activity of plants and protists for energy-binding. This creates a rather inefficient food chain, because much energy is lost in the process of conversion. Although selective breeding of plants and animals has reduced the amount of raw material needed to manufacture foodstuffs, 80–90 percent of the available energy is still dissipated in every link of the chain. Perhaps the longest food chain of all appears in the diet of Eskimos. An Eskimo must eat five pounds of seal to gain a pound of weight, each pound of seal being derived from five pounds of fish, a pound of which is manufactured from five pounds of shrimp or other invertebrates, each pound of which takes five pounds of algae to produce. In sum, it takes 625 pounds of algae to make one pound of Eskimo, with at least 99.84 percent of the original energy bound by the algae being lost in the process.

One method of shortening the food chain is to grow for direct human consumption plants that would satisfy nutritional requirements presently met by eating animals. For instance, it is possible to manufacture edible protein from otherwise inedible leaves. Similarly, the use of marine protists or yeasts for food is a possibility but the deeply ingrained preferences people hold for certain food makes utilization of such possibilities difficult.

Another complication is the fact that most plant proteins are deficient in certain amino acids essential for the synthesis of proteins in human cells, which lack the appropriate enzymes to manufacture them. Hence, supplementation of a plant diet with synthetically produced amino acids or development of strains of plant food with higher levels of these amino acids may be needed. At least two mutations in corn that increase the amounts of the amino acids lysine, tryptophan, and methionine have already been found. These three substances are among those that man needs and obtains, at present, mostly from animal proteins. Methods using microorganisms to produce high-grade protein from such nonliving materials as petroleum are also being developed. The ultimate technology of food production may depend entriely on synthetic processes, although human dietary habits and palatability standards may have to be modified. Perhaps the need for these adjustments will be circumvented, however, by the manufacture of synthetic material indistinguishable from familiar foodstuffs.

The costs, of course, will be enormous. It is estimated that to feed the population of Southeast Asia alone in 1980 more than 22 billion pounds of bulk protein would have to be produced. At present prices this would cost about 55 billion dollars a year.

In any case, the present doubling rate of the population is such that even if the nutritional deficit could be erased completely, other problems raised by overpopulations would not be solved. Various kinds of limits to the number of people on earth have been imagined, including, for instance, eventual scarcity of nitrogen, which is necessary to make living beings, although this is unlikely. Perhaps, the grimmest picture, relieved by a light touch, has been painted by the British physicist J. H. Fremlin.

He has suggested that the absolute limit to the human population on this planet will be determined by terrestrial overheating. People and their activities generate heat that must be dissipated. If the population increased to one quadrillion people, temperatures throughout the world would reach those currently known in equatorial areas. Adequate cooling devices would make it possible to have 60 quadrillion people on earth. The population density would then be 120 million per square kilometer; today it is 18. When the population rose to 10 quintillion, overheating would literally cook people. At the present rate of population growth, this would happen in about 900 years.

Fremlin imagines many difficulties even if the population stabilized at 60 quadrillion, for example, the housing problem. Perhaps technological advances would permit us to build 2,000-story buildings, covering both land and sea, with 1,000 stories of each housing food-production and refrigeration machinery. Of the rest of the space half would be occupied by wiring, piping, ducting, and elevators, leaving 3¾ square meters of living space per person. Food would have to be liquid, clothes would not be worn, cadavers would be immediately processed into food, and each area of a few square kilometers, containing several billion people, would have to be nearly self-sufficient.

Very little movement of people would be tolerated, but still "each individual could choose his friends out of some ten million people, giving adequate social variety," and world-wide television of unexcelled quality would be available. With the present size of the human population, the birth of a Shakespeare is an exceedingly rare event. In the world of 60 quadrillion some ten million Shakespeares ("and rather more Beatles") might be expected to be alive at any given time.

This apocalyptic vision is not likely to become reality. Our problem is how to put a brake on the increase in the number of people on earth before it does. The main causes of the population explosion are considered in Box 5.C. In brief, they lie in the exponential (Malthusian) nature of population growth and in the increase, owing to advances in sanitation and medicine, in the per-

---

BOX 5.C SOME CAUSES OF THE POPULATION EXPLOSION

A few data gathered from various sources will illustrate some of the reasons for the current population explosion. To start with, if the birth rate is greater than the death rate, population size will increase exponentially, so long as the difference is greater than zero. Other factors also increase the rate of population growth. A minor one is the current tendency to marry younger. In Europe, the average age at which persons enter into marriage contracts is 0.5–2.8 years younger than it was two or three decades ago. The effects of this change are shown in the following table, which gives the average number of children in a sample of families.

Socioeconomic status	Age at first marriage	
	20-24	30-34
Professional	1.8	1.1
Skilled labor	2.3	1.1
Unskilled labor	3.1	1.3

Of more significant effect are the great increases in life-span in this century, largely owing to the rapid progress in prophylactic and therapeutic methods of controlling infectious disease.

Life expectancies in different periods of history have been estimated as follows:

Period	Life-span in years
8000–3000 B.C. (Stone and Bronze ages)	18.0
A.D. 800–1200	31.0
1600–1700	33.5
1800–1900	37.0
early 1900's	57.4
mid-20th century	66.5

Thus, only 11.8 percent of dated Paleolithic skeletons represent human beings who lived more than 41 years; today in the United States, 95 percent of the people survive past 40. Some examples of recent changes in life expectancy may be instructive:

Country	Period	
England-Wales	1910-12 53 years	1958 71 years
U.S.S.R.	1896-97 32 years	1955-56 66 years
Jamaica	1919-21 38 years	1950-52 57 years

Especially dramatic changes have been observed in the underdeveloped countries because of the introduction of sulfa-drugs, antibiotics, DDT, and other means of controlling the spread of infections. At the present time, 60 percent of the world's adults—but 80 percent of the world's children—live in underdeveloped areas. Examples of lowered infant mortality are given by the table below, which shows the percentage of infants surviving a year after birth:

Place	Period	
London, England	1860 70.0	1960 98.0
India	1901 77.0	1962 90.5

One evolutionary effect of the increased probability of surviving until the reproductive age is that, whereas survival per se was an important concomitant of Darwinian fitness in the past, today, with the high level of survival, most of the selection in human population is based on differential fertility. As voluntary contraception becomes more widespread and standards of living improve, philoprogenitiveness may become the main selective agent. In other words, natural selection will lead to an increase in the proportion of the more prolific parents, a fact that may eventually negate the population-regulating efficacy of birth control.

centage of human beings who survive to an age at which they can produce offspring.

Many suggestions have been made as to how population increases can be controlled in addition to the very obvious method of contraception. Ireland's population growth has been limited by a traditional prolongation of the period of celibacy, a method that seems increasingly unlikely to catch on elsewhere in the world. Japan has slowed down its population explosion by encouraging abortion. Legalizing abortion, although it is meeting some religious opposition in the United States, seems a sensible move, but the medical and psychological effects of requiring repeated and numerous abortions for the same woman may rule out its value as a method of population control. Sterilization has been suggested as still another means. Yet it has been computed that the scale on which it would have to be undertaken is not a practical one. For instance, in India, the birth rate (42 per thousand) and the death rate (19 per thousand) might be brought into equilibrium at 16 per thousand by 1991, with the population stabilized at 657 million (it was 438 million in 1961). But this would have required an increasing rate of sterilization, with everybody above the age of 22 having been sterilized by the time the equilibrium were reached. And if the population were to be reduced, the extent of sterilization would have to be even greater. Reduction of population size by any humane means is in general a very slow process. For example, to reduce the present population of Britain to that of 1910 by any reasonable methods might take 200 years.

Even the suggestion that encouragement of homosexuality could keep down population size has been made. Now, so far, no clear-cut genetic basis for homosexuality, or other types of sexual gratification that do not result in conception, has been demonstrated. Should there be one, obviously in the long run this method of population control would be self-defeating: natural selection will tend to weed out genotypes for preferences for sexual behavior not leading to production of offspring (see the remarks on philoprogenitiveness in Box 5.C).

Visionaries who suggest that the problem of overpopulation can be solved by exporting mankind to other planets can hardly take comfort in the fact that it would take only 50 years at the present rate of population growth to bring Venus, Mercury, Mars, the moon, and the satellites of Jupiter and Saturn to the same population density as the earth. Colonization of Saturn and Uranus would give only another 200 years' breathing space. Besides, going outside of our solar system presents what now seem to be insurmountable problems of time and cost.

So contraception seems to be the logical method to use. Cheap and efficient techniques are already available, and only ignorance, religious dogma, and socio-political considerations seem to stand in the way of universal acceptance of family planning. Opposition from organized religious groups appears to be gradually crumbling, and ignorance is being dispelled by education, but other problems still exist. For example, advocacy of limiting the number of children per family in minority groups sounds hollow indeed, when wealthy men raise huge families.

Among those scholars who attempt to foresee the future, there are some who believe that man faces an inescapable dilemma because of the rivalry among nations. If, on the one hand, a given country pursues a vigorous policy of limiting the growth of its population, it will (other things being equal) incur a political disadvantage vis-a-vis a country that does not: on the other, lack of restraint will increase the intensity of the struggle among nations for resources. Others, less bleak in their forecasts, hope for an eventual world-wide society—whether a totalitarian state or a free association is envisaged depends on the optimism of the forecaster—without national boundaries and with demographic policies that may make this world a good place to live in. It is possible that in such a society sterilizing chemicals will be added to drinking water, and conceptions will be the result of a premeditated act*, rather than occurring by default, as most do now. This could imply the licensing of reproduction, an uninviting prospect, but, in the view of some demographers, an unavoidable one.

There are many other things to be considered in any attempt to view man's future. But since our concern here is with the effect of genetic mechanisms, we must leave historical considerations and turn to the machinery by which genetic messages are transmitted within individuals and between generations, and to the biological bases underlying the various evolutionary forces.

---

* As a consequence, one of the best known nursery rhymes may have to be revised:
Mother, may I conceive a child?
Yes, my darling daughter.
Hang your clothes on a hickory limb,
But don't go near the water.

6
INFORMATION MACHINERY OF THE CELL

6.1 CHEMICAL STRUCTURE OF HEREDITARY MATERIAL

Among the most spectacular achievements of modern biology are the deciphering of the language in which genetic information is transmitted, and the construction of plausible models, some of which have been verified, of how the language is translated into action by the cell. An international group of geneticists, microbiologists, biochemists, and crystallographers participated in these discoveries. Nobel prizes have been awarded to American (G. W. Beadle, A. Kornberg, J. Lederberg, S. Ochoa, E. L. Tatum, J. D. Watson), British (F. H. C. Crick, M. H. F. Wilkins), and French (F. Jacob, J. Monod, A. Lwoff) scientists for their contributions to the understanding of the information machinery of the cell. Others, too, have played important roles in elucidating the complicated and beautifully elegant mechanism by which a cell receives instructions, carries them out, and passes them on to its descendants.

No full historical account of these recent discoveries will be given here. Rather, a capsule description of current theory, very much simplified, will be given. Details unessential to the understanding of the remaining chapters of this book will be omitted. But it is strongly urged that those for whom the

BOX 6.A THE STRUCTURE OF NUCLEIC ACIDS

The nucleic acids, DNA and RNA, are chains made up of subunits called **nucleotides**, each consisting of phosphoric acid, a nitrogenous ring compound, and sugar. In DNA the sugar is deoxyribose, and in RNA it is ribose. The nitrogenous compounds, or bases, are five in number, two purines, **adenine (A)** and **guanine (G)**, and three pyrimidines, **cytosine (C)**, common to both DNA and RNA, **thymine (T)** present only in DNA, and **uracil (U)** present only in RNA.

The structure of a nucleic acid is then

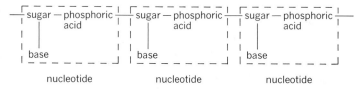

The chains are of varying length, some known to contain as many as 200,000 nucleotides. In the base position at any place there may be either one of the purines or one of the two pyrimidines characteristic for DNA or RNA. The following are some of the possible sequences of bases

    DNA: AACGTAGCTGGT   RNA: UCUGGUCACAUG

The number of different sequences is clearly enormous. Each molecule of DNA consists of two strands of nucleotides joined by hydrogen bonds and intertwined in a helix (excepting some single-strand DNAs found in viruses). The bonding, because of the structural properties of the bases, is always between A and T, and between G and C. On a flat surface the DNA molecule would look as follows:

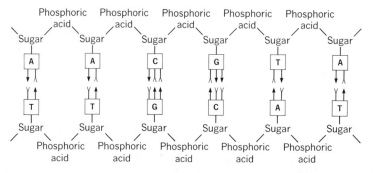

A three-dimensional view of a stretch of DNA might be represented in the following way according to the model first proposed by Watson and Crick:

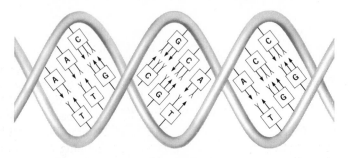

There is thus a complementarity between the two strands of DNA, since specification of the base of one also specifies the base of the other. RNA taking part in protein synthesis is single-stranded. The replication of DNA occurs by separation of the two strands, each of which then has a complement synthesized along its length, as shown in the diagram. (From F. H. C. Crick, "Nucleic Acids." Copyright © 1957 by Scientific American, Inc. All rights reserved.)

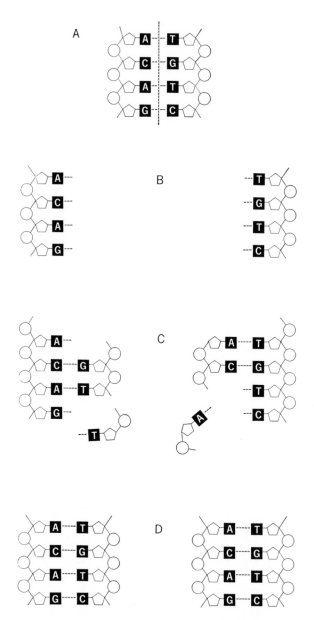

beauty of the genetic apparatus presents an intellectual or esthetic fascination become acquainted with further particulars of molecular genetics by additional reading.

It may be recalled from Section 2.1 that the bearers of the genetic message are nucleic acids. DNA is a substance, found in cell nuclei, that contains the specifications for the manufacture of proteins by the cell. Its structure, as well as that of RNA, the second type of nucleic acid involved in protein synthesis, is described in Box 6.A. The fact that DNA is the vehicle of hereditary information was first proven by the experiments of the American biologists O. T. Avery, C. M. MacLeod, and M. McCarty, in which rough nonvirulent bacteria were changed to smooth virulent forms by supplying them with DNA from smooth virulent strains. The transformed bacteria produced smooth virulent offspring. This process, **transformation**, has been unequivocally demonstrated only in protists. Nevertheless, DNA appears to be the almost universal hereditary language and to have a common structure in all forms of life where it exists (some viruses have only RNA).

The language of DNA might be described as having three-letter words, each representing a triplet sequence of bases. Since there are four different bases in DNA, there can be 64 (4^3) different "words," such as ACC, CTG, and GCA. Through the brilliant investigations of Marshall W. Nirenberg and others, the meaning of each of the 64 different triplets, or **codons**, has been deciphered. Each one, except for three, ATT, ATC, and ACT, specifies one of the twenty common amino acids that make up the polypeptide chains of proteins. Figure 6.1 shows the genetic code for both DNA and RNA. It may be noted that although some of the amino acids are coded for by only one triplet (for example, methionine by TAC), others have as many as six codons representing them (e.g., serine, AGA, AGG, AGT, AGC, TCA, TCG). The property of having several codons for the same amino acid is described as the **degeneracy** of the code.

What the sequence of codons in the DNA does is to specify the sequence of the amino acids in the polypeptide chain manufactured by the cell. When

Figure 6.1.

The genetic code.

The DNA codons appear in boldface type; the corresponding RNA codons are in italics

The names of the amino acids have been abbreviated.

Second nucleotide

		A or U		G or C		T or A		C or G		
A or *U*	**AAA** *UUU* Phe, **AAG** *UUC* / **AAT** *UUA* Leu, **AAC** *UUG*		**AGA** *UCU* \ **AGG** *UCC* Ser **AGT** *UCA* / **AGC** *UCG*		**ATA** *UAU* Tyr **ATG** *UAC* / **ATT** *UAA* Stop **ATC** *UAG*		**ACA** *UGU* Cys **ACG** *UGC* / **ACT** *UGA* Stop **ACC** *UGG* Trp		A or U / G or C / T or A / C or G
G or *C*	**GAA** *CUU* \ **GAG** *CUC* Leu **GAT** *CUA* / **GAC** *CUG*		**GGA** *CCU* \ **GGG** *CCC* Pro **GGT** *CCA* / **GGC** *CCG*		**GTA** *CAU* His **GTG** *CAC* / **GTT** *CAA* Gln **GTC** *CAG*		**GCA** *CGU* \ **GCG** *CGC* Arg **GCT** *CGA* / **GCC** *CGG*		A or U / G or C / T or A / C or G
T or *A*	**TAA** *AUU* \ **TAG** *AUC* Ile **TAT** *AUA* / **TAC** *AUG* Met		**TGA** *ACU* \ **TGG** *ACC* Thr **TGT** *ACA* / **TGC** *ACG*		**TTA** *AAU* Asn **TTG** *AAC* / **TTT** *AAA* Lys **TTC** *AAG*		**TCA** *AGU* Ser **TCG** *AGC* / **TCT** *AGA* Arg **TCC** *AGG*		A or U / G or C / T or A / C or G
C or *G*	**CAA** *GUU* \ **CAG** *GUC* Val **CAT** *GUA* / **CAC** *GUG*		**CGA** *GCU* \ **CGG** *GCC* Ala **CGT** *GCA* / **CGC** *GCG*		**CTA** *GAU* Asp **CTG** *GAC* / **CTT** *GAA* Glu **CTC** *GAG*		**CCA** *GGU* \ **CCG** *GGC* Gly **CCT** *GGA* / **CCC** *GGG*		A or U / G or C / T or A / C or G

First nucleotide

Third nucleotide

UAA, UAG, or especially UGA, the RNA equivalents of the three DNA exceptional codons mentioned in the previous paragraph, appear in the chain, probably a halt to protein synthesis is called for: they are the stops of the molecular language.

We have provisionally defined the gene as a unit of heredity. We can now redefine it in terms of molecular structure, although in later discussion of Mendelian and population genetics we may at times revert to the original definition. More strictly specified, *the gene is a stretch of DNA coding for a particular polypeptide.* The average number of nucleotides in a gene is about 1,500; the average polypeptide of a protein has, perhaps, a sequence of 300 amino acids. The number of genes in different organisms varies from no more than three in small viruses, which use RNA for coding, to several thousand, or enough to code for 2,000–3,000 different proteins, in the bacterium *E. coli,* and, perhaps, to some hundreds of thousands, in man. In the egg of the frog *Xenopus* it has been estimated that there is enough DNA to constitute 756,000 genes exclusive of those coding for ribosomal RNA (see Box 6.B). In cattle sperm there may be enough DNA for 6–7 million genes, although this may, in fact, be a hundredfold overestimate of the actual number. Whereas a quarter to a third of the genes in *E. coli* are known, only a small fraction has been identified in higher organisms. It is highly probable that the number of proteins coded for in man is considerably lower than the number of genes, some of which may code for the same protein (the property of *redundancy*) or have other functions than directing the order of amino acids in polypeptides. The general properties of the code can be summarized in this way: It is based on nonoverlapping triplets of nucleotides; it is universal, degenerate, and contains punctuation.

6.2 PROTEIN SYNTHESIS

The machinery of protein synthesis in the cell is described in Box 6.B. The DNA of the cell nucleus performs two operations. In the course of cell division, it replicates itself, transmitting the genetic message to the daughter cells. This process is illustrated in Box 6.A. DNA also directs protein manufacture by synthesizing **messenger RNA (mRNA)** complementary to itself, just as it produces complementary DNA strands in replication. The only differences between the two processes lie in the fact that the single strand of RNA is detached, and that U replaces T as the complement to A. In the course of RNA synthesis, the message is said to be **transcribed**, each DNA codon being replaced by the complementary RNA codon (Figure 6.1). Only one of the DNA strands is transcribed in this way, although it is not exactly known how the correct one is chosen. Possibly a polarity of organization of DNA governs the choice.

Messenger RNA enters the cytoplasm, through the nuclear membrane (Box 2.C and Figure 2.2), where it attaches itself to the ribosomes, which are the sites of protein synthesis. Here the genetic message is translated. Another form of RNA, **transfer RNA (tRNA)**, or soluble RNA, is found in the cytoplasm. Still another form of RNA, present in ribosomes (rRNA), apparently

BOX 6.B PROTEIN SYNTHESIS

Nucleic acids control the synthesis of proteins. The relationship between the two kinds of substance may be represented diagrammatically as follows:

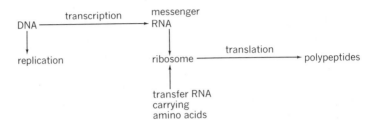

The ribosomes are the sites of synthesis and apparently do not operate as single factories but in clusters. The electron micrograph shows groups of more than 50 ribosomes of the polio virus, enlarged 100,000 diameters. (Courtesy of Alexander Rich.)

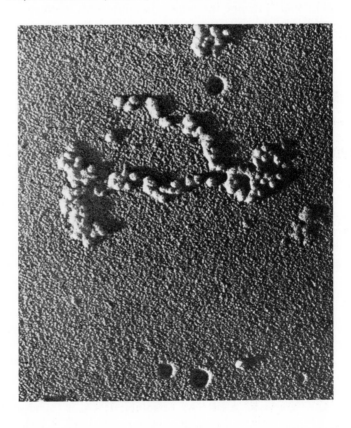

The four-stage process of assembly of a polypeptide chain is shown in the following diagram. (From Marshall W. Nirenberg, "The Genetic Code: II." Copyright © 1963 by Scientific American, Inc. All rights reserved.)

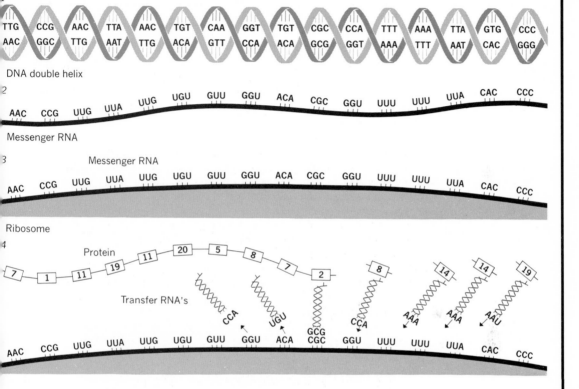

A schematic illustration of the adapter role of tRNA is shown below. The complementary shapes of tRNA and mRNA reflect the different amino acids to be placed in sequence in the polypeptide chain.

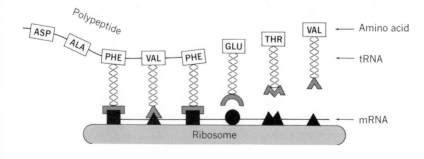

does not have translatable genetic information in it. The units of which tRNA is composed are essentially small adapter molecules, each one carrying an anticodon specific for a particular amino acid. As shown in the third illustration of Box 6.B, tRNA molecules pick up the appropriate amino acids and take them to the ribosomes. Then the amino acids are fitted together in the sequence dictated by the original nuclear DNA, and eventually are released

BOX 6.C THE REGULATORY SYSTEM

The diagram below shows the genetic machinery of protein synthesis as proposed by François Jacob and Jacques Monod. Two structural genes, constituting the **operon** whose DNA specifies the amino acid sequence of two proteins or polypeptides of a molecule, are under the control of a contiguous operator gene. In turn, an operator gene is controlled by a regulator gene located some distance apart. The model works in two different ways. In certain systems, the regulator produces a substance (not yet isolated), the *repressor*, which is bound to some metabolic product (a regulatory metabolite). This allows the operator to direct the structural genes to manufacture the appropriate mRNA, and protein synthesis is carried out. When the regulatory metabolite is all used up, the repressor is free to attach itself to the operator gene, and inactivates it. This switches off the production of mRNA. If the operator gene is destroyed or the repressor is ineffective because of mutation, protein synthesis is not regulated and goes on continuously.

In other systems, regulation may proceed in reverse of the path described. The regulatory metabolite, which could be the end product of protein synthesis, combined with the repressor, shuts the operator off. The process, in both systems, is a feedback process, and is end-directed. This model is based on experiments with bacteria, and although some attempt has been made to apply it to higher organisms, it is likely that the regulatory systems in them are more complex. (From Jean-Pierre Changeux, "The Control of Biochemical Reactions." Copyright © 1965 by Scientific American, Inc. All rights reserved.)

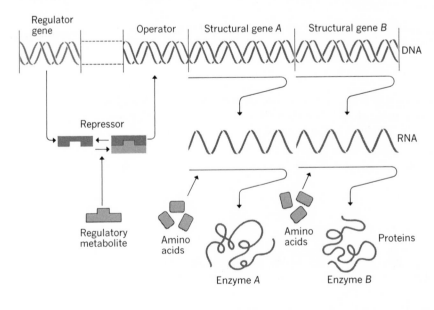

as a completed polypeptide. Enzymes in the cell, themselves manufactured in a similar way, mediate the assemblage of these into proteins.

The minutiae of protein synthesis can vary from species to species. Thus, for example, there are differences among various organisms with respect to the longevity of RNA molecules. In some bacteria, mRNA lives only one or two minutes because their needs for one or another protein can be drastically changed by changes in their environment. On the other hand, in the homeostatic environment of vertebrate cells that are manufacturing, let us say, hemoglobin, mRNA can be very long-lived and carry out its functions for a considerable period of time.

The whole operation does not proceed in a haphazard fashion, but rather, at least in bacteria, is under the delicate control of a regulatory system. A model proposed for the regulatory system is described in Box 6.C. An important feature of the system is that the turning on and off of protein synthesis is based on a feedback. Accumulation of the final (or an intermediate) product of the synthesis in the cell, or alternatively, exhaustion of some building material, turns the factory off. In lower organisms, an operon may contain many structural genes that participate in the manufacture of a single product. Thus, in the bacterium *Salmonella*, the histidine operon makes ten different enzymes and has around 11,000 nucleotides. In one virus some 75 genes, organized in blocks controlling DNA synthesis, its timing, and the assembly of the virus from its component parts, have been identified. Such operons are not known in higher forms, but there is evidence that some higher organisms have gene-complexes that comprise two or more contiguous genes affecting the same developmental process. Perhaps, in the course of evolution, operons became fragmented and their constituent parts distributed among different chromosomes.

Most of the machinery described has been worked out in viruses and bacteria. As we move from protists to multicellular forms of life, many complexities arise. For instance, a virus consists merely of a stretch of nucleic acid and a protein coat; a bacterium can have a single circular chromosome carrying the DNA. Chromosomes of plants and animals, most of which are rod-, J-, or V-shaped, are structurally much more complicated. They contain, in addition to DNA, proteins of the class of histones, which are apparently involved in regulatory functions of RNA production. The processes whereby chromosomes replicate and serve as directors of ribosomal activity are bound to be more complicated than described here, and much is to be learned about them. But the basic principles that have evolved by natural selection to ensure the transmission of genetic instructions from cell to cell (intraorganismal heredity) are, no doubt, general throughout all forms of living matter.

6.3 DEVELOPMENTAL GENETICS

Another important feature of multicellular organisms that does not have a counterpart in bacteria is differentiation of parts and supercellular organs. The study of this process from the genetic point of view is one of the most important areas of modern biology, but experiments are only beginning to give

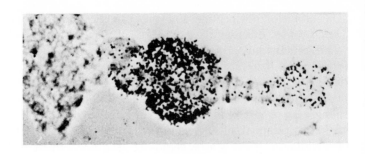

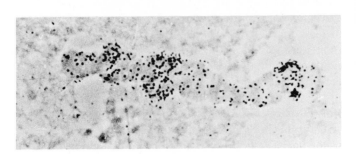

Figure 6.2.

RNA synthesis and puffs in the salivary-gland chromosome of a midge. The black spots record the presence of radioactive U-carrying RNA. The upper picture shows a chromosome with an active puff; the lower, a chromosome in which RNA synthesis has been inhibited. (By Claus Pelling.)

clues of how differentiation is controlled as an embryo develops.

One of the significant problems in differentiation is the manner in which different cells in the body, all originating from a single zygote, and, therefore, carrying exactly the same instructional information, do different things. Cells of the pancreas manufacture insulin, but not hemoglobin; red blood cells contain hemoglobin, but not insulin or the enzyme used in the metabolism of alcohol, and so forth. There must, therefore, be machinery that regulates the activities of different cells and, presumably, inhibits production of one kind of mRNA while stimulating synthesis of another kind in the differentiated cells.

The salivary glands of Drosophila, the midge, and other insects show evidence for such machinery. Enlargements and puffs appear in different parts of their chromosomes at different times in the course of development. By introducing into the cells radioactive uracil, which is incorporated into the RNA manufactured, it is possible to see that these puffs are, indeed, associated with RNA synthesis (Figure 6.2). In other words, the instructions a cell receives from the nucleus are under regulatory control, which directs the particular activity the cell is to undertake at a particular time.

A higher control, which instructs a differentiated cell to manufacture a specific substance, must also exist. It operates in two ways. First, the cytoplasm of different cells may contain different materials. Although the total genetic message is passed from mother to daughter cells in the chromosomes, the cytoplasm may be unequally distributed at each cell division. Experiments with sea urchins and other organisms have shown that differentiation of cytoplasmic contents does occur. In part it might be directed by the position of the cells in the developing organism. Thus, outer cells may have different potentialities for development than those surrounded by other cells.

Second, it has also been demonstrated that nuclei themselves become differentiated as development proceeds. Embryologists have destroyed the nucleus of an amphibian egg and by a kind of micro-surgery introduced a nucleus from another cell. In a series of such experiments, if the age of the replacement nucleus is varied, it is found in some experiments that progressively older nuclei have an increasingly reduced repertory of activities. That is, the differentiated nuclei have become unable to direct the manufacture of all the substances specified in the total genetic message and now instruct cells to perform only certain activities. The activities, of course, are different in different tissues, and eventually lead to the distinct shapes and functions of various body organs.

Many other considerations of developmental genetics might be mentioned, but enough has been said to indicate existing problems and the type of answers that are being sought (see also Section 17.2). Another role of RNA in cellular activities, although it does not technically belong to the subject of developmental genetics, may be discussed here.

The Swedish neurologist Holger Hyden has developed a theory that memory storage in the brain occurs through the production of specific proteins. Nucleic acids would, according to this theory, be expected to control the accumulation of information in the brain. Significantly enough, Hyden has found that the RNA content of human nerve cells rises progressively from the time a person is three years old until he is 40 and declines precipitately when he is about 60, thus showing a correlation with the temporal pattern of the efficiency of brain function.

Other investigators, in particular, the American J. V. McConnell, reported that the simple cannibalistic planarian flatworm, which has a very rudimentary central nervous system, can be trained to respond to light and electrical shock stimuli. When trained worms were fed to untrained ones, the latter seemed to acquire a memory of the training. The question immediately arose whether it was RNA that incorporated the learned responses into the brain machinery of the untrained worms.

Many similar experiments with injection of brain extracts specifically, of RNA, between organisms have been carried out. There is strong disagreement about the interpretation of the results obtained, and the issue is still speculative. Yet, effective transfer of learning of various types of responses by injecting extracts of brains of trained hamsters into rats, or of brains of trained rats into untrained rats or mice, has been reported. Some experiments with injection of RNA from trained to untrained worms indicate success in transfer; others are negative. The majority of the tests suggest that the effective material is not RNA, but possibly a polypeptide or protein. In other words, the learning process is coded not in the RNA but in the products synthesized during training. The whole issue is still in doubt. If it is confirmed that learning can be transferred by injection, classroom instruction may receive a brand new dimension, in which the brains of learned professors could be served to students instead of lectures. However, learning by ingestion at present seems to be a more likely prospect for creatures like worms than for humans. Unlike humans, worms can incorporate into their tissues whole proteins or even whole cells that they have ingested, and they lack the immunological response to foreign antigens.

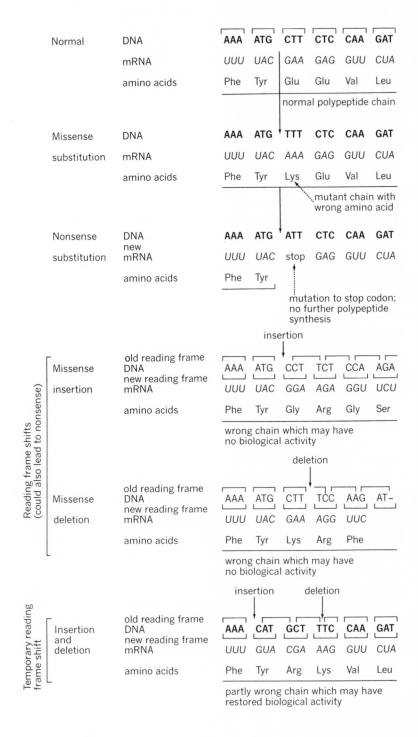

Figure 6.3.

The molecular basis of

point mutation.

6.4 POINT MUTATION

Just as the genetic code provides for heredity, so it also provides for the production of variation. In Chapter 14, we shall discuss the various kinds of mutation that can occur. Here we shall consider only one kind, which, perhaps, is the most important supplier of variation for selection to work upon: the class of mutations known as **point mutations**, which are intragenic.

In the course of transmission of the genetic message from cell to cell (somatic) or from parent to offspring (germinal), errors can occur. A wrong base may be substituted for any correct base in the original message. A base may be deleted from any part of the message, or one may be inserted. In all three situations, the meaning of the message will be changed, as shown in Figure 6.3. Once a change has been made, it will be remembered and transmitted to the following generations of cells or of organisms, unless the distortion is so severe as to prove **lethal** before any descendants are produced.

The severity of the effect of a mutation depends on many factors. If, for instance, the DNA codon AAA mutates to AAG, no observable effects will ensue, since both code for the same amino acid, phenylalanine. Slight changes involving only a few wrong amino acids in a polypeptide, such as the last one shown in Figure 6.3, may have only a small effect. Other self-correcting errors, for instance the deletion of a whole codon, such as appears to account for one of the abnormal hemoglobins, may have trivial genetic consequences. At the same time, as will be shown later in this section, a change of even a single nucleotide may have spectacular phenotypic effects.

But some mutations, like the missense examples in Figure 6.3, may produce proteins that will have no biological activity, or that cause significant abnormalities. And others, those in which the stop codon appears in the wrong place in the instructions, may prevent the cell from manufacturing a necessary enzyme or protein, thereby creating a **metabolic block**. It should be apparent that the position of a mutation in the DNA sequence is an important determinant of the severity of its consequences. A changed codon at the end of a DNA sequence is likely to have small effects, because most of the protein will continue to be made according to the unchanged instructions that precede it. A stop introduced by a mutation at the beginning of a chain will prevent further synthesis of mRNA, and hence, of the protein.

Clearly, the potentialities for the number of mutations that a single gene may undergo are enormous, since each of the 1,500 or so of its nucleotides theoretically can mutate three different ways. Perhaps some of these possibilities cannot occur because of chemical considerations, but even so, a huge variety *is* possible. Indeed, wherever a search was feasible and undertaken, a large number of different forms of the same gene, as judged by their effects on the phenotype, were found. Alternative forms of the same gene in a given species, presumably due to one or more changes in codons, are known as **alleles**, and existence of many forms of a gene as **multiple allelism**. We shall now examine two instances of changed instructions in human genes, to both of which we shall have reason to refer again. The first relates to the effects of a base substitution in one of the genes controlling the manufacture of hemoglobin. The other deals with blocks in the metabolic pathway of the amino acid phenylalanine.

Box 6.D describes two mutations that so change instructions to red blood cells that they produce abnormal, instead of normal, hemoglobins. In both instances, only a single codon is affected, and, probably, only one base (out of the 438 coding for the 146 amino acids molecules of the beta chain) has been changed. The phenotypic effects of the substitution are very dramatic. Persons whose cells make hemoglobin S instead of hemoglobin A suffer from a severe disease, called **sickle-cell anemia** or sicklemia, so named because, under reduced oxygen tension, the defective hemoglobin molecules clump together in rods and assume the shape of sickles (Figure 6.4). The disease is a very severe one and has grave consequences to its carriers as shown in Figure 6.5. The sickling phenomenon is probably caused by the structural difference between valine and glutamic acid that gives rise to a different shape of the folded protein, including a projection from the beta chain that can fit into an adjacent alpha chain and cause a sort of stacking of the hemoglobin molecules.

Hemoglobin C does not cause sickling, but like hemoglobin S, produces anemia. The interplay with evolution of these and related defects will be considered in Section 7.4.

Our second example deals with complete metabolic blocks, which appear if there is a failure of production of specific enzymes essential to the normal functioning of the human body. They are described in Box 6.E. The block in the pathway between tyrosine and melanin has the unpleasant consequence of producing albinism (Figure 6.6). The inability of the liver to manufacture the

---

BOX 6.D HEMOGLOBIN

The molecules of all vertebrate hemoglobins, except for those of the lamprey and hagfish, are composed of amino acids assembled into two pairs of chains. There are five chains in human hemoglobins, differing in their amino acid sequence. The production of each of the globins (the protein part of hemoglobin) is controlled by a separate gene; these genes probably arose in the course of evolutionary history from a single gene that carried instructions for the alpha chain. Altogether four normal kinds of hemoglobin are found in man. The subscripts indicate that two chains of each kind make up the hemoglobin molecule.

Adult hemoglobin	α_2	β_2
Fetal hemoglobin	α_2	δ_2
Kunkel's component (about 10 percent of the total hemoglobin in the adult)	α_2	γ_2
Embryonic hemoglobin (disappears after 12 weeks of gestation)	α_2	ϵ_2

Each chain has approximately 140 amino acids, and the exact sequence of amino acids is known for four of the chains.

The alpha and beta chains differ in 21 amino acids, the beta and gamma in 23, and the beta and delta in not more than 10. The epsilon chain was discovered very recently. The reconstruction of the evolution of genes determining hemoglobin production from a gene controlling production of muscle protein (myoglobin) can be diagrammed as follows:

myoglobin

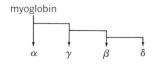

α γ β δ

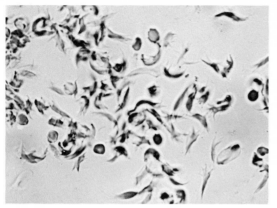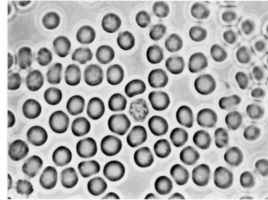

Figure 6.4.
The left photomicrograph shows red blood cells of individuals with sickle-cell anemia, and the right, normal red cells. (By Anthony C. Allison.)

enzyme phenylalanine hydroxylase has the more deleterious effect of causing the disease **phenylketonuria (PKU)**. PKU deserves discussion at some length.

The accumulation of phenylalanine and of phenylpyruvic acid in the bloodstream of PKU individuals causes, in a manner unknown, severe mental re-

The beta and delta chains, incidentally, form a gene complex, such as referred to in Section 6.2. Numerous mutations in the genes controlling the different chains are known. We shall consider in particular some of the abnormal hemoglobins resulting from mutations in the gene responsible for the beta chain. The differences between the normal and two mutant amino acid sequences in a short stretch of the beta chain are shown below:

Position in chain	Normal adult Hemoglobin A	Hemoglobin S	Hemoglobin C
4	Threonine	Threonine	Threonine
5	Proline	Proline	Proline
6	Glutamic acid	Valine	Lysine
7	Glutamic acid	Glutamic acid	Glutamic acid
8	Lysine	Lysine	Lysine

In both abnormal sequences an amino acid in the sixth position in the chain has been substituted. Although it is not known which of the glutamic acid codons is actually present in the corresponding position in the DNA, it is possible to see that each change may be only the substitution of a single nucleotide. Thus CTC, which codes for glutamic acid, could have been changed to CAC (valine) and to TTC (lysine) to produce the abnormal types. There are many further examples of how such single nucleotide substitutions could give rise to deviant hemoglobin types:

Position in beta chain	Amino acid change	Possible nucleotide substitution
7	Glutamic acid to Glycine	CTC ⟶ CCC
26	Glutamic acid to Lysine	CTT ⟶ TTT
63	Histidine to Tyrosine	GTA ⟶ ATA
63	Histidine to Arginine	GTA ⟶ GCA
67	Valine to Glutamic acid	CAT ⟶ CTT

We shall return to defective hemoglobins in Section 7.4.

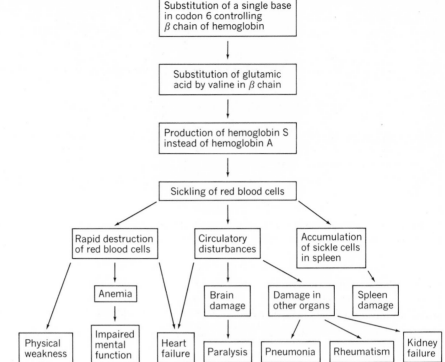

Figure 6.5.
A simplified
sequence of events
in sickle-cell anemia.
(Adapted from
J. V. Neel and
W. J. Schull.)

tardation. Indeed, the disease was discovered by observing a high concentration of phenylpyruvic acid in the urine of mentally retarded inmates of a Norwegian institution. The range of I.Q. of PKU patients falls from below 20 to over 80. The incidence of the disease in populations varies, and no exact figures are available. Estimates of babies born with the defect run from one in 10,000 to one in 20,000 among the white U.S. population and considerably lower among Negroes. To pick a number, perhaps 500 white PKU babies are born per year in the United States, and another 1,000 born per year carry a newly arisen mutant gene for the disease without its being phenotypically expressed.

In recent years, tests have been devised to identify high phenylalanine blood levels in newborn babies. The *diaper test* depends on change in the color of the urine when ferric chloride is added to it. The more efficient bacteriological *Guthrie test* is based on the ability of certain strains of bacteria to grow only when high levels of phenylalanine are present in their diet. To perform this test, blood from babies is added to bacterial cultures lacking phenyalanine. If they grow, it is an indication that the phenylalanine level of blood is high. Some 37 states now make the Guthrie test compulsory for all newborn babies in order to identify PKU infants. The test is not one hundred percent effective, and errors in both directions, false positives and false negatives, occur.

Phenylalanine is highly concentrated in such foodstuffs as bread, cheese, eggs, fish, and milk. Since PKU babies cannot perform the normal metabolic breakdown of this amino acid, treatment consists of placing them on a regime

BOX 6.E PHENYLKETONURIA

The first step in the metabolic breakdown of the essential amino acid phenylalanine is mediated by a liver-produced enzyme, phenylalanine hydroxylase. This enzyme is responsible for the substitution of an OH group for an H atom in phenylalanine, converting it to the amino acid tyrosine. Tyrosine, in turn, through a series of intermediate steps is converted into **melanin**, the skin pigment, and other substances. It is also broken down further along the pathway illustrated, in which the existence of intermediary steps is indicated by dotted arrows. If phenylalanine hydroxylase is absent, phenylalanine is in part converted into phenylpyruvic acid, which accumulates, together with phenylalanine, in the bloodstream. These substances are toxic to the central nervous system and lead to phenylketonuria. Other genetic metabolic defects in the tyrosine pathway towards oxidation are also known. As indicated in the diagram, absence of enzymes operating between tyrosine and melanin is the cause of **albinism**. Two other blocks illustrated produce tyrosinosis, a rare defect that causes hydroxyphenylpyruvic acid to accumulate in the urine, but requires no treatment, and **alkaptonuria**, which makes urine turn black on exposure to air, causes pigmentation to appear in the cartilage, and produces symptoms of arthritis. Another block in a different pathway, somewhat more complex, produces thyroid deficiency leading to goiterous cretinism.

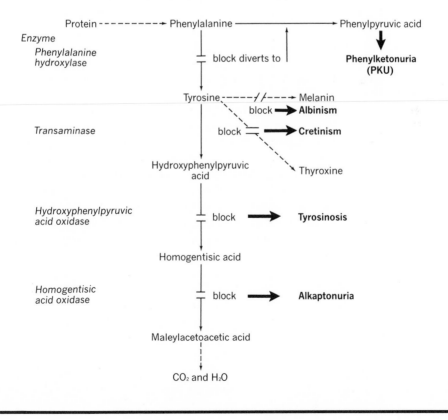

Figure 6.6.

An albino.

(Courtesy of L. Gedda.)

of vegetables and fruit and a special protein mixture, low in phenylalanine. It is not a particularly palatable diet, but apparently an adequate one for these babies.

Success has been reported for this treatment when it is initiated early in life. In one study 14 out of 17 children who had been placed on the diet soon after birth were within the normal I.Q. range; children who began eating the special diet after six years of age, showed no improvement. On the surface then, we have here an example of nutritional management of a genetically caused effect. However, there are still a great many unsolved PKU problems.

To start with, diet alone is not really known to be responsible for the improvement. Possibly, the successfully treated children belong inherently among the higher range of I.Q.; if this were the case, the test results would not be an index of improvement as a result of nutritional therapy. It is also possible that the extra attention paid to them is a cause of the rise in I.Q. Other nongenetic complications enter the picture. Thus, untreated PKU mothers can induce the disease in their genetically non-PKU children, apparently by providing a toxic environment during gestation. Besides mental retardation in the offspring, maternal phenylketonuria may cause abortions and other pathological effects.

Furthermore, if an error of diagnosis is made and a normal baby is placed on the PKU diet, mental retardation can occur because of phenylalanine deficiency. Other forms of protein malnutrition can have similar effects. We shall discuss the population genetics of PKU in Section 12.3.

6.5 INDUCTION OF GENETIC CHANGE

A fuller discussion of mutations and the factors involved in **mutagenesis**, their origin, is to be found in Chapters 14 and 15. Here, only some further comments on the role of nucleic acids in the production of variation will be made.

If mutations are viewed as changes in the genetic instructions, it is clear that they have to be incorporated in the vehicle that carries the message, the DNA of the chromosomes. In bacteria, this can be accomplished by transformation, a process already described, or by **transduction**, in which a virus can carry a piece of DNA from one bacterium to another, which then incorporates it into its own chromosome. Many attempts to demonstrate these phenomena in higher organisms have been made, but no unequivocal successes have been obtained, although a Russian report on success in changing the genotype for egg color in silkworms is on record. One experiment for which positive results were claimed involved injection of DNA from one breed of ducks into another, after which the recipients began producing ducklings of a different type from either original strain. But the uncertainty of origin of the experimental birds and the failure of follow-up experiments to duplicate the positive results throw doubt on this claim.

In general, believers in the inheritance of acquired characters suggest that transformation of the genetic message can be obtained by means not involving DNA. One such alleged method is blood transfusions, not only in organisms such as chickens, whose red blood cells have nuclei and therefore DNA, but also in mammals, which have no nuclei in the mature red blood cells. The official party line in the USSR regarding genetics upheld the idea of inheritance of acquired characters for nearly twenty years (until 1964), but it is now apparent that the successful experiments reported there were fraudulent (see Chapter 21). No carefully controlled blood-transfusion experiments since the one by Galton (Section 3.6) may be said to have given positive results although there are a couple of doubtful reports from France and Switzerland. Indeed, in the light of what we now know about the chemical nature of hereditary instructions, it seems highly improbable that acquired characters can imprint themselves on the DNA transmitted to the next generations. And the fact that experiments with cutting off the tails of successive generations of mice failed to produce a tailless strain should not surprise us. After all, circumcision has been practiced by Semitic people for countless generations, yet Semitic males continue to be born with foreskins.

This is not to say that artificially produced changes in genetic instructions are not possible. Many mutagens of a physical nature (such as ionizing radiation) or a chemical nature (such as nitrous acid, among numerous other substances) are known. But all of these produce their effect by changing, in some way, the DNA of the cells or their descendants.

The genetic aspects and consequences of spontaneously or artificially induced mutations are discussed in various succeeding chapters. Important somatic considerations, however, are also involved.

A possible instance of a spontaneous change in the genetic message of somatic cells in man has been reported. There is a virus causing tumors in rabbits that is not pathogenic to humans. Infected rabbits were found to have acquired the ability to synthesize an enzyme, a form of arginase that operates in the metabolism of the amino acid arginine, which they could not do before. Probably, genes carried by the virus somehow became incorporated into the informational machinery of rabbit liver cells. Support for this explanation is provided by synthesis of the new kind of arginase in tissue culture infected with the virus. When blood serum of scientists who had worked with the virus for a long time was examined, indications were obtained that the genetic information coding for the new arginase had also been incorporated into their cells. This is not a property that would be transmitted to offspring, because there is no chance for the new DNA to find its way into the gonads, where germ cells are produced. But, if the report is substantiated, this work will provide the first step towards the eventual potentiality of changing the genetic messages in a human body by what has been called euphenics and **genetical engineering** (Section 20.2).

Viruses are known to interfere with the hereditary information of cells in other ways too. For instance, at least 40 different viruses that induce formation of tumors in animals have been identified. Hereditary information normally regulates cell division. Cancer, in general, is the result of uncontrolled cell division, and any factors that interfere with the control of normal cellular growth could be carcinogenic.

To move to an even broader topic: Nucleic acids must play a role in the process of aging. Although the exact nature of senescence is not understood, it is clear that aging and eventual death are somehow programmed into the hereditary apparatus. One possibility that has been suggested is that somatic mutations producing metabolic blocks accumulate gradually throughout the lifetime of an individual until the loss of many vital functions causes death. It is easy to speculate that it might be eventually possible to replace the erroneous genetic messages with correct ones as the body ages, and thus produce the immortal man, *Homo continuus*, as we might then rename our species.

7

BIOLOGICAL COMMUNICATION BETWEEN GENERATIONS

7.1 CELL DIVISION

Most bacteria reproduce by simple fission, although sexual reproduction can occur in some strains. Each daughter cell may receive directly from the mother cell a set of genetic instructions carried on the bacterial chromosome. In somatic cell division of higher organisms the process is much more complex, but the principle is the same: the hereditary apparatus replicates itself and each daughter cell receives the full set of the genetic information contained in the chromosomes. The number of chromosomes of normal cells remains constant. The process of replication and distribution of chromosomes to daughter cells is called **mitosis.**

In the reproduction of higher organisms, however, this process for the transmittal of genetic messages would lead to an absurd situation. If both of the germ cells supplied by the parents contained a full set of chromosomes, the zygote would have a double number of them, the next generation four times as many, and so on *ad infinitum*. This, of course, does not happen. Instead, a reduction division occurs in the course of germ-cell formation, which is called **meiosis**. This division halves the number of chromosomes in a highly regular fashion. The original number is reconstituted at fertilization, giving the zygote the full somatic set of chromosomes. Mitosis and meiosis are illustrated in Box 7.A.

The particularly important aspect of the regularity of meiosis lies in the fact that in multichromosomal organisms, each pair of chromosomes, one member

BOX 7.A MITOSIS AND MEIOSIS

The life cycle of diploid sexually reproducing organisms can be diagrammatically illustrated as follows. ♂ is the symbol for male; it represents the shield and sword of Mars. ♀ is the symbol for females; it represents the mirror of Venus.

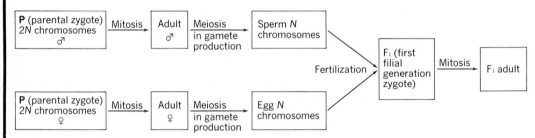

A simplified version of the distribution of the chromosomes in mitosis is shown in the following diagram. (From Curt Stern, *Principles of Human Genetics*. Copyright 1960. San Francisco: W. H. Freeman and Company.)

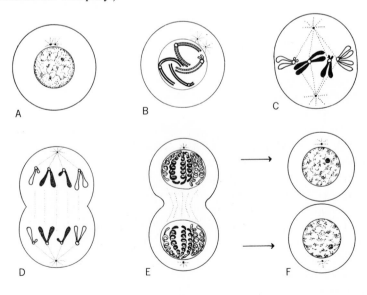

derived from the paternal germ cell, the sperm, and the other from the maternal egg, has its own individuality. Thus, if we label three chromosomes of some animal A, B, and C and assign subscripts S and D to indicate their origin from the sire and the dam respectively, a zygote would have a genotypic formula of $A_S A_D B_S B_D C_S C_D$. It would have a **diploid (2N)** number of chromosomes. When it, in turn, starts producing gametes, only one member of each pair of chromosomes will enter each germ cell. The number of chromosomes in these germ cells will be **haploid (N)**.

Because different chromosomes **segregate independently** of each other, dif-

Similarly, the next diagram (also from C. Stern) shows a simplified version of meiosis, including the reduction division, for an organism with two chromosomes. The chromosomes of paternal origin are dark; those from the mother are light. A shows the nucleus in a premeiotic stage; B and C show the pairing of homologous chromosomes; D and D′ show alternative arrangements of the chromosomes leading to the production of four (2^2) kinds of gametes.

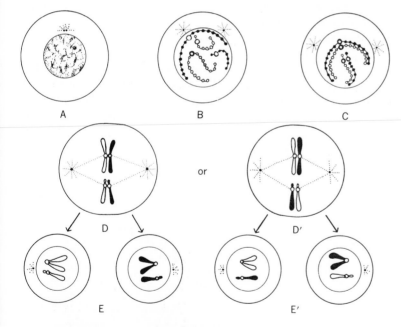

The difference between meiosis in males and in females should be noted: The prereductional cell in the male divides twice, producing four sperm. In the female there are also two divisions, but only one of the four cells becomes an egg; the other three form **polar bodies** and are abortive.

ferent kinds of gametes are produced. In our example, eight kinds are to be found: $A_SB_SC_S$, $A_SB_SC_D$, $A_SB_DC_S$, $A_DB_SC_S$, $A_SB_DC_D$, $A_DB_SC_D$, $A_DB_DC_S$, and $A_DB_DC_D$. Eight is, of course, 2^3, and, in general, the number of different kinds of gametes possible is 2^N, where the exponent stands for the haploid number of chromosomes. We shall see later that in reality the potential number of kinds of gametes is tremendously greater because of crossing over, an exchange of parts between members of a homologous chromosome pair. Should fertilization occur at random, that is to say, should chance govern which of the many different gametes produced by an individual unites with a similarly chosen gamete from the other parent, it is statistically easy to compute the proportions of the various genotypes expected among the progeny. The number of genotypes possible in our three-chromosome example is 27, or, in general, 3^N.

7.2 SIMPLE MENDELISM

The elementary statistical consequences of this scheme of inheritance were described for garden peas by Mendel (Figure 7.1) in 1865. The significance of Mendel's results was not generally appreciated for many years although a Russian botanist, I. F. Schmalhausen, had stressed their importance soon after they were published. It was only in 1900 that independent experiments carried out by the Dutch biologist Hugo deVries, the German botanist Carl Correns, and the Austrian Erich Tschermak (who, however, failed to interpret his findings properly) led to universal recognition of the fact that Mendel had, indeed, provided the basis of formal transmission genetics. To round out the international character of the rediscovery of Mendelism, it was the French zoologist L. Cuenot and biologists **William Bateson** (British, 1861–1926) and W. E. Castle (American) who within a few years accumulated data to show that animals as well as plants follow Mendel's laws. Bateson (Figure 7.2) actually coined the term *genetics* (in 1906), and contributed to our knowledge of the many ramifications of Mendelian inheritance.

Figure 7.1.

Johann Gregor Mendel as he appears on the medal struck by the Czechoslovakian Academy of Sciences in celebration of the Mendel Centennial. (Designed by V. A. Kovanič.)

Figure 7.2.

John Kimber, a successful and public-spirited California poultry breeder, in appreciation of the significance of genetics, established in 1956 the annual award of a medal by the U.S. National Academy of Sciences to a geneticist for meritorious work. The medal portrays Charles Darwin, Gregor Mendel, William Bateson, and Thomas Hunt Morgan. Among the contributors to genetics cited in this book, the following have been recipients of the medal: H. J. Muller, S. Wright, Th. Dobzhansky, T. M. Sonneborn, G. W. Beadle, J. B. S. Haldane, C. Stern, N. V. Timofeev-Resovsky, and B. McClintock. (Courtesy of John Kimber.)

We may illustrate the operation of Mendelian principles by considering the transmission of sex-determining instructions in man. Figure 7.3 shows photomicrographs of the diploid set of human chromosomes. It may be seen that 22 pairs of the chromosomes are common to both sexes: these are called **autosomes**. The twenty-third pair comprises the sex chromosomes and is different in the male and the female. The female has two similar chromosomes, the pair of **X-chromosomes**. The male has only one X, which pairs with the **Y-chromosome**, different in size and shape. It is this Y-chromosome that carries the instructional information that a zygote containing it should develop into a male rather than into a female.

In the course of human reproduction, the sex chromosomes segregate and recombine as shown here:

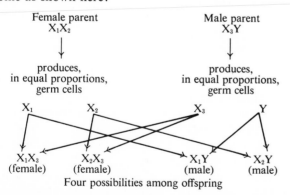

Four possibilities among offspring

The diagram, of course, does not imply that if two individuals mate and produce four offspring, two will be male and two female. If a large enough group of offspring is looked at, however, a **1:1 ratio** of females to males is expected. This is the most primitive Mendelian ratio, corresponding to that found in a **backcross** or the testcross.

The discreteness of the inheritance, or its particulate nature, is demonstrated by the fact that the genetic message indicating maleness remains intact as it

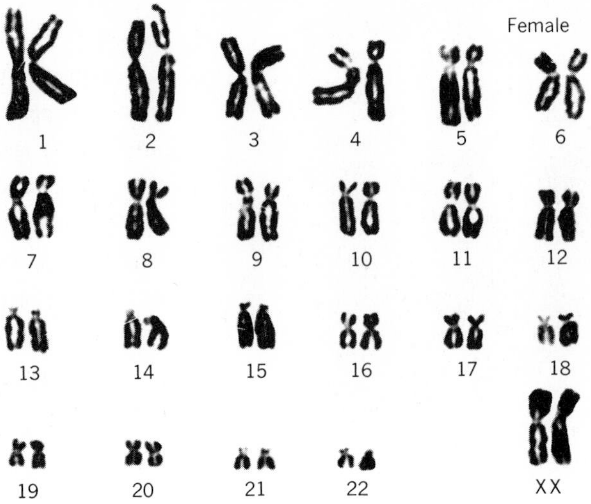

Female

1 2 3 4 5 6

7 8 9 10 11 12

13 14 15 16 17 18

19 20 21 22 XX

Figure 7.3.
Female and male human
chromosomes. (Courtesy of M. Grumbach
and A. Morishima.)

passes from grandfather, through father, to son. It does not become contaminated by the presence in the zygote or adult of the X-chromosome derived from the individual's mother. We may note, by mentally extending the diagram to another generation, that the X-chromosome of a grandfather (X_3 in our example) may be passed through a second-generation female to a grandson. Genetic messages carried by individual genes on the autosomes also remain intact throughout inheritance, with occasional exceptions.

Determination of human maleness by presence of the Y-chromosome is similar to another Mendelian property, **dominance**. When an organism receives from its parents alleles that are different, it is said to be **heterozygous** for those alleles. For some genes, or we might say for their loci, the phenotypic expression of heterozygosity may be intermediate, in which case no dominance or **partial dominance** is observed. (The singular of loci is **locus**, which refers to the place at which a gene lies along the length of a chromosome.) At other loci, only one of the two unlike alleles expresses itself. When this happens, the allele recognizable in the phenotype of the offspring is dominant; the other one is **recessive**. A third situation, in which both alleles are expressed, as, for instance in the ABO blood-group system, is also possible. Here the two alleles show **codominance**. In general, however, the distinction between these different kinds of effects is an arbitrary one. For example, the allele for the defective hemoglobin S can be viewed as a dominant if anemia is considered: individuals whose genotype is $Hb^A Hb^S$ have anemia. With respect to the sickling phenomenon, however, there is no dominance, since $Hb^A Hb^S$ red blood cells show a degree of sickling intermediate between that of $Hb^A Hb^A$ and $Hb^S Hb^S$ when under low oxygen pressure. So far as hemoglobin production is concerned, the alleles are codominant, since the heterozygotes produce both hemoglobin A and hemoglobin S (Figure 7.4).

Units of transmission are not completely discrete. Since there are in man many thousands of genes and only 23 pairs of chromosomes, it follows that

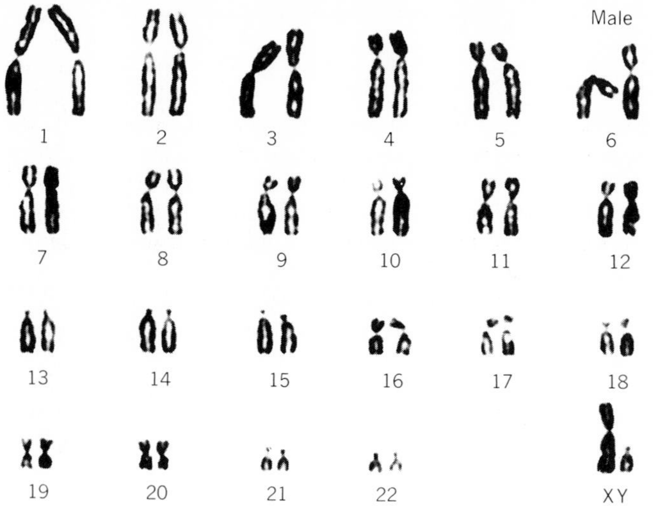

Male

each chromosome contains a great many genes. Genes lying on the same chromosome are said to be **linked**. They tend to be transmitted in blocks and are subject to crossing over, the exchange of sections between homologous chromosome pairs.

Genes located on the X-chromosome are **sex-linked**. It is not definitely known what function other than sex determination the Y-chromosome performs (see Sections 8.3 and 8.4), but no crossing over between the X and the Y normally occurs. In the human female, sex-linked alleles may be in a heterozygous state or in a **homozygous** state (meaning that the two alleles are identical). Since males have only one X-chromosome and the Y does not carry homologous alleles, all sex-linked alleles, whether dominant or recessive in the female, will be expressed in the male. The male, in having these unpaired genes, is said to be **hemizygous**. Box 7.B shows an example of sex-linked inheritance. Note in particular the difference in outcome of mating 2 and the **reciprocal mating** 3.

Phenotype	Genotype	Fitness	Hemoglobin Electrophoretic Pattern origin → +	Hemoglobin Types Present
Normal	Hb^A ┤ ├ Hb^A	0.98	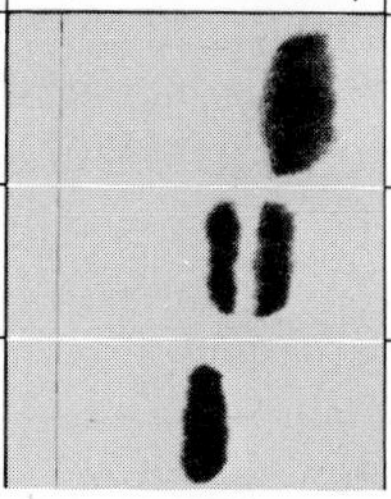	A
Sickle-cell trait	Hb^A ┤ ├ Hb^S	1.24		S and A
Sickle-cell disease	Hb^S ┤ ├ Hb^S	0.19		S

Figure 7.4.
Electrophoretic patterns of human hemoglobins A and S. (By Anthony C. Allison.)

BOX 7.B SEX-LINKED INHERITANCE IN MAN

Although some 120 phenotypic characteristics that are believed to depend on sex-linked genes have been described in man, only about 70 of them have been clearly proven to show such inheritance, one being the inability to distinguish green from red. We shall designate the allele for normal vision as B, and the one for color blindness as b. The six possible matings between individuals of different genotypes, and their results, are illustrated in the table below.

Because this defect is sex-linked, we would expect that its incidence would be much higher in males, an expectation borne out by observation.

If we look at mating 5, we observe that although there are two genotypes among the female offspring, the homozygotes and the heterozygotes, they are phenotypically undistinguishable. One way to tell them apart is to subject them to a **progeny test**. The homozygotes will breed true, but the offspring of the heterozygotes will show phenotypic segregation. Thus an $X^B X^B$ mated to a color-blind male will produce only normal daughters; half of the female offspring of $X^B X^b$ mated to a color-blind male, will be color blind.

	Mating					
	1	2	3	4	5	6
	Homozygote normal x normal	Homozygote normal x color blind	Homozygote color blind x normal	Homozygote color blind x color blind	Heterozygote x normal	Heterozygote x color blind
Genotypes of parents						
♀	$X^B X^B$	$X^B X^B$	$X^b X^b$	$X^b X^b$	$X^B X^b$	$X^B X^b$
♂	$X^B Y$	$X^b Y$	$X^B Y$	$X^b Y$	$X^B Y$	$X^b Y$
Germ cells						
♀	X^B	X^B	X^b	X^b	X^B, X^b	X^B, X^b
♂	X^B, Y	X^b, Y	X^B, Y	X^b, Y	X^B, Y	X^b, Y
Genotypes of offspring						
♀	$X^B X^B$	$X^B X^b$	$X^B X^b$	$X^b X^b$	$X^B X^B,\ X^B X^b$	$X^B X^b,\ X^b X^b$
♂	$X^B Y$	$X^B Y$	$X^b Y$	$X^b Y$	$X^B Y,\ X^b Y$	$X^B Y,\ X^b Y$
Phenotypic ratio						
♀	all normal	all normal	all normal	all color blind	all normal	1:1
♂	all normal	all normal	all color blind	all color blind	1:1	1:1

We turn next to autosomal inheritance, which is the type that Mendel himself studied. If we designate two alleles as A_1 and A_2 and assume that there is a cross between two homozygotes A_1A_1 and A_2A_2 (the **P** or parental generation), all of the first filial generation (F_1) will be heterozygotes of genotype A_1A_2. Here, contrary to what we observed for sex-linked traits, reciprocal crosses do not produce different results. Two of these F_1 heterozygotes mated with each other will, as Mendel discovered, produce an array of three different genotypes in the next generation (F_2):

		Sperm	
		A_1	A_2
Eggs	A_1	A_1A_1	A_1A_2
	A_2	A_1A_2	A_2A_2

Among a large enough F_2 population, the three genotypes will be in the ratio of **1:2:1**. If there is no dominance this will also be the F_2 phenotypic ratio. In Shorthorn cattle, for instance, red coat color characterizes one homozygote, the heterozygote is roan, and the other homozygote white. If in the P generation a cross is made between a homozygous red and a white animal, all of the F_1 will be roan. In the F_2, the phenotypic ratio will be 1 red:2 roan:1 white. It is customary to designate dominant alleles by capital letters and recessives by lower-case letters. The genotypes of the three kinds of animal, are then RR, Rr, and rr, respectively.

Apparently a single dose of gene R cannot manufacture enough of the enzyme needed to produce redness. Therefore a dilute color appears in the heterozygote.

When dominance is manifested, two of the genotypes are undistinguishable and the common phenotypic F_2 ratio of **3:1** is obtained. Biochemically, dominance reflects the fact that a single dose of an allele manufactures enough of the primary gene product to permit full expression of the dominant phenotype.

Mendel reported results from crosses of garden peas involving seven independent sets of alternative characters, four of which are shown below. The numbers of plants showing the contrasting traits in the F_2 of Mendel's experiments are shown in the next-to-last column.

Alternative characters of parents	F_1 genotype	F_1 phenotype	F_2 phenotypes	Percentages of alternative characters in F_2
Smooth *vs* angular wrinkled seed	*Ss*	smooth	5,474 smooth	74.74
			1,850 angular	25.26
Yellow *vs* green albumen	*Yy*	yellow	6,022 yellow	75.06
			2,011 green	24.94
Long *vs* short stem length	*Ll*	long	787 long	73.96
			277 short	26.04
Grey-brown *vs* white seed color	*Gg*	grey-brown	705 grey-brown	75.90
			224 white	24.10

Notice that the first two crosses involved many more individuals than the last two and that the F_2 percentages of the first two crosses come closer to the 3:1 ratio theoretically expected. Statistical laws indicate that the larger the number of observations, the closer will the outcome be to the expectation, provided, of course, the prediction was based on correct premises. Mendelian experiments generally show that this holds true.

The discussion so far has been based on examples in which it is assumed that for each locus there are only two different alleles. Normally, of course, a diploid organism can have only two alleles of each gene in its genotype. But in the population as a whole, numerous multiple alleles usually exist. A certain blood-group locus in cattle appears to have some 250 alleles. In sweet clover 200 alleles for one locus make the plant self-sterile. (Self-fertilization is impossible.) In *Drosophila melanogaster*, a group of three neighboring loci have a long series of eye-color alleles with such flashy names as apricot, blood, buff cherry, coral, ecru, eosin, honey, ivory, peach, satsuma, and plain white.

7.3 GENOTYPE *vs* PHENOTYPE

We have seen that one of the reasons that there is not a perfect correlation between a genotype and its phenotypic expression is the phenomenon of dominance, which is basically an interaction between alleles at the same locus. Another form of such interaction that can have important evolutionary implications is **overdominance**, in which the character expressed in the heterozygote is outside the range of both of the homozygotes. Suppose that in some organism there is a locus controlling height. The various forms of allelic interaction govern the expression of this trait, as is shown in the following diagram:

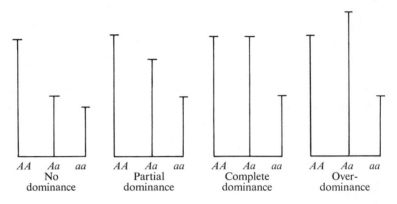

AA	*Aa*	*aa*	*AA*	*Aa*	*aa*	*AA*	*Aa*	*aa*	*AA*	*Aa*	*aa*
	No dominance			Partial dominance			Complete dominance			Over- dominance	

Dominance sometimes is a matter of the scale on which the measurement is made. For instance, if the expression of A_1A_1, A_1A_2, and A_2A_2 is respectively on some scale 121, 36, and 1, A_2 is partially dominant. Should we choose to transform the measurement to logarithms, the figures change to 2.08, 1.56, and 0, with a reversal of partial dominance to A_1. If we used squared roots instead, the numbers become 11, 6 and 1, and no dominance is observed. However, no simple scale transformation can eliminate overdominance.

Another source of variation between a genotype and its phenotypic expression is environmental. If a gene does not have a suitable environment in which to produce a specific substance, its phenotype may not appear as expected. Thus, PKU, a recessive gene leading to one form of mental retardation, will fail to express itself fully when a homozygous infant is placed on a low phenylalanine diet. In these circumstances the three possible genotypes pertinent to mental development or retardation will be difficult to distinguish phenotypically. Similarly, being homozygous for the gene that makes a man sensitive to ragweed pollen would cause him to exhibit the character in the Middle West but not in Alaska where he would not be exposed to the irritant. Fuller implications of such genotype-environment interactions will be explored in Chapters 10 and 11.

Some ambiguity between phenotype and genotype accrues from the phenomenon of incomplete **penetrance**. Some genotypes do not, for a variety of reasons, have a phenotypic manifestation in all individuals possessing them. A number of such incompletely penetrant genes are known in man. For instance, a dominant gene that causes a bent and stiff little finger belongs to this category.

Finally, another form of gene interaction can also be responsible for absence or modification of the predicted expression of a gene in the phenotype. This is interaction between genes at different loci, nonallelic interaction, or epistasis, a subject that is discussed in Section 9.1.

At this point, we shall turn to the consideration of an important instance of overdominance in man, that of sickle-cell anemia and some related diseases.

7.4 DEFECTIVE·HEMOGLOBINS REVISITED

It has been noted in Section 7.2 that the Hb^S allele may be considered to be dominant, without dominance, or codominant, depending on which phenotypic property is examined. We shall now see that with respect to fitness, or reproductive capacity, this locus (as well as some others connected with red blood cells) exhibits overdominance in certain circumstances.

The group of diseases caused by defective hemoglobins comprises, among others, (1) sickle-cell anemia, in which persons homozygous for the recessive allele show a severe and often lethal effect, (2) **hemoglobin C disease**, a milder form of anemia, (3) **thalassemia**, for which many genes are imperfectly known, including one for β-thalassemia, an anemia caused by defective hemoglobin and by a partial suppression of the formation of the β-chain of normal hemoglobin.

Still another anemia-producing genetic defect is controlled by a number of sex-linked alleles that specify deficient production of the enzyme, **glucose-6-phosphate dehydrogenase (G6PD)**. Under ordinary conditions, carriers of one of the G6PD deficiency genes are normal, but if an antimalarial drug, primaquine, or sulfanilamide is administered to them they will develop anemia. G6PD disease can also be generated in carriers by naphthalene or by inhaling pollen of the broad bean, *Vicia fava*. Indeed, the disease, which is called favism in Italy, was originally associated with prolonged diets of raw beans.

These various diseases are found in many populations of Africa and Asia, particularly in the Mediterranean Basin, but are unknown among northern Europeans, Japanese, American Indians, and certain other populations. Computations based on current frequencies of the sickle-cell trait among West Africans suggest that at least 22 percent of the Negroes who were brought to the American continent two or three centuries ago had it. Indeed, by checking the present-day frequency of the trait among American Negroes (about 9 percent) and allowing for the differential mortality, which, as we shall see presently, occurs in the different genotypes for this locus in Africa and in America, it is possible to estimate the degree of gene interchange or **gene flow** between American white and Negro populations (see Section 16.4).

The remarkable thing about these diseases is their high frequency in many populations, despite the facts that they can be exceedingly severe and that natural selection would be expected to operate against the persons homozygous for the recessive alleles. Some examples of current frequencies, compiled from various sources, may be given. The frequency of the sickle-cell trait in West Africa, may be above 20 percent. As much as 27 percent of a population on the Gold Coast carry the hemoglobin C gene. On mainland Italy the frequency of heterozygotes for β-thalassemia may rise to 20 percent; in some Sardinian populations it goes up to 38 percent. In Israel, there are great differences in G6PD frequency, ranging from less than a half percent among male Israelis of European origin to 60 percent or higher among Kurdish Jews (Section 12.1).

These frequencies of phenotypes reflect different **gene frequencies** of different communities, demes, or gene pools. Since we are dealing with diploid organisms, the number of genes at a given locus is twice the number of individuals in any such group. Gene frequency, then, refers to the proportion that a given allele constitutes of the total number of genes at a given locus. For sex-linked alleles, such as those specifying production of G6PD, the frequency in males is easily determined since the gene pool is on the haploid level and a phenotypic census gives a direct gene-frequency estimate. The concept of gene frequency as applied to autosomal genes is further developed in Chapter 12. Meanwhile, we can make use of it in connection with studies on the geographical distribution of the genes under discussion.

When frequencies of the anemia-producing alleles are examined, it becomes apparent that they are high in areas of high incidence of malaria and low, or even zero, where malaria is unknown. For example, as shown in Box 7.C, in Sardinia the frequencies of the genes for thalassemia and G6PD deficiency are high at low coastal altitudes where malaria is endemic and drop with increasing altitude (mountainous regions being free from malaria).

One form of malaria is caused by a protist parasite, *Plasmodium falciparum*, which is carried by mosquitoes and transmitted to man by mosquito bites. After an individual has been bitten, his red blood cells become infected and the malarial symptoms of chills, fever, and anemia follow. Carriers of defective hemoglobins, however, do not show these symptoms. It seems that their red blood cells do not provide a suitable diet for the parasite. Possibly, when such cells are infected, they adhere to blood vessel walls, become starved of oxygen, change shape (as in the sickle-cell disease), and are destroyed together with the invaders by the body's defensive mechanisms.

It does seem probable that possession of the gene for the defective hemoglobin affords a certain protection against malaria. Indeed, the British biologist A. C. Allison infected some volunteers with malaria and found that, while 14 out of 15 normal individuals developed the disease, only two out of 15 carriers of the sickle-cell gene did.

The picture with respect to fitness in a malarial environment is then as follows. Homozygotes for the hemoglobin variant genes are at a selective disadvantage because they have severe anemia. Homozygotes for normal hemoglobin are at a similar disadvantage because they are subject to malaria. The heterozygotes, however, do not develop anemia and are protected from malaria and, therefore, have the highest fitness of the three genotypes. It is because of this overdominance that the defective genes continue to exist in high frequency in malarial regions.

This situation provides an example of selection in man continuing to operate in our times. When people migrate to nonmalarial regions or when mosquitoes are removed from an environment by DDT or other methods, the heterozygotes lose their advantage and defective-gene frequencies begin to drop.

Comparison of the distributions of the Hb^S and Hb^C alleles shows that

BOX 7.C DISTRIBUTION OF ABNORMAL HEMOGLOBIN GENES IN SARDINIA

The diagram (adapted from M. Siniscalco, *et al.*) illustrates the correlation observed in Sardinian villages between altitude and the concomitant incidence of malaria, and the frequencies of the thalassemia and G6PD deficiency genes. Each unshaded circle gives the average gene frequency for thalassemia in a group of villages at the altitude indicated; the shaded circles show similar figures for G6PD deficiency.

Of particular interest are Carloforte and Usini. In these two villages the low frequencies of the diseases are related to the geographical origins of the inhabitants. Carloforte is a coastal village close to the malarial plains and would therefore be expected to have a high incidence of the defective alleles. The actual low incidence can be explained by these facts: the village was only established in 1700 and its founders were Genovese fishermen from nonmalarial areas, and, until recently, it was reproductively isolated. Indeed, according to genealogical records the few carriers of thalassemia and G6PD deficiency genes there are of Sardinian ancestry.

Usini is another village with a relatively lower frequency of the defective genes than expected, and for the same general reason. Its inhabitants are also of non-Sardinian origin, deriving from ancestors who emigrated from Genoa and Spain.

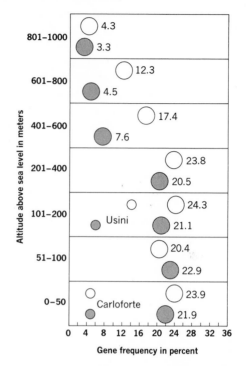

In fact, the local dialect shows definite influences of the Catalan language. More intermixture with Sardinians has taken place here than in Carloforte, as is reflected by the gene frequencies shown.

wherever they coexist, the latter tends gradually to replace the former: hemoglobin C also affords antimalarial protection, but does not have such drastic effects in the homozygous state as hemoglobin S (most homozygotes for hemoglobin S die long before reaching reproductive age).

In general, these diseases illustrate the interaction between man's biological and cultural evolution. Recently, S. L. Wiesenfeld presented some interesting evidence in support of the hypothesis that there is mutual feedback between the frequency of sickle-cell anemia and the dependence on agriculture among different African populations.

Anthropological information suggests that it was the introduction of agricultural practices and crops from Malaysia that permitted Negroes in Africa to penetrate tropical rain forests and exploit new niches. This development led to increases in population numbers that could be supported. Probability of malarial infection was increased, giving a selective advantage to the individual carrying a gene for sickle-cell anemia or other genes protecting from malaria. The enlarged proportion of individuals immune from malaria by virtue of their heterozygosity in turn permitted further expansion of the adopted agricultural practices. Mathematical models of the spread of the sickle-cell gene have been investigated, and apparently the present-day frequencies can be accounted for by the evolutionary changes that have occurred in the gene pools concerned over the 60 generations, or 1,500 years, since the introduction of Malaysian agriculture into Africa.

For perhaps the last twenty generations the frequencies have remained reasonably constant, but at present the situation has become dynamic once more, partly because of the control of the mosquito population and partly because of medical advances in treating malaria. Gene frequencies at the loci concerned are very likely to change because of these cultural changes. And when treatment that permits survivial of the homozygotes for the defective alleles is developed, a still different type of environmental pressure will be brought into the picture of ongoing natural selection in man.

In Section 7.2 we used the inheritance of sex as a model of Mendelian genetics. Having considered autosomal inheritance, we now return to a fuller consideration of sex determination in man and other organisms.

8
SEX

8.1 SEX DETERMINATION SYSTEMS

Sexual reproduction is both a progressive and a conservative evolutionary force. The replacement of fission by sexual reproduction in the course of evolution tremendously increased the potential genetic variability available. A great many genotypes are produced, tested by natural selection, and stored, if need be, in a sexually reproducing diploid species. An organism reproducing itself by fission can multiply very rapidly and propagate the best adapted genotypes at the expense of others. Sexually reproducing organisms never leave offspring genetically identical to themselves; an organism whose genotype is highly successful leaves descendants that, on the average, are less well adapted than itself. Nevertheless, judging from the prevalence of sexual reproduction among living beings, this mode of propagation provides more advantages than disadvantages.

The mechanism of **sex determination** are highly varied, with different groups of organisms coding for maleness and femaleness in different ways. All of these mechanisms, of course, evolved. For some groups evolutionary trees of sex-determining machinery can be reconstructed on much the same basis as trees of morphological or biochemical traits. Only a few of the systems of sex determination found in nature will be reviewed here.

The system wherein it is the presence of a Y-chromosome that determines development into males is shared by man and other mammals with a plant of the pink family known as Melandrium. Populations of these organisms, most of which are diploids, may include individuals with three sets of chromosomes (**triploid**) or four (**tetraploid**). The general term for multiplicity of sets is **polyploidy**. In diploids and triploids of Melandrium, a single Y produces males. But if a plant has tetraploid autosomes and X-chromosomes, a single Y does not suffice for this, and a **hermaphrodite**, possessing both male and female gonads, is produced. Apparently, although the power of Y to direct development is great, it is not complete, and a certain balance between genetic male determinants on the Y-chromosome and the autosomes is involved.

In asparagus sex seems to be determined by alleles at a single locus rather than by a whole chromosome. In the animal whose genetics is known best, the fruit fly *Drosophila melanogaster* ($2N = 8$ chromosomes), a system of balance between the number of autosomes and X-chromosomes determines sex. The following table illustrates this mechanism.

Sex chromosomes	Number of sets of autosomes	Ratio of X to autosomes	Sex
XXX	2	1.50	Super or meta female (sterile)
XX	2	1.00	female
XXY	2	1.00	female
XX	3	0.67	male
XY	2	0.50	intersex
XY	3	0.33	super or meta male (sterile)

There are, however, also single genes that govern transformation from a female genotype into that of a sterile male. In other Drosophila species, strains are known in which some females produce no males at all; preservation of such a line requires that every generation use males of other strains for reproductive purposes. This deficiency of male offspring can be cured by heat treatment, and can be transmitted to females of other strains by injection. Apparently, the abnormality is caused by infection of the females with a treponema, a parasite related to the organism that causes syphilis in man. The infection is lethal to male zygotes; thus we are dealing here with a congenital disease selectively killing one sex.

Grasshoppers have no Y-chromosomes: the males have a single X (XO chromosome complement), the females two (XX). In birds and in moths the system is much like that in man, but reversed: the males are XX and the females XY or XO, although no proof that the Y carries coding for femaleness as it does for males in man (see Section·8.3) is available. Since the individual of XY chromosome complement produces two kinds of gametes, in birds and moths it is the female which represents the **heterogametic** sex. The males, producing only one kind, are **homogametic**. Sometimes, the notation used for this type of sex-determination is ZW and ZZ, to distinguish it from the kind found in man.

In certain tropical fish, the guppies and the platyfish, both systems are known to exist within the same species. In domestic strains females are ZW and males ZZ; in wild strains the chromosome complements for female and male are XX and XY, respectively. The two kinds of fish can be crossed with each other, and departures from the ordinary **sex ratio** of 1:1 are then observed. The male chromosome complements are ZZ, ZX, ZY, XY, YY; the female, ZW, YW, XW, and XX. No WW complements are known, since they could arise only if both parents were female. The cross of XX and ZZ yields only male (ZX) offspring; the cross of XW and ZX produces a sex ratio of 1:3.

In some bees and related insects there are no sex chromosomes. Sex is determined by the males' being haploid, that is, having only one set of autosomes. They develop from unfertilized eggs and present a curious paradox: they have no fathers, but do have grandfathers on the maternal side. Fertilized eggs develop either into queens, which are normally functional females, or into sterile female workers. In some species, the differentiation between the two types of female depends on nutrition. In others, it is genetically determined by two or three pairs of genes, all of which have to be heterozygous to give rise to a queen.

A parasitic wasp, *Habrobracon*, has a similar mechanism, with females being diploid and males haploid. However, there can be diploid males, and these are always homozygous for a locus at which multiple alleles exist. Femaleness, therefore, is determined by heterozygosity at one particular locus.

In the marine worm, *Bonellia*, sex determination is nearly entirely environmental. Larvae that are free-swimming throughout their entire larval stage become females. Some larvae attach themselves to the bodies of mature females and are turned into males by a masculinizing hormone from the females. A certain economy of not having any surplus males in search of mates is thereby achieved.

Many other forms of sexual or parasexual (producing recombination) reproduction exist. There are hermaphroditic forms that reproduce by self-fertilization, and others that have to be cross-fertilized. There are forms that have a number of different mating types with rules as to which can mate with which, and so forth. Enough, however, has been said to show the inventiveness of nature in maintaining genetic variability by sexual reproduction.

8.2 SEXUAL DIFFERENTIATION

Sex determination is the process that decides the gender of the zygote; **sexual differentiation** is the developmental pathway by which genetic instructions are carried out. In normal embryology of higher organisms, sexual differentiation must operate under the direction of powerful switch genes to avoid unnecessary and useless intersexes. Development must be **canalized** in such a way that either one or the other kind of gonads appears in the adult individual, rather than something in between. Perhaps an analogy of a train arriving at a point on the railroad line where it can turn into one or another direction may be suggested. A switch must be used to send it to one of the alternative tracks, rather than have it make its own choice of tracks or even meander aimlessly in the field between tracks. Just as a train does occasionally jump the track, errors of development do occur, and result in intersexes, hermaphrodites, and gynandromorphs (see Figure 8.1), which are sex **mosaics**, with different parts of the body exhibiting properties of one or the other sex.

Embryos develop without sexual differentiation until the switch mechanism operates. Eventually, functional gonads are produced, but there are many admixtures of elements of both sexes in an adult. For instance, both male and female hormones are produced (although in different amounts) by both sexes. Occasionally, even after normal adulthood is reached, **sex reversal** may occur.

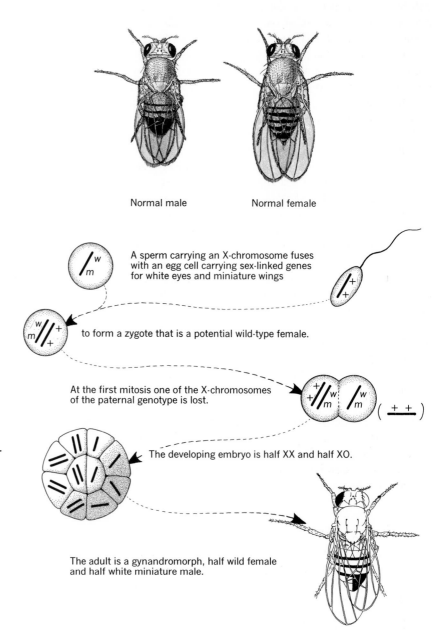

Normal male   Normal female

A sperm carrying an X-chromosome fuses with an egg cell carrying sex-linked genes for white eyes and miniature wings

to form a zygote that is a potential wild-type female.

At the first mitosis one of the X-chromosomes of the paternal genotype is lost.

The developing embryo is half XX and half XO.

The adult is a gynandromorph, half wild female and half white miniature male.

Figure 8.1.
Normal and gynandro-morphic *Drosophila melanogaster*. (From Adrian M. Srb, Ray D. Owen, and Robert S. Edgar, *General Genetics*, 2nd Ed. San Francisco, W. H. Freeman and Company. Copyright 1965.)

Particularly instructive is sex reversal among the domestic fowl, where it is relatively common. In the avian gonad, the male component, the medulla, begins to develop first in both sexes. In due course of time, the female component, the cortex, begins to produce feminizing substances in the female, which inhibit medullary growth. But only the left ovary develops. The right one remains rudimentary. An adult hen, unlike a mammal, has only one working ovary. Now, if the left ovary is destroyed (spontaneously by disease, or artificially by surgery) compensatory growth begins in the right ovary. Depending on the proportions of medullary and cortical elements, this replacement gonad will become an ovary, an ovotestis, or a testis. If it becomes a testis, full sex reversal and production of sperm is possible. The sperm, however, is not functional. Sex transformation of this type in chickens has long been known. It can also be reversible, if a partially destroyed left ovary regenerates. Indeed, there is a record of a cock that was publicly burned in Basel in 1474 "for the unnatural crime of laying an egg." The one reported instance of a hen, which had laid fertilized eggs (thus being a mother) later turning into a cock and siring offspring, is very likely not reliable.

A somewhat similar situation obtains in cattle twins. They usually share a common placental circulation. Here masculinizing substances from a male twin affect the female and turn her into a sterile **freemartin**.

In general, sex differentiation in higher organisms, although programmed by the genes, is mediated by the hormones. As we go up the evolutionary scale, sex reversal by hormone treatment alone, without surgical intervention, becomes less probable. Nevertheless, experiments in which frog eggs and rabbit eggs were dipped in solutions of female sex hormones resulted in all of the frogs and 90 percent of the rabbits produced being female.

Because of the normal control of sexual differentiation by hormones, gynandromorphs are not as a rule found in higher vertebrates, since all parts of the body share common hormone circulation in the blood. But where the sex differences are based on chromosome constitution independent of hormones or controlled in some other ways, sex mosaics are possible. For example, facial hair growth is hormone-dependent, yet a case has been reported in man, where a beard developed only on one side of the chin.

Intersexes and hermaphrodites can be produced by errors of development in higher forms. From 1899 to 1962, at least 171 persons have been reported to be true hermaphrodites, that is, actually to have both ovarian and testicular tissues. Pseudohermaphrodites have only one of these kinds of tissue but exhibit sexual characteristics of both genders. Some other abnormalities of human sexual development produced by errors of chromosome distribution into germ cells are discussed in Section 8.4.

8.3 HUMAN SEX CHROMOSOMES

In 1949, M. L. Barr and his associates working in Canada, found in the nuclei of cells from the brain of a female cat some dark-staining material. It appears that a bit of such material, now named the **Barr body**, represents one of the inactivated or partially inactivated X-chromosomes.

BOX 8.A INHERITANCE OF HAIRY EARS

The photograph at right shows the left ear of a 54-year-old man from south India and illustrates the hairy ear gene, which some investigators believe is carried on the Y-chromosome. Because of the age at which this trait develops and difficulties of classification of phenotypes, others do not feel compelled to accept the hypothesis that the gene is sex linked.

A seven-generation pedigree of a family in which the hairy ear characteristic was studied is reproduced below, in one of the conventional forms of representing pedigrees. Marriages are indicated by short horizontal dashes from which longer vertical lines lead to offspring. Double lines are used to indicate consanguineous marriages. A male sign with a black circle indicates possession of hairy ears. When a sign is crossed out, the individual in question is dead. A number below a crossed-out symbol tells the age of the individual at the time of death. Numbers given

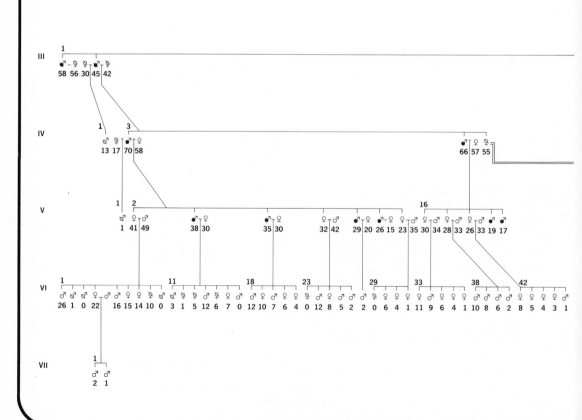

for all other individuals are their ages at the time
the study was made. Close examination of the
pedigree will show that all the male descendants
of the original patriarch who lived beyond a certain age appear to have inherited the gene, while
no females have exhibited it. (The photograph
and pedigree are reproduced by courtesy of the
author of the investigation, Krishna Dronamraju.
The pedigree is reprinted from *Journal of Genetics*, **57**:230, 1960.)

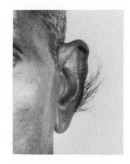

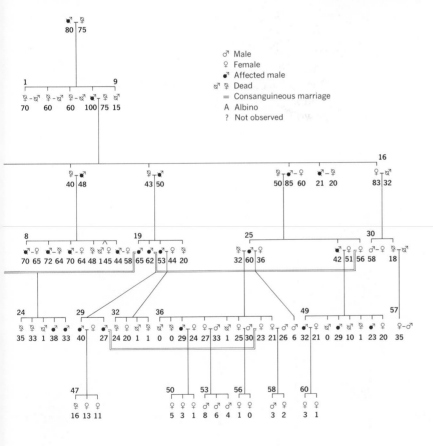

There always existed a puzzle as to why male cells can get along with one X-chromosome, while the female cells have two. In Drosophila, some "dosage-compensation" genes have been invoked to explain the phenomenon, and, indeed, no Barr bodies have been seen in these flies. Several years ago, independent suggestions that in mammals one of the two X's becomes inactive in each cell in the course of development were put forth. This proposal is now referred to as the Mary Lyon hypothesis after the British geneticist who elaborated it. In some cell lines the inactivated X-chromosome may be of paternal origin, and in other cell lines of the same organism of maternal origin, as determined at random. Female mammals are thus mosaics for sex-linked genes. This hypothesis is now generally accepted, although some voices dissenting about its generality are still heard.

There is much evidence for the Mary Lyon hypothesis. Normal human females have a single Barr body; normal human males have none. In a series of abnormal chromosome complements with more than two X's (see Section 8.4), the number of bodies is always one less than the number of chromosomes (Figure 8.2). Freemartins, despite their masculinization, have a Barr body in accordance with their chromosome complement for femaleness. Tissue-cultured red blood cells from women heterozygous for G6PD deficiency (which as may be recalled is sex-linked) give rise to mixtures of cells some capable and others incapable of producing the enzyme. Finally, some indication that female identical twins are more variable than male identical twins in many measurable properties, as would be expected of mosaics, has been reported.

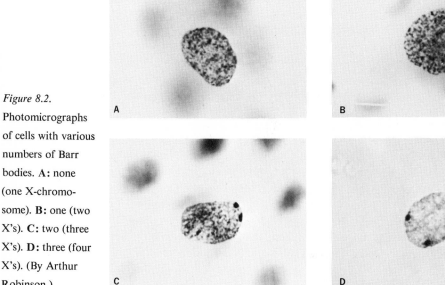

Figure 8.2.
Photomicrographs of cells with various numbers of Barr bodies. **A:** none (one X-chromosome). **B:** one (two X's). **C:** two (three X's). **D:** three (four X's). (By Arthur Robinson.)

Because of the discovery of Barr bodies, it is now possible to identify the sex of an unborn child at as early an embryonic age as three weeks. This is done by obtaining through a syringe fluids from foetal membranes, culturing cells from them, and looking for Barr bodies. Do-it-yourself kits for this purpose are not yet available!

Let us briefly examine two other aspects of human sex chromosomes here. First, it may be noted (Box 7.B) that by now some 70 X-borne genes in man have been definitely recognized as such, and another 50 or so postulated on basis of reasonable evidence. They represent a great variety of traits of physiological, biochemical, or anatomical expression. Besides the G6PD deficiency and the red-green color-blindness genes already mentioned, the list of sex-linked genes includes those for atrophy of the optic nerve, toothlessness, night blindness, one form of muscular dystrophy, brown teeth, a form of diabetes, total color blindness, sensitivity to the smell of hydrogen cyanide, and others (Section 17.2).

Second, we may give brief consideration to the question of genes other than sex-determinants that may be carried on the Y-chromosome. The property of such genes, of course, would be their transmittal only from father to son and never to a daughter. Several pedigrees of this type of inheritance have been published, including one for a defect described as porcupine skin and one for webbed toes. Fuller examination of the material has not lent any credence to them but the possibility that one other trait, hairy ears (Box 8.A), is Y-borne still exists. Meanwhile, it has been found from the study of chromosomal abnormalities that the Y-chromosome may have other than sex-determining effects.

8.4 X AND Y ABNORMALITIES IN MAN

The original proof that the Y-chromosome determines sex in man came from cytological investigation of abnormal genotypes. Because of errors in the distribution of chromosomes in the course of meiosis, aberrant individuals were produced. One such error, **nondisjunction**, causes unequal numbers of chromosomes to enter gametes. Figure 8.3 shows a diagrammatic representation of this process.

If the sex chromosomes are involved in nondisjunction, a gamete containing only a set of autosomes, a gamete containing two X's, or a gamete containing both an X and a Y could be produced. If each of these abnormal gametes united with a normal gamete, the zygotes would have genotypes for the sex chromosomes of YO or XO, XXY or XXX, and XYY or XXY. Indeed, all of these types except the first one have been observed. YO apparently cannot survive, probably because of a complete absence of the genetic information normally coded for by the X-chromosome. If a Y-chromosome is present, a male phenotype is found, and if it is absent the phenotype is female. The fact that, unlike the X, the human Y-chromosome can be dispensed with may suggest that no essential genes are carried on it. In Drosophila, however, Y-less males are sterile; a number of fertility genes or regions on the Drosophila Y-chromosome have been identified.

Figure 8.3.

The mechanism of nondisjunction schematically illustrated. Instead of each daughter cell receiving four chromosomes, one pair does not segregate and enters the same cell. As a result, gametes respectively containing three and five chromosomes are produced. (From Curt Stern, *Principles of Human Genetics*, 2nd Ed. San Francisco, W. H. Freeman and Company. Copyright 1960.)

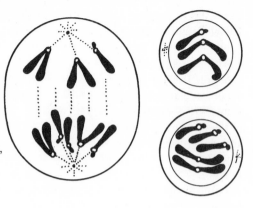

Some abnormal complements—whether simple, like those listed in the preceding paragraph, or complex—produce no observable phenotypic effects; others do. In particular, XO females display a series of morphological features such as short stature. They are usually of impaired intelligence, and, most significantly, are sterile, owing to the failure of the ovaries to develop. (An interesting side note is that female XO mice are fertile.) The totality of these properties is designated as **Turner's syndrome**. Similarly, males with super-

---

BOX 8.B ABNORMALITIES OF THE SEX CHROMOSOMES IN MAN

The incidence of various abnormalities of sex chromosomes in man is relatively high. One estimate places the average number of people who are afflicted with Turner's syndrome at one in 2,500, and an estimate for Klinefelter's syndrome, made from a study of a white Philadelphia population, is one in 500. All XY abnormalities together are estimated to occur at the rate of one in 250 births. Since many such abnormalities cause abortion, it is probable that abnormal complements of sex chromosomes constitute as many as one percent of all conceptions.

The abnormalities, other than those involving whole missing or extra chromosomes, include deletions or additions of parts of chromosomes. Two true hermaphrodites were found to be mosaics, one for loss of a section of the X, and the other for duplication of a section of the X.

The following table summarizes some of the kinds of abnormalities involving whole chromosomes, either in all cells or in some, found so far.

	Number of X-chromosomes					
	0	1	2	3	4	5
0	Not found	Turner	Normal	Normal or sterile	Female	Female
1	Not found	Normal	Klinefelter	Klinefelter	Klinefelter	Klinefelter
2	Not found	Normal	Klinefelter	Klinefelter	Klinefelter	Klinefelter

Number of Y-chromosomes

numerary X-chromosomes show lengthened limbs and other features. Their testes fail to develop so that they too are sterile. The abnormality is known as **Klinefelter's syndrome** (Box 8.B). (Probably tortoiseshell tomcats are sterile because they are Klinefelters.)

The human X-chromosome has two arms. Another X abnormality, besides those in Box 8.B, is deletion of one or the other arm, which may or may not be accompanied by duplication of the remaining arm. Ring-shaped X-chromosomes are also known.

There are a number of other pathological manifestations of some of the abnormal complements of sex chromosomes. Of particular interest is the fact that the effect of the abnormalities may extend not only to such physical traits as stature, but also to some behavioral characteristics.

Thus, in the general British population about 0.2 percent of males and 0.08 percent of females show abnormal numbers of Barr bodies, but the percentage in mentally subnormal institutionalized persons is 1.0 and 0.4 percent, respectively. Furthermore, a high proportion of such males with extra Barr bodies were found to have been placed in institutions because of antisocial behavior. In British studies, the incidence of XXY males among institutionalized patients requiring special security because of violent or aggressive and criminal behavior, was two-and-a-half times that among other patients. In a French investigation, the incidence of extra X- or Y-chromosomes among the mentally retarded was found to be 4 to 5 times that in the general population. Another interesting fact is that males with extra Y-chromosomes are unusually tall. In one study, in which the average height of males with single Y's was 67.0 inches, those with two Y's averaged 73.1 inches. Indeed, in this group the probability that a male over 6 feet in height would be XYY was 50 percent.

The X- and Y-chromosomes themselves can vary in length. Especially with respect to the Y, it has been found that there exist considerable differences between individuals. Because the measurable length of a given chromosome may be affected by variations in preparation of cells (usually white blood cells in culture), in order to standardize the measurement, Y length is usually expressed as a ratio; that is, it is divided by the length of some other chromosome or chromosomes in the culture. Significant differences in such ratios have been reported between different ethnic groups, with Indians, for example, showing relatively short Y's, and Japanese, long Y's.

Variability between individuals has been suggested as a possible diagnostic tool in cases of disputed paternity, since the single Y is transmitted from father to son. The two-fold limitation of this method is (1) that it can only be used for boys, and (2) that it cannot be used to determine which of two brothers is the father; their Y's, both originating from the Y of the boy's grandfather, would be identical.

As a final word on sex chromosome abnormalities we may note that they can lead to the production of identical twins of opposite sex. At least two such cases have been reported. The origin of identical twins is discussed in Section 11.1. Here it need only be said that they are produced when a single zygote divides and separates into two organisms. Should the Y-chromosome be lost at this stage, as was the Drosophila X-chromosome in Figure 8.1, an XY zygote will produce a normal XY male and a twin XO Turner female.

8.5 THE HUMAN SEX RATIO

Sex ratios are sometimes given as percentages of males in the population. The alternative convention, to which we shall adhere, is to divide the number of males by the number of females: thus, a sex ratio of 106 indicates that there are 106 males for every 100 females.

The **primary sex ratio** is that at the time of fertilization. Since many zygotes fail to be implanted and foetuses may abort before their sex has been determined, the actual primary ratio for man is not known. The use of the Barr body technique for early identification of the sex of embryos will eventually bring us closer to the knowledge of the primary sex ratio. For the present it may be inferred to be higher than the **secondary sex ratio**, that at the time of birth, largely because the number of male embryos aborted or stillborn is considerably higher than that of females. Up to four months of embryonic age, sex ratios of the stillborn tend to run (these figures are not very accurate) from 200–400, gradually decreasing, but still over 130 after 9 to 10 months of pregnancy. From these figures, various estimates of the primary sex ratio running from 110 and upwards have been made.

The secondary sex ratios tend to vary: in the U.S. the ratio is about 106 for whites and 103 for Negroes, in Greece 113, in Cuba 101. The **tertiary sex ratio** refers to any specified time after birth. The comparison of tertiary ratios at different ages shows a systematic decline with age. Some approximate ratios are as follows:

birth	106
18 years of age	100
50 years of age	95
57 years of age	90
67 years of age	70
87 years of age	50
100 or more years of age	21

Figure 8.4 shows the typical sex ratio decline with age. Indeed, it is as if in the human species the male is weaker than the female. Thus, deaths of infants younger than one year (1961, U.S.) are one-third more numerous among boys than girls, and the higher mortality persists throughout life. Of the 64 specific causes of death listed by the U.S. census, 57 show a lower rate among females at all ages. Of the remaining seven only diabetes and pernicious anemia, which do cause more deaths among females than among males, seem to be relevant to this comparison. The others include breast and uterine cancer and child-bearing, which are not expected to affect males.

The reasons for the difference in viability between the two sexes are obscure. Perhaps lethal sex-linked recessive traits, arising from either germinal or somatic mutations, can account for some of it, because they would be expressed in hemizygous males but not in heterozygous females; this is unlikely, however, to be the full explanation.

The sex ratio is known in part from thereotical consideration and in part from experimental evidence to be under genetic control. In general, a 1:1 sex ratio appears to be the best evolutionary strategy for a species, though, perhaps, not under all circumstances. Its advantages include the facts that it

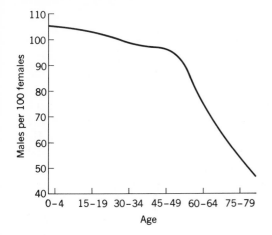

Figure 8.4.

1960 data of human sex ratios

by age in England and Wales.

(Redrawn from A. S. Parkes.)

provides for maximum genetic variability and maximizes the probability of male-female encounter. Among the experimental evidence is the observation of genetic differences in sex ratio between selected strains of mice because of differing genetic specifications, of the magnitude of 40 points (111.8 *vs* 71.8). In crosses between such strains, incidentally, it is the father's genotype that apparently determines the sex ratio of the progeny.

There are many possible ways in which a high primary sex ratio can be obtained. Among them are: (1) More Y-bearing than X-bearing sperm are produced; (2) More Y-bearing than X-bearing sperm reach the egg; and (3) Y-bearing sperm have a competitive advantage over X-bearing sperm.

All of these are supported by observations on mice. The first, in particular, is highly probable, since the phenomenon of **segregation distortion**, unequal representation of the two sex chromosomes in gametes produced by heterozygotes, has been well-established in nonhuman material.

Some other general features of the human secondary sex ratio may be listed. More males than females appear among firstborn than among subsequent children. The ratio in one study dropped from 106.6 for firstborns to 104.5 for children born to couples who had already produced ten or more children. The sex ratio in single births is higher than in twins, which in turn is higher than among triplets. Proportionately more males are found among legitimate than illegitimate children. Formerly, proportionately more males were born to parents in rural than in urban communities. The socioeconomic class has an effect on the sex ratio: in England and Wales, the upper- and middle-classes show a secondary sex ratio of 106.1, skilled workers, 105.7 and unskilled laborers, 103.4. All of these facts are consistent with the general idea of the relative weakness of the male sex. The increases in the sex ratio may be associated with improved nutritional and physiological state of the mothers, who can then provide a better uterine environment, in which more males would survive.

But the picture has many other more puzzling aspects. The age of the father has a bearing on the sex ratio. Even the father's occupation has been claimed to have an effect. There are seasonal differences, with a higher sex ratio in the births between June and August than at other times of the year. Similarly puzzling are the sex ratio differences between different countries and between regions of the same country. Again, the slight but significant tendency for the sex of successive children in a family to be the same has as yet received no adequate explanation.

A rise observed in the secondary sex ratio during or shortly after wars (Figure 8.5) has been commonly misinterpreted as the way in which Nature restores the proportion between the sexes to compensate for the soldiers killed. Actually, of course, there is no conceivable reasonable mechanism by which Nature could know about the need for adjustment, nor by which it could mediate the rise, and much more sensible explanations can be found. Many of the factors listed that promote a higher secondary sex ratio are present during wars. The less than one percent rise observed after World War II could be easily accounted for either by these factors or by the amplitude of normal fluctuations in the secondary sex ratio from year to year.

The obvious question concerning human sex determination is whether man could ever come to dictate the gender of babies to be produced. In some lower forms, such as silkworms, methods for producing only males or females have been developed (see Section 15.3). In higher forms many attacks on the problem have been made. At one time, sodium bicarbonate introduced into the vagina was claimed to speed up the relative rate of travel of Y-bearing sperm and thereby to increase the proportion of male conceptions. The claim was not substantiated.

More promising are methods in which X-bearing and Y-bearing sperm are separated outside the body and then used in artificial insemination. Although some positive results have been reported in rabbits and in cattle, for which it would be a very useful technique from the economic point of view, no repeatable and efficient ways of accomplishing the desired end are as yet available. But with extensive work along these lines being carried out in Great Britain, Germany, the Soviet Union, the United States, and probably elsewhere, it is almost certain that success is imminent.

Various forms of separation of the two kinds of sperm have been tried. They include (1) ordinary centrifugation, based on differences in the weight of X-bearing and Y-bearing sperm; (2) electrophoresis, based on the assumption

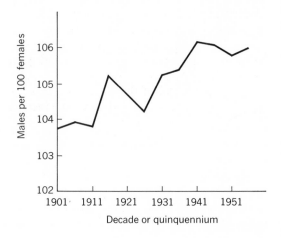

Figure 8.5.

Secondary sex ratios in England and Wales. Note rises connected with two world wars. (Redrawn from A. S. Parkes.)

that the two kinds of sperm have different electric charges; (3) high-speed centrifugation, based on density differences; and (4) differential sedimentation methods. A more visionary possibility, permitting natural matings, might lie in immunizing wives against the X- or Y-chromosomes of their husbands. Particular antibodies interfering with implantation of zygotes of one or the other sex might thus be produced. Still another distant prospect is to fertilize an egg outside the mother's body, culture the zygote, identify its sex from the number of Barr bodies, and implant it within the mother only if it is of the desired sex. Although external fertilization of eggs of rabbits and pigs has been accomplished, the actuality of reported successes with human eggs is not clear. However, an alternative technique is available by which eggs fertilized naturally may be removed from the mother's body before they are implanted, and grown in tissue cultures to the stage at which sex determination is possible. (The practicability of either of these procedures may, however, be questioned by considering another alternative: with the same moral accommodation and simpler technological and medical manipulations, the sex of a normally conceived and implanted zygote could be determined and it could be aborted if it were of the undesirable sex.)

Should any of these or other methods be found efficient—and there is little reason to doubt that a working technique will be developed reasonably soon—new problems of personal and social responsibility will face us. Some social critics think that even today determination of the number of children a given couple may have is the responsibility not only of the parents but also of society. The making of choices to predetermine sex of offspring would have similar implications. If left to the parents, what would govern the decision? It might be the prediction of happiness of a girl, living in a world overpopulated by boys. It might be the Freudian proclivities of the parents. It might be, in the view of some, even the welfare of the commonwealth. And, in any case, with our system of monogamy can we risk throwing the sex ratio out of balance, as might happen if parents freely chose the sex of their progeny?

8.6 PARTHENOGENESIS

Development of an egg without fertilization by sperm, or **parthenogenesis** is a normal method of reproduction in some organisms. It can also occur among normally sexually reproducing forms, such as some species of *Drosophila*, in which its occurrence may be genetically determined. This has been demonstrated by experiments in which its frequency has been increased by selection. Such experiments have had as subjects both Drosophila and such an advanced form as the domestic turkey. In various strains of turkeys, several generations of selection led to increases from 16.7 to 40 percent, from 4.0 to 21.1 percent, and from 1.1 to 18.6 percent. The interesting revelation was that parthenogenesis occurs in high frequency in the presence of viruses in eggs that have been produced by vaccinated hens or by hens whose dams had been vaccinated. This suggests that viruses may interfere with the normal genetic message specifying development. The parthenogens are always male, and some of them have proven to be fertile and heterozygous for some genes determining plumage color. This could be the result of a number of different processes. Among them are failure of reduction of the egg, fertilization of the egg by the polar body, and the doubling of the chromosome number after reduction, although this method would always lead to the production of homozygotes. These same processes are relevant to other diploids among which parthenogenesis occurs.

One laboratory reported that it had experimentally produced parthenogenetic rabbits. Extensive repetition of this experiment, which stimulated parthenogenetic development by heat shocks or treatment of eggs with sodium chloride, has failed to create additional surviving parthenogens, although many treated eggs have developed to an early stage.

In humans, claims of parthenogenetic births have been often advanced, especially by unmarried ladies. If the offspring are boys, the claim can be rejected out of hand, unless miraculous intervention forms part of it. Since human females have no Y-chromosome, they can give rise parthenogenetically only to girls. Biological tests for parthenogenetic origin of daughters are also available. One involves blood groups: no blood group present in the parthenogenetic daughter would be absent in the mother. A very sensitive test is provided by grafting of tissues. Since all the proteins of a parthenogenetic daughter would be manufactured under the direction of genes that the mother supplied, none of them would act as foreign antigen *vis-a-vis* the mother. Grafts from such a daughter to the mother would then always be accepted, barring rare cases of somatic mutation. Grafts from a nonparthenogenetic daughter would be rejected, because they would contain antigens derived from the paternal genes.

Further fanciful speculation on the immortal man, *H. continuus* derives from this topic. Should human parthenogenesis be possible, women could produce by this process daughters, who in turn could be used to produce similar granddaughters. These could be kept in storage and used to provide the mother with an infinite series of acceptable tissues and organs to replace those worn out as she ages. Males, of course, would be biologically completely superfluous under such a development, and might be kept only for amusement. Some men, however, find the prospect of being maintained as a pet in Fremlin's world (Section 5.3), a world populated by sixty quadrillion women who have numerous daughters in cold storage, a somewhat depressing one.

So far we have considered Mendelian inheritance of single genes or such units as the sex chromosomes. In all organisms, however, Mendelian phenomena occur simultaneously and with interacting effects at many loci. We may now turn to the more complex considerations involving more than one gene.

9

GENE INTERACTION

9.1 POLYHYBRID RATIOS

The basic cross used in Mendelian investigations in which differences in only a single trait are considered, leads to an F_2 ratio of 1:2:1 if there is no dominance, or to an F_2 ratio of 3:1 if there is dominance. These are ratios of **monohybrid** crosses. Mendel, however, did not confine his observations to them. He also studied crosses in which the parental types differed in two characters (**dihybrid** crosses) and in three (**trihybrid**). The general term for crosses in which more than one contrasting trait is considered is **polyhybrid**.

In his experiments with peas, Mendel studied a total of seven different traits, some singly and some in combination. It so happened that in the multiple trait experiments he studied characters that were determined by genes located on different chromosomes. (The significance of this fact will become apparent in Section 9.2.) From these experiments he established that, in the transmission from the F_1 to the F_2 generation, genes may **assort independently** of each other.

Thus, if we designate the allele that codes for round shaped seed as R, and its recessive variant, which codes for angular wrinkled seeds, as r; the dominant allele for yellow albumen (the nutritive part of the seed) as Y, and its recessive green-producing allele as y, then the dihybrid cross may be represented as follows:

P generation

phenotype	round, yellow	×	angular, green
genotype	*RRYY*		*rryy*
gametes	*RY*		*ry*

F₁ generation

phenotype	round, yellow
genotype	*RrYy*
gametes	*RY, Ry, rY, ry*

The proportions in which the four kinds of gametes will be produced by the F_1 will be $1:1:1:1$. If they unite randomly to form the F_2 zygotes, we may expect the following proportions of F_2 genotypes:

Sperm

		RY	*Ry*	*rY*	*ry*
	RY	*RRYY*	*RRYy*	*RrYY*	*RrYy*
Eggs	*Ry*	*RRYy*	*RRyy*	*RrYy*	*Rryy*
	rY	*RrYY*	*RrYy*	*rrYY*	*rrYy*
	ry	*RrYy*	*Rryy*	*rrYy*	*rryy*

For each gene separately, a $3:1$ ratio prevails. In combination, the ratio becomes $(3:1)(3:1) = 9$ (round, yellow): 3 (round, green): 3 (angular, yellow): 1 (angular, green). The genotypic ratios can be readily observed from the above square.

One of Mendel's experiments dealt with the dihybrid cross illustrated. The numbers he obtained in the F_2, indeed, conformed with his expectation:

F₂ phenotype for shape

		RR	*Rr*	*rr*	*Total*		*Approximate ratio*
	YY	38	60	28	126		
						397 yellow	3
F₂ phenotype for color	*Yy*	65	138	68	271		
	yy	35	67	30	132	green	1
		138	265				
Total		403 round		126 angular			
Approximate ratio		3	:	1			

The combined phenotypic ratio is 301 ($38 + 60 + 65 + 138$ round, yellow): 102 ($35 + 67$ round, green): 96 ($28 + 68$ angular, yellow): 30 (angular, green), or approximately $9:3:3:1$.

In the same way, the trihybrid F_2 ratios expected are $(3:1)(3:1)(3:1) = 27:9:9:9:3:3:3:1$. Such expressions can be extended to any number of genes, but study of the higher polyhybrid ratios becomes experimentally impractical, because of the increasing numbers of organisms required.

So far we have dealt with genes that are located on different chromosomes

The following table presents various results that have been reported for independent assortment of genes at two loci. The first line shows an ordinary Mendelian F_2 ratio. The second line also shows a 9:3:3:1 ratio, but because of epistasis the double dominant produces a phenotype not shown by either parent of the P generation: the original cross was between rose-combed and pea-combed fowl, and all of the F_1 had a walnut-shaped comb. In the F_2, a segregate with a single comb, the double recessive homozygote appears. The rest of the examples through No. 9 illustrate various combinations of phenotypic expressions. The last line involves no interactions: both A and B have the same effect on kernel color, which is determined merely by the dosage of dominant alleles, ranging from four for the deepest color to none for white.

Organism	Character	Ratio	AABB 1	AABb 2	AaBB 2	AaBb 4	AAbb 1	Aabb 2	aaBB 1	aaBb 2	aabb 1	Type of interaction
			Genotype and number									
1. Peas	Seed shape and color	9:3:3:1	Gray-brown round				Gray-brown angular		White round		White angular	Regular F_2 ratio
2. Chickens	Comb shape	9:3:3:1	Walnut				Rose		Pea		Single	Regular with interaction
3. Mice	Color	9:3:4	Agouti*				Black		White		Albino	Complementary (for Agouti)
4. Squash	Color	12:3:1	White						Yellow		Green	Inhibitor (A) of color
5. Swine	Color	9:6:1	Red				Sandy				White	Complementary (for red)
6. Sweet peas	Color	9:7	Purple				White					Complementary (for purple)
7. Chickens	Leg feathers	15:1	Feathered								Clean	Duplicate genes
8. Chickens	Color	13:3	White						Colored		White	Inhibitor of color
9. Mice	Color	10:3:3	White spotted				White		Colored		White spotted	Complex interaction
10. Wheat	Kernel color	1:4:6:4:1	Dark red	Medium dark red		Medium red		Light red	Medium red	Light red	White	Multiple genes

*Black hair with a yellow-reddish band, giving gray appearance.

and that affect independent biochemical pathways. But in many crosses the specific enzymes produced by genes may interact with each other and modify phenotypic expressions of the various genotypes. Interaction between products of genes at different loci is known as **epistasis**. Originally, Bateson suggested this term for one form of interaction only, but today the tendency is to use it for any kind of interaction between nonallelic genes.

Box 9.A shows a variety of dihybrid ratios, some of which show epistasis. The various combinatorial schemes, many of them worked out by Bateson and his associates, produce the different F_2 phenotypic ratios. Explanation of two of the examples will give some idea of how the different ratios come about. Apparently, two interacting enzymes are needed to produce color in sweet peas. Absence of either (or both) of these enzymes will lead to colorlessness. Hence, the 9:7 ratio. In chickens it seems that two different dominant genes control the appearance of feathers on the legs. Presence of one dose of either produces feathering, and only the double recessive has clean legs; the ratio, therefore, is 15:1.

9.2 CHROMOSOME ORGANIZATION

As may be recalled, each species is normally characterized by a constant chromosome number. These numbers range from a single pair in the round-worm *Ascaris*—although it should be mentioned that in the somatic cells of this organism they break up into a number of smaller chromosomes—to over 800 pairs in the marine animal *Aulacantha*. In plants the number of chromosome pairs may vary from two or more to more than 500, with some ferns having the highest number.

BOX 9.B CROSSING OVER

The process of crossing over may be schematically and numerically represented as follows. The data deal with the color of poppies and were reported originally by J. Philp. Only two loci are shown here, but the principle applies to situations with many genes, and multiple crossovers also occur. The genes in question are the dominant for white petal edge, W, and the recessive d, which dilutes normal color and produces some other effects. If one parent is a double recessive $\dfrac{d\ w}{d\ w}$, any cross-overs will have no effect, since exchange between the upper and lower chromosomes would merely reconstitute a *dw* gamete. For the other parent, the genotype $\dfrac{d\ W}{D\ w}$ may be used. Here a crossover will result in the production of two kinds of gam-etes as shown in the diagram. The particular form of representation is based on the fact that crossing over occurs when the chromosomes are in a double strand stage.

In Philp's experiment the numbers of the differ-ent phenotypes (a) expected on the basis of inde-pendent assortment, (b) expected on the basis of complete linkage, and (c) actually recovered, were as follows:

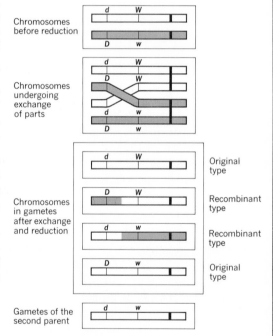

The heterozygous parent in the cross received a *dW* chromosome from one and a *Dw* chromo-some from the other grandparent. In the off-spring, out of a total of 798 plants, 791 were of the grandparental types. Seven out of 798, or 0.9 per-cent, were new *recombinant* types.

	Normal with white petal edges (*ddWw*)	Dilute with white petal edges (*DdWw*)	Dilute (*ddww*)	Normal (*Ddww*)
a) Expected (independent assortment)	199.5	199.5	199.5	199.5
b) Expected (complete linkage)	399	0	0	399
c) Observed	400	3	4	391

BOX 9.C CYTOLOGICAL PROOF OF CROSSING OVER

The diagram illustrates the classical experiment reported in 1931 by Curt Stern, giving the cytological proof of crossing over. In the experiment he used some abnormal X-chromosomes of *Drosophila melanogaster*. The one represented first in the diagram was a broken X-chromosome, a small portion of which had become attached to an autosome. The recessive gene for carnation eye-color and the dominant gene for bar-shaped eyes were present in the main portion of the X. In the other, a small piece of the Y-chromosome, shown in outline, was attached to the X-chromosome. By making the cross shown and comparing the phenotypes of the offspring with the cytological appearance of their chromosomes, Stern was able to demonstrate that recombination between the genes for eye color and shape was accompanied by a physical exchange of parts of the X-chromosomes. A similar experiment with corn was performed by the American geneticist, Barbara McClintock. (Diagram after Stern, *Biol. Zentr.*, **51**: 586, 1931.)

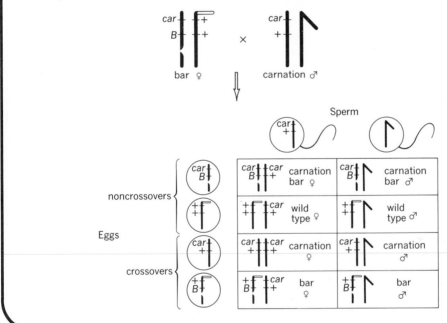

The question arises of what happens when two genes entering a dihybrid cross are located on the same chromosome. In fact, it has been found that in such a situation, independent assortment fails and the alleles entering the gametes of the F_1 tend to retain the association they had in the P generation. For example, in Drosophila an F_1 male from a cross between a female with scarlet eye color and curled wings (both recessive genes) and a male normal for both eye color and wing shape will be heterozygous at the two loci. If back-crossed to his mother the expected ratio among the progeny, should the traits assort independently, is 1 scarlet eyes, curled wings : 1 normal eye color, curled wings : 1 scarlet eyes, normal wings : 1 normal for both eye color and wing shape. However, because these two genes are located on the same chromosome, the F_1 male will produce only two kinds of gametes: one containing the

BOX 9.D LINKAGE MAPS

The bacterium *Escherichia coli* has one circular chromosome, although at certain stages of the life cycle it may have two to four replicates. Between one-fifth and one-third of all the metabolic reactions in this organism are already known. About one hundred loci on the chromosome have been mapped, some of which are shown in the illustration to the right. All the genes listed control requirements for some amino acid. There are many loci at which the same requirement is involved: for instance, at least eight for arginine. Other known genes control such biochemical characters as requirements for various substances, resistance to lethal effects of certain substances, and presence of antigens; others cause variation in morphological traits essentially through biochemical processes.

Of all plant linkage maps the most complete one is for corn, with about 100 loci known on its ten chromosomes. *Drosophila melanogaster*, the representative of the animal kingdom best known to geneticists, has about 500 loci mapped on its three autosomes and X-chromosome. The diagram below, redrawn from Th. Dobzhansky, illustrates the correspondence between the position of some Drosophila sex-linked genes as deter-

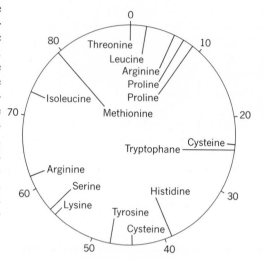

mined by frequency of crossing over between them (mapped along the dark bar) and their actual location on the chromosome (pictured at the top of the diagram) as established from cytological evidence.

One hundred genes have been mapped in the mouse, and 30 in the chicken.

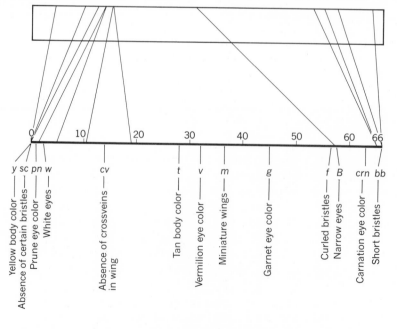

scarlet and curled recessive genes and the other the dominant normal alleles. As a result, only two kinds of individuals will appear among the backcross offspring, one like the male and the other like the P generation female.

Complete linkage, however is, not the rule. In the process of meiosis there may be an exchange of sections between members of homologous pairs of chromosomes, a process known as **crossing over**. In Drosophila males, in general, the process is suppressed; hence, the results described. But different species differ in their behavior. Thus, in the silkworm it is also only the heterogametic sex, but this time the male, that shows crossing over. In some birds the heterogametic male sex shows less crossing over than the female. In mice, the frequency of crossing over is higher in females. In the pea, it is equal in the two sexes.

Crossing over is a very complex process and much is still to be learned of its physics, chemistry, and biology. For our purposes, we will treat it in the simplest possible way (see Boxes 9.B and 9.C).

The understanding of linkage and crossing over was greatly increased by the development of the concept of a linear order of genes on the chromosome. This concept was first proposed and later brilliantly confirmed by the first

---

BOX 9.E AUTOSOMAL LINKAGE IN MAN

Data are still extremely scarce largely because detection of linkage in a species in which experimental breeding is not possible depends on finding families with two or more segregating genes. Whereas in Drosophila, for instance, thousands of flies can be examined for construction of linkage maps, in man only very few individuals may be studied. An example of the sparse data on which human autosomal linkage information rests is given below (from V. A. McKusick). It involves a blood-group locus, known as Lutheran, alleles for which are written L^+, L^-. When it is not known whether a given chromosome carries L^+ or L^-, the allele is designated as l. The other gene shown causes certain substances to be secreted into the saliva; the alleles for the secretor locus are written S, s. Sixteen families comprising 70 individuals in which segregation for these two loci exists have been described.

The proportion of crossover phenotypes is 9 out of 70, giving a recombination value of 13 percent. Other linked loci known in man are occupied by the genes for the Rh blood group and for elliptocytosis, a form of anemia (3 percent recombination); the ABO blood group and the nail-patella syndrome, which exhibits abnormalities in nails and the knee cap (10 percent recombination); a serum protein, transferrin, and a serum enzyme, cholesterase (16 percent), and another serum protein, the so-called group-specific component of globulin and a variant of serum albumin (1.5 percent). The former has also been reported to be closely linked to another form of serum albumin. That only these five pairs of linked genes are known in man may be contrasted with the detailed maps of linked genes that have been made for other species, as mentioned in Box 9.C.

Mating		Nonrecombinant offspring		Recombinant offspring	
$L^+\|\|l$ $\;$ $L^+\|\|l$		$L^+\|\|l$	$L^-\|\|l$	$L^+\|\|l$	$L^-\|\|l$
$S\|s$ $\quad$ $s\|s$		$S\|s$	$s\|s$	$s\|S$	$S\|s$
Number: (one of the l's must be L^-)		15	17	0	6
$L^+\|L^-$ $\;$ $L^-\|l$		$L^+\|\|l$	$L^-\|\|l$	$L^+\|\|l$	$L^-\|\|l$
$s\|S$ $\quad$ $s\|s$		$s\|s$	$S\|s$	$S\|s$	$s\|s$
Number:		16	13	2	1

geneticist to receive a Nobel prize, **Thomas Hunt Morgan** (1866–1945; Figure 7.2), and a group of his students. The probability that crossing over will occur between any two genes on the same chromosome is proportional to the distance separating them. As a result, by making experiments involving three or more genes a **linkage map** may be produced, much as the arrangement of stations along a railway may be deduced by the number of hours a train, traveling at a constant rate, takes to cover the distance between them. Thus, if it takes the train 2 hours to travel from A to B, three hours from A to C, and one hour from B to C, it is reasonable to infer that the order of the stations is A, B, C, with relative distances of two and one between them. There are many complexities in chromosome mapping that we shall ignore here. Box 9.D gives some examples and Box 9.E gives the information on autosomal linkage in man.

Some aspects of crossing over need emphasis. The first is the evolutionary

---

BOX 9.F PRODUCTION OF MOSAICS

Mosaics may result from somatic crossing over, as well as from losses of chromosomes as illustrated in Figure 8.1. Suppose that in a heterozygote for eye color there was crossing over during the first division after the zygote was formed. (*BB* and *Bb* are genotypes expressed as brown eyes; *bb* as blue.) The following course of development might occur.

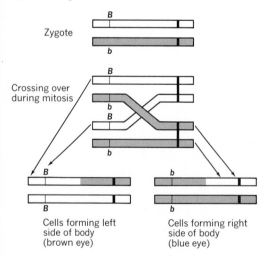

Cells forming left side of body (brown eye)

Cells forming right side of body (blue eye)

The photograph of a human mosaic, showing effects on hair and eye color is reproduced by courtesy of Y. R. Ahuja and permission of L. Gedda from *Acta Genet. Med. Gemell.*

Not all mosaics are caused by chromosome abnormalities. Thus, Siamese cats and Himalayan rabbits have a system of regulation, in which genes producing melanizing enzymes are turned on only at certain temperatures. Differences in the temperature of the different parts of the body during development may lead to a mosaic or variegated phenotype. In plants, variegation in leaf color depends on differences between green and colorless plastids in the cytoplasm (see Box 2.C and Section 9.4).

significance of this process. Without crossing over, the number of different genotypes possible in a species would be limited by the number of chromosomes. With crossing over, the number of potential genotypes becomes astronomical, since, theoretically, an exchange may occur between any pair of adjacent nucleotides. The potential diversity of human genotypes, given multiple allelism and crossing over, becomes so fantastically huge that it exceeds the total number of particles in the universe. The contention that no two human beings that ever existed or will ever exist would have identical genetic constitutions is not unrealistic under these circumstances. Identical twins might be an exception, but even they would differ from each other, if mutation took place in one very shortly after twinning. In any case, because of the way cytoplasm is distributed, identical twins may still differ in cytoplasmic material. Another point about crossing over is that it can occur in somatic cells as well as in germ cells. This process in a heterozygote is one possible cause of mosaicism (Box 9.F).

9.3 COADAPTATION

The epistatic gene interactions that were considered in Section 9.1 have been analyzed on a formal Mendelian basis. Directly or indirectly, however, all genes must be interacting to produce an adapted individual and an adapted population. The complicated biological machinery that transforms single-celled zygotes into a successful population of mature organisms must have extensive regulatory aspects. This is to say that alternative alleles at a locus are selected not only for what they themselves do, but also for their interactions with the totality of all alleles carried by an individual, and, beyond that, with the total contents of the gene pool.

The evolutionary process of selection for a balanced combination of genes in an individual, and of individuals in a population, is known as **coadaptation**. Darwin used this term to describe correlated modifications of different structures in the course of the evolution of an organism to produce a harmonious living being. Its meaning, however, can now be extended to the genic level, on the one hand, and to the species level, on the other.

One example of genic coadaptation is provided by *synthetic lethals*. As already noted, many genes have detrimental effects, some of which may be fatal or sterilizing. But, in Drosophila at least, some genes are harmful or lethal only when present in some epistatic combination with certain others. In analyzing the effects of whole chromosomes on viability, it is sometimes found that a chromosome, which had no detrimental effects originally, becomes lethal after crossing over. However, another crossover can remove the lethal effects. Clearly an interaction between genes on different parts of such chromosome must exist. Another and even simpler example of interaction or balance on the genic level is, of course, provided by overdominance. Still other examples can be found in the biochemically determined *position effect*, that is, the modification of genic expression by a change in the location of a given gene on the chromosome, as may happen when an inversion (Figure 3.8) occurs.

On the population level, coadaptation can take the form of *frequency-*

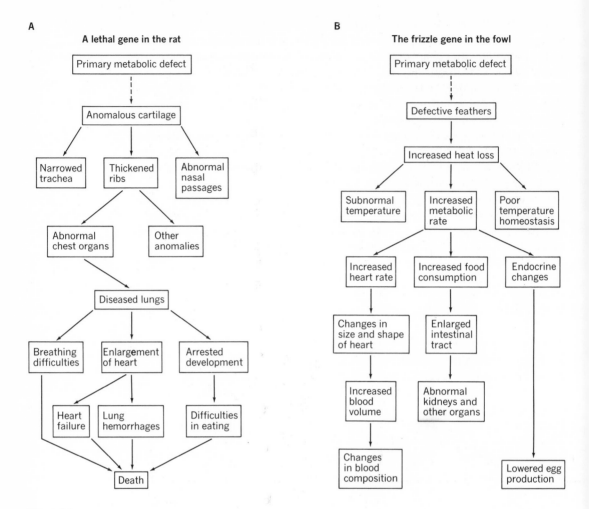

A

A lethal gene in the rat

Primary metabolic defect

Anomalous cartilage

Narrowed trachea | Thickened ribs | Abnormal nasal passages

Abnormal chest organs | Other anomalies

Diseased lungs

Breathing difficulties | Enlargement of heart | Arrested development

Heart failure | Lung hemorrhages | Difficulties in eating

Death

B

The frizzle gene in the fowl

Primary metabolic defect

Defective feathers

Increased heat loss

Subnormal temperature | Increased metabolic rate | Poor temperature homeostasis

Increased heart rate | Increased food consumption | Endocrine changes

Changes in size and shape of heart | Enlarged intestinal tract

Increased blood volume | Abnormal kidneys and other organs

Changes in blood composition | Lowered egg production

Figure 9.1.
Pleiotropic effects of two genes. **A:** a lethal gene in the rat. (After H. Grüneberg.)
B: a detrimental gene in the chicken. (After W. Landauer.)

dependent selection. That is to say, the relative fitness of a given allele may depend on its frequency in a gene pool. When a certain allele is rare, it may confer a reproductive advantage on the individual carrying it; if it becomes common it may prove to be disadvantageous. A nonbiological analogy in human society would be in the supply and demand situation controlling, let us say, the number of watchmakers in a community. When few watchmakers are available, they prosper, but as their numbers increase, their prosperity may vanish. The exact biological nature of frequency-dependent selection is not known but it could be related to exploitation of particular niches or to mating preferences.

Another consideration dealing with balance relates to the phenomenon of **pleiotropy**, the multiple phenotypic effects that a particular gene may have. A gene is, of course, responsible for a single specific product, a polypeptide or protein. But the enzyme that a single gene produces will participate in a variety of reactions, each one of which may have ever-spreading consequences in the functioning of an organism. Figure 9.1 shows two examples of the pleiotropic action of single genes. Part A pictures a series of developmental events resulting from the presence of a lethal gene in the rat. Part B shows the effects of the frizzle gene in the chicken, stemming from the production of defective feathers.

Pleiotropic effects have been often confused with very close linkage. If crossing over between two adjacent genes is very rare, in many instances they may be considered to lie at a single locus. Only in the lower organisms, which can be grown by the millions in the laboratory, or those in which biochemical techniques permit study of the fine structure of genes, is it possible to distinguish unequivocally tight linkage from pleiotropy.

In many organisms, balance lost by the appearance of a deleterious mutation can be recovered through **suppressor mutants**, which are genes that may correct the detrimental effects of genes at a different locus. They do so by restoring organismal balance—perhaps biochemically—through shifts in DNA reading frames that reestablish the meaning of the original genetic message (Figure 6.3).

9.4 NONNUCLEAR GENETIC EFFECTS

So far we have largely confined ourselves to the action and interaction of genes carried on the chromosome. But the products of genes also interact with extrachromosomal determinants of the phenotype. We may briefly mention here two kinds of such interaction, **cytoplasmic inheritance** and **maternal effects**. In a sense, the former might be included in the latter, because the greatest part by far of the cytoplasm of the zygote (that originally in the egg) is contributed by the mother. In this discussion, however, the two are best separated, since clear-cut cytoplasmic inheritance has been demonstrated only in lower forms of life, unless one includes direct transmission to the offspring of viruses, bacteria, or particles carried in the egg. Maternal genetic effects, however, are exceedingly common in man.

Cytoplasmic inheritance may take many forms. In plants and some protists, self-reproducing plastids, some of which are involved in photosynthesis, are commonly transmitted through the maternal cytoplasm; for example, those referred to in Box 2.C. In some instances, they, as well as mitochondria, have been demonstrated to contain DNA and thus could be described as nonnuclear genes. In other protists, such cytoplasmic inclusions as antigens are known to be under the control of nuclear genes or to show various kinds of interactions with gene products. In general, nonnuclear genes are difficult to study because the cytoplasm is not as regularly distributed to daughter cells as the nuclear material. Furthermore, while the bulk of the zygote's cytoplasm comes from the egg, the sperm also makes some cytoplasmic contribution.

In at least one instance, the direction of coiling in certain snails, the phenotype of the offspring is determined not by its own genotype, but by that of its

Figure 9.2.

The effects of maternal environment
in horses. All data are on females; hence,
sex linkage cannot account for the
differences between reciprocal crosses, and
they must be attributed to maternal
effects. (Redrawn from A. Walton
and J. Hammond.)

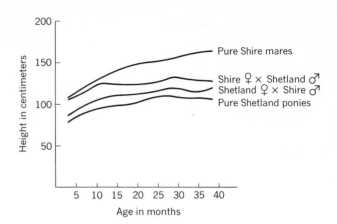

mother. Thus, in reciprocal crosses, the direction of the coiling expressed in the F_1 is that of the mother, while all F_2 snails from both crosses show the dominant right-hand coiling. One quarter of the F_2's, however, are genetically homozygous for left-hand coiling; females of this genotype will produce offspring that show left-hand coiling regardless of the phenotype or genotype of the sire to which they are mated.

Cytoplasmic factors in some animals can have practical significance for man. For instance, in different strains of mosquitoes, cytoplasmic differences lead to incompatibilities between the chromosomes of one strain and the cytoplasm of another. Crosses between two such strains result in eggs that fail to develop. Males of one such strain may be released at appropriate times in massive numbers in a locality in which an incompatible strain may be a vector of malaria or other diseases. A high proportion of the native female mosquitoes, the ones inseminated by the visitors, would then fail to reproduce, because in mosquitoes all zygotes derive from sperm introduced at first copulation. Complete eradication of mosquitoes is possible in some places by this method.

In mammals maternal effects mediated through differences in prenatal intrauterine environment or in postnatal nutrition provided by the mother are more common than those based on cytoplasmic differences. A classic example is illustrated in Figure 9.2. Some further details of this phenomenon are discussed in Section 10.3.

So far our emphasis has been on phenotypic expressions of single genes and interactions between them. There are, however, many characters that depend on a larger number of genes. Their inheritance presents special problems that we shall consider next.

10

POLYGENIC INHERITANCE

10.1 CORRELATION AND CAUSATION

This chapter and a good share of the next three will be devoted to a discussion of the genetics of **polygenic** traits, that is, traits whose expression is controlled by many loci. The main properties of polygenic inheritance can be summarized as follows:

1. Most **metric** and **meristic** traits are affected by a number of loci. (Metric traits are those measurable on a continuous scale, like stature; meristic traits are countable, like the number of ribs in pigs.) There are, however, exceptions, such as the single genes for human dwarfism and for stem length of garden peas, one of the characters studied by Mendel.

2. The effects of allelic substitution at each of the segregating loci are usually relatively small and interchangeable, in the sense that identical phenotypes may be displayed by a great variety of genotypes.

3. The phenotypic expression of polygenic characters is subject to considerable modification by environmental influences.

4. Most populations have great reserves of genetic variability, often carried in the gene pool in balanced systems.

5. Biochemically, there is nothing exceptional about genes controlling polygenic inheritance. They still control production of enzymes or other proteins.

Many genes that have major effects on certain characters may have pleiotropic effects on others. For example, a gene for white feather color in chickens also inhibits growth rate.

6. Polygenic traits show a **continuous** rather than a **discontinuous** distribution (Box 10.A).

Because of these properties, the methods of studying polygenic or, generally speaking, quantitative characters, have to be different from those employed in

---

BOX 10.A THE NORMAL DISTRIBUTION

Phenotypic manifestations of genes with major effects tend to be discontinuously distributed. In this illustration, the top diagram shows the distribution expected in the F_2 of a monohybrid cross, such as one involving stem length in peas. But in reality, such distribution would prevail only if the two phenotypes were classified simply as long or short. Since there is some environmental modification of stem length, the phenotypes would probably cluster around some **mean** value. Other measures of central tendency are the **mode**, the value of the most numerous group, and the **median**, the value of the middle item in the whole array. If the relative frequencies are plotted against the phenotypic value, curves such as those shown in the second diagram are often obtained. The distribution within each phenotypic class becomes continuous. For the total population, however, a discontinuity between AA and Aa, on the one hand, and aa, on the other, still exists.

If we now remove the condition of dominance, the expected distribution of phenotypes can be computed from the coefficients of the expanded binomial $(a + b)^N$, shown in the third part of the illustration, which is known as Pascal's triangle. When the relative frequencies of phenotypic classes are plotted, a *normal* continuous distribution, characterized by a bell-shaped curve is approached, as shown on the bottom diagram. The larger the number of classes and the more individuals in the sample, the closer will be the approximation.

A characteristic property of a normal distribution is that the mean, mode, and median coincide. In addition to the measures of central tendency, we shall also have recourse to a measure of dis-

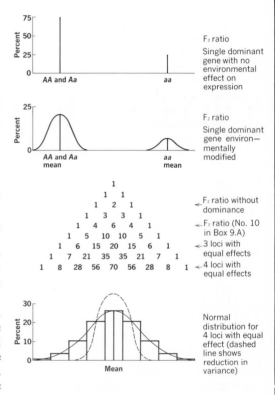

persal, that is, the degree to which individuals tend on the average to deviate from the mean. A statistical measure of this property is known as the *variance* of the distribution. We shall not discuss the methods of computing it, but the dashed line in the lowest diagram illustrates a normal distribution with reduced variance from the solid curve.

ordinary Mendelian analysis. Each locus involved, of course, probably segregates in the ordinary manner delineated by Mendel. But because there are many loci, and because a great many genotypes cannot be phenotypically distinguished from each other, special statistical techniques have been developed for the study of continuous variation. They form the field of biometrical genetics and stem from **biometry**, the statistical study of biological observations, a science developed by Francis Galton (Box 10.B).

BOX 10.B SIR FRANCIS GALTON (1822–1911)

Francis Galton, one of the most eminent Victorians, was a man of insatiable curiosity and remarkable industry and ingenuity. His experiments on the genetic consequences of blood transfusion have already been cited in Section 3.6. He is credited with being the founder of biometry, although this honor might more properly be given the French astronomer L. A. J. Quetelet (1796–1874). Galton was also the founder of mental testing, and a pioneer student of the individuality of fingerprints. Fingerprint classifications actually were independently devised by an Englishman in India and another in Japan, and then adopted by the British police in 1901. Galton conceived the idea of using twins in research on heredity, and coined the term **eugenics** for programs of improvement of mankind by selective breeding, although Plato had first suggested this possibility, basing it on the success of dog breeders. Galton's views on eugenics happened to be wrong, if not entirely because he was the product of his class, then certainly not in spite of his origin. Although he devised the correlation coefficient, he failed to distinguish between the environmentally and the genetically induced portions of the correlation between phenotypes of near relatives. In his book on hereditary genius (1883) he examined pedigrees of judges, statesmen, military commanders, literary men, scientists, painters, divines, oarsmen, and wrestlers, coming to the conclusion that eminence in these fields is largely governed by biological inheritance. The fallacy of the argument is clearly shown by the fact that a man becomes a king usually not because of his genotype but by accident of birth in a king's family, although this does not fully apply to founders of dynasties.

There seem to be very few subjects that did not

interest Galton. He even published an article in a scientific journal discussing the optimum ways of cutting a cake to preserve its freshness. In 1872 he created a furor amid the Victorian establishment by publishing an investigation on the efficacy of prayer. Reasoning that the most-prayed-for people are royalty ("God save the King"), he failed to find evidence that kings outlived commoners. Not being satisfied with this result, he extended his study from those prayed for to those who pray, that is, the clergy. Here, once more, the net conclusion was not conducive to the belief that praying is beneficial. Galton's influence in genetics, psychometrics, anthropology, and many other fields, has been exceeded by few men. (The photograph is reproduced by permission of the Royal Society, courtesy of John R. Freeman.)

In particular, great use in biometry is made of the analysis of variance and of covariation of quantitative characters, that is, the manner in which one trait changes with changes in another. Particularly useful is the **correlation coefficient** (usually indicated by *r*), which measures the degree of association between two or more variables.

Suppose it is found in comparing the speed at which an automobile travels and the distance it takes to brake to a stop, that for every increase of 10 miles of speed per hour, 20 feet of stopping distance is added. If this exact relation holds in every test, the correlation coefficient is positive and has a value of 1.0. Or, if it were observed that doubling the number of men on a construction project invariably halved the time for its completion, the correlation would be negative and have a value of −1.0. In reality, few perfect correlations are found: there is almost always a degree of variation in the variables compared— one automobile may take 40 feet to stop, and another, traveling at the same speed, only 35. The value of the coefficient is then reduced. Thus, correlations range from −1.0 through 0 (which indicates that there is complete independence among the variables) to + 1.0.

A very important consideration must be kept in mind when speaking of correlation. In the examples given the speed of the automobile and the number of men employed may reasonably be assumed to be *causes*, while the distance traveled and the time taken to complete the job are *effects*. But generally speaking, we cannot infer merely from the presence of a high correlation which of two correlated items is the cause and which is an effect. Or, just as important, whether either one is a cause: they both may be the effects of a common cause.

For example, if a comparison were made between the number of storks found in the various districts of a country and the number of babies born in them, a positive correlation might well be established. It would, however, be rash to conclude that storks bring babies. A more plausible explanation is that storks abound in the countryside and are rare in cities, and that birthrates are lower in urban than in rural communities. The causal factor here is the degree of urbanization of the districts, and the two variables originally compared are both effects. Hence, shooting half the storks in a district should not be expected to lower its birthrate.

Interpretation of correlations can thus be very tricky. Galton, for instance, assumed that the correlation between parents and children for eminence in a profession was produced by community of inheritance. But, as parents and children also tend to have a similar environment, at least two causes contributed to the correlation. We shall see later that there are biometrical techniques that can help to untangle nature from nurture, or genotype from environment. Such techniques are highly effective in experiments with plants and animals, in which much of the environment can be randomized and made independent for parents and offspring, but less so in the study of man. Meanwhile, we may profit by viewing the relationship between genotype (*G*), environment (*E*), and phenotype (*P*) as shown in the diagram, which uses single-headed arrows to point from cause to effect and double-headed arrows to indicate correlation:

This may also be written as $G + E + r_{GE} = P$. The diagram may be extended to two generations, with subscripts S for sire, D for dam, and O_1 and O_2 for two offspring:

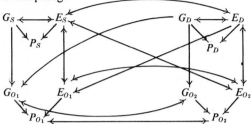

If the parents were genetic relatives by birth, there would also be a double-headed arrow between G_S and G_D. To disentangle the various components represented in this diagram is no simple matter, and for human data it is possible only with a low degree of accuracy—with some exceptions, which we shall examine.

10.2 HERITABILITY

Three of the architects of biometrical genetics and its closely related fields were the British statistician **R. A. Fisher** (1890–1962; Figure 10.1), the American geneticist **Sewall Wright**, and J. B. S. Haldane (Box 2.7). Much of what appears in these chapters is based on their work and that of the British geneticist and biometrician Kenneth Mather and the American geneticist Jay L. Lush. Among the important concepts developed by the latter is that of **heritability**.

If a quantitative character is measured in a population, it will exhibit a certain degree of phenotypic variability. Part of this variation arises from the fact that the different individuals constituting the population have different genotypes, and part, that they developed in different environments. Ignoring for the moment the interaction between genes and environment, we might say that if it were possible to equalize all the environments, all environmental variation would disappear, but genetic variation would still be present. It is this fraction of the total phenotypic variation that is called heritability. Usually designated by the symbol h^2, heritability may be determined by a variety of statistical methods. If we designate genetic, environmental, and phenotypic variation by G, E, and P, we have the relation

$$G + E = P.$$

Dividing by P, we obtain

$$\frac{G}{P} + \frac{E}{P} = \frac{P}{P} = 1,$$

or

$$h^2 + e^2 = 1,$$

where e^2 is the complementary term to heritability, indicating the fraction of the phenotypic variation that would be left were all genetic variation to be removed.

It is clear that h^2 values can range from 1, when no environmentally caused

BOX 10.C DETERMINATION OF HERITABILITY FROM SELECTION EXPERIMENTS

Let us assume that there is a normal distribution of a metric character in a population. We may consider two extreme conditions: When all variation is determined by environmental differences, h^2 may be 0, or it may be 1 when variation observed among the phenotypes is entirely due to genetic differences. We may understand these two conditions better if we examine the effects they would have on the offspring of only the parents that exceed the mean of their own generation. Under the first condition, provided the environments of the parents and the progeny are not correlated, the average degree of expression of the trait in the offspring would be not at all dependent on the phenotypes of the parents. Whether the parental phenotypes were above or below the mean, the average phenotype of the filial generation would still equal the average of the total parental generation and not that of the selected parents.

Under the second condition ($h^2 = 1$), the offspring would inherit the genes of the selected parents, causing them to exceed the mean of their generation. On the average, the phenotype of such progeny equals the mean phenotype of the *selected* parents.

Intermediate degrees of h^2 produce intermediate results. Heritability thus may be estimated by dividing the **gain** obtained by the **selection differential**, as shown in the diagram.

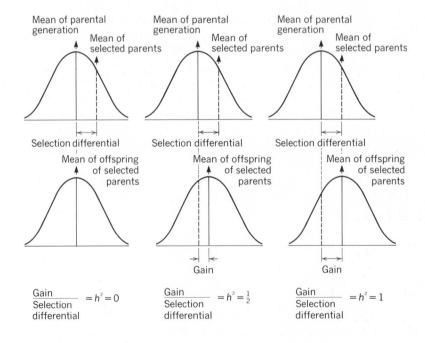

An example of differences in offspring produced when heritabilities differ is shown in the following diagram of the results of an experiment carried out at the University of California at Berkeley.

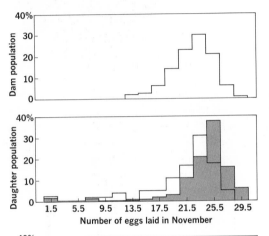

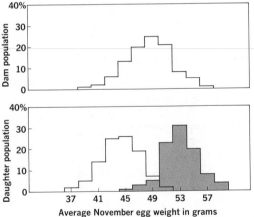

The top diagram shows the November egg production of a group of Leghorn pullets. The most prolific layers among them were selected for mating, and the performance of their daughters is shown by the shaded distribution in the next diagram. The lowest layers from the original group also produced progeny. Their egg production is shown by the outlined distribution in the second diagram.

The third and fourth diagrams show distributions from a corresponding experiment in which the average weight of eggs rather than their number was the objective of selection. The difference in the results of the two experiments is apparent: whereas the h^2 of egg number in this experiment is 0.25, that of egg weight is 0.75.

Precise heritability figures for humans cannot be obtained by these methods. Actually using selection is not the problem, for the necessary calculations could be carried out on paper, that is, by comparing offspring of groups of parents classified as high or low for expression of a specific trait as in the following example. The complication lies in the impossibility of disentangling genetic correlations from environmental correlations. For instance, in the following set of data (from F. J. Kallman), a clear relationship between longevities of parents and their offspring is shown, but how much of the effect can be attributed to G, and how much to E, is impossible to tell.

Country	Date of study	Life-span of offspring from short-lived parents, in years	Life-span of offspring from long-lived parents, in years
U.S.A.	1903	39.4	41.8
U.S.A.	1918	32.8	52.7
U.S.A.	1931	40.9	45.8
China	1932	31.5	39.8
Scandinavia	1951	36.2	48.1
U.S.A.	1956	49.5	57.9

Figure 10.1.

Sir Ronald Fisher, as well as working
on genetics and evolution, was
one of the foremost statisticians
of our time. He developed a
number of powerful tools of
biometry. (Courtesy of Godfrey Argent.)

variation is present (as in blood groups) to zero, when all variation is environmental. It must be understood that when a statement is made that stature has an h^2 of 0.50 or 50 percent, it does not mean that the height of any given individual is determined half by heredity and half by environment. Heritability is a population concept, and what it means is that half of the *variation* in the population is produced by genetic differences between its members.

Since

$$h^2 = \frac{G}{P} = \frac{G}{G + E},$$

it follows that changes in any component of the fraction will cause changes in its value. Indeed, it is found that by inbreeding (see Chapter 19), genetic variation within groups is reduced, and h^2 for a given character decreases. Similarly, if changes in environment cause increases in environmentally generated variation, h^2 will drop; if they cause decreases, h^2 will rise.

Essentially, h^2 is a measure of correlation between genotype and phenotype. If we represent the respective correlations in the diagram appearing in the previous section, by r_G and r_P,

$$h^2 = \frac{r_P}{r_G}.$$

This gives one clue as to how heritabilities may be determined. In cases where no environmental correlations are present, theoretical genetic correlations can be computed. Since each parent provides half of the genes of each offspring, the genetic correlation between parent and immediate progeny is 0.5. Because identical twins have identical genotypes, the genetic correlation between them is 1.0. In a similar way, it can be shown that the genetic correlation between **sibs** (sisters or brothers) is 0.5. Between half-sibs, sharing one parent in common, it is 0.25, between first cousins 0.125, and so forth.

Phenotypic correlations can be computed from observed data. Thus incubator-hatched chickens can be reared and maintained in a random environ-

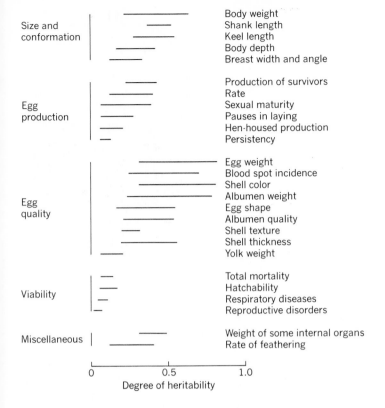

Figure 10.2.

Range of heritabilities

reported for various

economically important

characters of the

domestic fowl.

(I. M. Lerner.)

ment independent of the environment of their parents, except for the food material which the hen provides in the egg. If it is then found that the phenotypic correlation between full sister hens for the average weight of eggs they lay is 0.375, the h^2 of this trait will be 0.375/0.500 or 0.75. The less closely related the individuals considered in computing heritabilities are, the less useful is this method because its reliability goes down with the drop in r_G.

Another method, which is described in Box 10.C, is provided by experiments on artificial selection. Figure 10.2 shows the range of values of h^2 reported for chickens. Many other heritability studies have been carried out. Those done on domestic animals assist in the choice of efficient selection systems (see Section 13.3). Thus, in cattle, birth weight is 40–50 percent heritable, and milk is 30 percent; in sheep, staple length of wool about 25 percent; in swine, body weight at different ages around 30 percent.

10.3 PARTITIONING OF VARIATION

We have been discussing the division of the total phenotypic variation into two component parts: that due to genetic differences among the members of a population and that due environmental ones. Not only can each of the components be partitioned further, but some of the phenotypic variation may be the result of interaction between genotype and environment. In the examples

Figure 10.3.

Some diagrammatic examples of
genotype-environment interaction. Comparing
the phenotypes produced by G_1 and G_2, it
may be seen that E_1 is optimal for G_1 but
substandard for G_2. Moving G_2 to E_2 equalizes
the phenotypes if G_1 stays in E_1, while E_3 can
make G_2 superior to G_1 in any tested
environment. The genotype dealt with here
could be intelligence; the environment,
schooling or parental socioeconomic class.

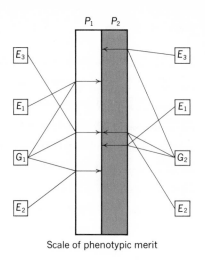

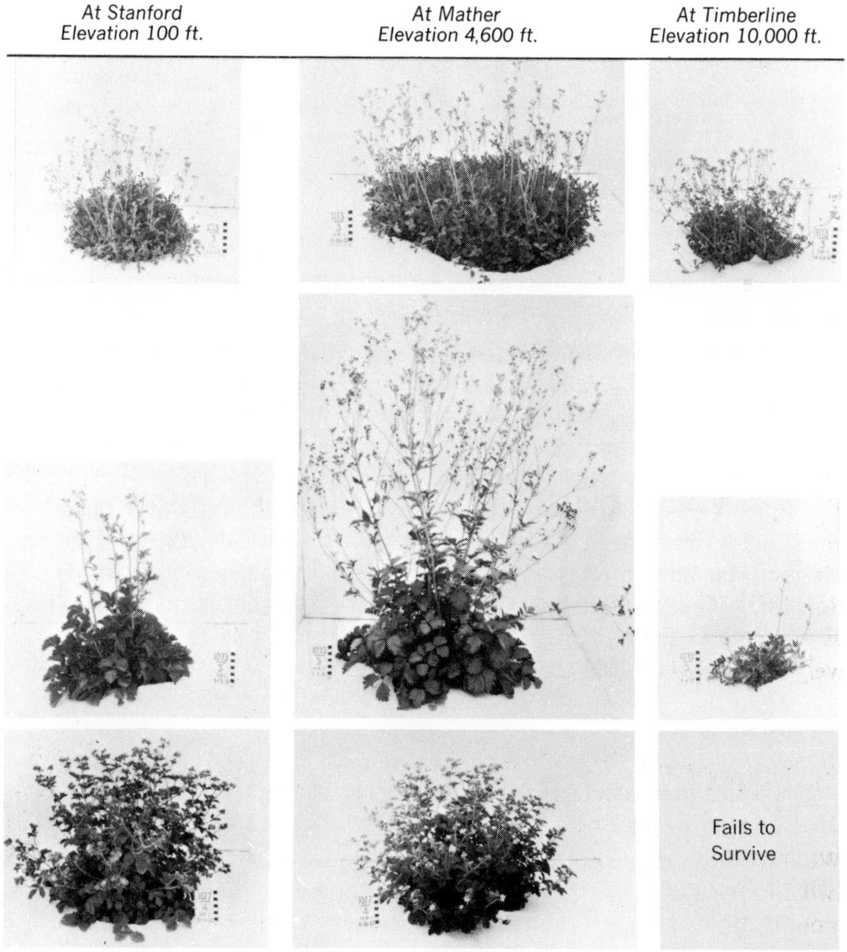

Scale of phenotypic merit

| At Stanford Elevation 100 ft. | At Mather Elevation 4,600 ft. | At Timberline Elevation 10,000 ft. |

Figure 10.4.

The top row shows
the appearance of a
subalpine subspecies of
Potentilla glandulosa
native to Timberline,
grown in three environ-
ments; the second row
that of a meadow
subspecies; and the
third row that of a
coast species. In each
case, the plants came
from cuttings from a
single individual.
(Courtesy of J. Clausen
and the Carnegie
Institution of
Washington.)

Fails to
Survive

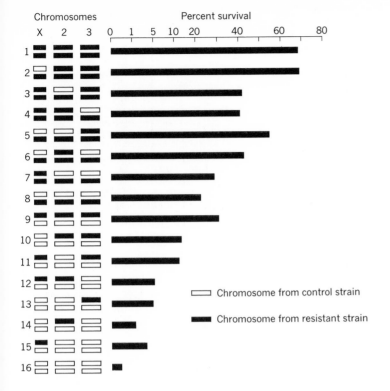

Figure 10.5.
James F. Crow's analysis of the
effects of the three large chromosomes of *Drosophila melanogaster*
on resistance to DDT. The
sixteen different combinations of
chromosomes from a resistant
strain and a control strain
indicate that each of the three
chromosomes carries some genes
for resistance. (From Crow,
Annual Review of Entomology,
2:228, 1957.)

of human sensitivity to ragweed pollen, or of PKU, the phenotypic expression
of a given genotype depends on the environment in which the phenotype develops. But beyond that, differing genotypes that produce identical phenotypes in differing environments will produce other phenotypic patterns if the
environments are interchanged. For instance, a strain of chickens adapted to
a warm climate and maintained in indoor cages may have an average annual
production of 250 eggs. Another strain living in a moderate climate and kept
in outdoor pens may have a similar phenotype for egg number. Yet if the environments are switched, the production of the first may drop to 220 eggs, and
that of the second to, let us say, 180. Similarly, two strains *differing* in egg production in one environment may reverse their ranking in another (Figure 10.3).

In general, natural populations are adapted to their habitats by selection.
A change in environment may then produce suboptimal (from the standpoint
of fitness) phenotypes. For example, in experiments with a rosaceous plant,
Potentilla glandulosa, strains from sea-level, mid-elevation, and high mountains were grown in all three environments, with the results shown in Figure
10.4.

It is possible to isolate traits resulting from interaction between genotype and
environment in plants and animals experimentally, but there are few data on
humans that are suitable for this purpose. Hence in interpreting the heritability of human traits, it is important to keep in mind that h^2 estimates in man
are subject to error because of lack of information on the interaction between
genotype and environment and on the extent of uncontrolled environmental
correlation between relatives.

BOX 10.D PARTITIONING GENETIC VARIANCE

The table at right (from El Oksh *et al.*) shows the partitioning of variation in body weight of mice of different ages. In this experiment weight at birth had an h^2 of zero. The negative value for the postnatal maternal influence may be a statistical artifact and hence may be viewed as zero. As the animals grew older, the influence of the genetic component increased and that of the prenatal maternal effects decreased. The postnatal influence of the mother at first rose, but by the time of weaning (3 weeks) it had begun to drop. (The symbol m_u^2 stands for intrauterine effects, m_n^2 for nutritional ones.)

		Source of Variation		
			Maternal	
Age in weeks	*Genetic* (h^2)	*Prenatal* (m_u^2)	*Postnatal* (m_n^2)	*Environmental* (e^2)
0	0.00	0.52	−0.14	0.62
1	0.11	0.27	0.30	0.31
2	0.23	0.25	0.38	0.14
3	0.30	0.12	0.30	0.29
6	0.26	0.17	0.23	0.34

The diagram below illustrates the partitioning of sources of variation in human birth weight (data of L. S. Penrose and M. Karn). It may be seen that the greatest of the recognized causes of variability is the maternal genotype for ability to provide an optimum environment for the foetus. The influence of the paternal genotype is included in the 15 percent that the foetal genotype contributes to the variation in birth weight. The other factors are self-explanatory.

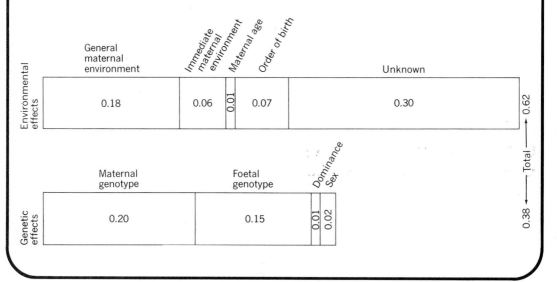

The *G* fraction of the phenotypic variation can be further subdivided into fractions attributable to dominance, epistasis, and straightforward additive effects of genes. In Drosophila, genetic analysis based on many gene markers and on cytological observation has been brought to a high degree of precision, and it is possible to estimate the effects of individual chromosomes or even parts of chromosomes on polygenic characters. Figure 10.5 provides an example of one such analysis. Although this kind of refined analysis is not possible for many organisms, partitioning of the genetic variance in a variety of different ways is feasible even for man, as can be seen in the diagram in Box 10.D.

The phenotypic variation due to environment is also subject to subdivision. Thus, in many experiments, e^2 can be divided into the effects produced by tangible influences and those produced by intangible ones. Among the former may be the effects of maternal influences, which will be common to all offspring of a given dam; effects resulting from the nutritional state or health of the mother during a particular pregnancy; effects common to a group of individuals raised in a specific environment; and so forth. The environmental variation not thus accounted for is considered to be due to intangible and uncontrolled differences in the environments of the members of the population studied.

Box 10.D provides two illustrations of the partitioning of variance in mammals, that on human birth weight being the most completely analyzed example of partitioning in man as yet available.

Variance partitioning of metric traits is essentially one aspect of the more general problem of nature-nurture interaction, which has occupied mankind for a long time. It is only recently that techniques which provide reasonably meaningful estimates of the role of these two forces have been perfected.

There are few good data available on heritability in man. Yet it appears that in a human population that is homogeneous with respect to income, geographical location, and genetic origin, the genetic fraction of phenotypic variance of such morphological metric traits as weight or stature is generally similar to that found in other animals. But with such complex traits as intelligence or personality, we are still facing many unsolved issues not only of interpretation, but also of methodology.

11
NATURE AND NURTURE

11.1 TWINS

The heritability of anatomical and physiological traits of plants and animals is of great concern to agriculturists, since the choice of breeding methods used in plant and animal improvement depends on it. In man, the h^2 of stature or of skin pigmentation is mostly a matter of intellectual curiosity. The heritability of such human characteristics as intelligence, temperament, and behavior, however, are of social significance today and will be, perhaps increasingly so, in the future.

High heritability must not, of course, be confused with the impossibility of modifying a phenotype. A person is born with a fixed genetic endowment, but its phenotypic expression can, in principle, be modified at will by supplying an appropriate environment. The degree of modification possible increases as our knowledge of genetics and development progresses.

Few disagreements or controversies among informed and well-meaning men have raged for so long and with such bitterness as that over the nature-nurture interaction in man. Extreme views of what are the important determinants of differences in human mentality and behavior have been held by proponents of various theories since the time of the Greek natural philosophers. The most disparate views may be represented by the ideas of the English philosopher John Locke (1632–1704). who believed that the minds of men were blank at birth (*tabula rasa*) and that all later differences between them were environmentally produced, and those of the French diplomat and writer J. A. Gobineau (1816–1882), who, in his essay on the inequality of human races, declared that differences in abilities of men were entirely innate.

Locke's position was forcefully restated by the French philosopher C. A. Helvetius (1715–1771), who believed that "the inequality of minds is the effect of a known cause, and this cause is the difference of education," Gobineau's viewpoint was later amplified by the English-German political theorist Houston Stewart Chamberlain (1885–1927), and acted upon by racists in the southern United States and elsewhere, and, in the most drastic form, by Adolf Hitler and his followers in Europe. Regrettably, not only demagogues but also some scientists of reputation, even a few geneticists and psychologists, have upheld near-extremist positions clearly unsupportable by scientific facts; both extremes of the controversy have had such supporters.

Clearly, the stance taken by an individual on this subject is correlated with his social and political views and is beclouded by prejudices generated by upbringing, social milieu, and psychological factors. Hence, it would be surprising if the contents of this book were detached from and free of influences in the writer's personal history. What is to follow should, therefore, be understood as a mixture of reported data and authorial interpretation. Although I am trying to be impartial and enlightened, the warning *caveat lector* must, in fairness to the reader, be spelled out.

The most useful material available to students of the genetics of human behavior comes from studies of twins. Before proceeding with the discussion of the genetics of intelligence and personality, therefore, we will consider the subject of these studies.

There are two kinds of twins: **monozygotic**, also known as **identical** or one-egg twins, and **dizygotic**, **fraternal** or two-egg twins. Monozygotic twins originate from a single zygote that splits into two at an early division and develops into two genetically identical individuals (see exceptions in Section 8.4). Such

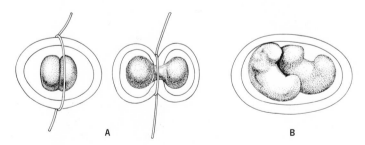

Figure 11.1.
The classical experiment of the German embryologist and Nobel Prize winner Hans Spemann, producing monozygotic twins in a salamander. **A** shows the constriction of a zygote with a fine hair loop along the plane of the first cleavage; and **B**, the resulting twin embryos. (After Spemann, *Embryonic Development and Induction*. New Haven, Yale University Press, 1938.)

identical twins have been produced experimentally in animals, as, for example, is shown in Figure 11.1. There are now more elaborate ways of producing identical twins in toads and frogs than that shown for salamanders in the illustration. Nuclei from the cells of a frog are transplanted into a number of unfertilized frog eggs, whose own nuclei have been destroyed by irradiation. Such transplants give rise to genetically identical individuals. This process may be repeated to produce any number of frogs, which would (provided the same frog supplied the replacement nuclei) belong to the same **clone**, a term originally applied to plants of identical genotype reproduced in a vegetative fashion—like *Potentilla*, which is pictured in Figure 10.4. (The possible immortality of man, should such methods become available, could be extended to males

BOX 11.A CONJOINED TWINS

Normal monozygotic twins become separate very early in their development, but late duplication or failure of separation sometimes also occurs, with a frequency estimated at 1 in 600 twin births. The doubling in such cases involves anything from a finger to a complete functional individual. Most conjoined twins are born dead, but many have survived for a long time. On occasion surgical separation is possible, as in the case of two San Francisco girls shown below.

The photographs are by Robert David Wong, medical illustrator/photographer, San Francisco.

They are reproduced by permission of Peter A. de Vries and the National Foundation, and first appeared in "Conjoined Twins," a publication of the National Foundation (April 1967).

The most publicized conjoined twins and source of the eponymic designation "Siamese" were Chang and Eng. They were sons of a Chinese father and a Chinese-Siamese mother. In later life they settled in North Carolina and took the family name of Bunker.

As shown in the illustration (reproduced by courtesy of the National Foundation), the twins

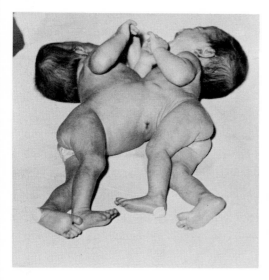
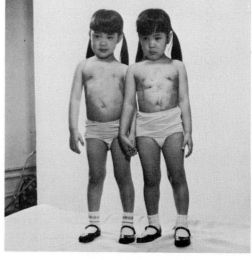

as well as females.) Monozygotic twins sometimes fail to separate, with the result that monsters of various degrees of viability are produced (Box 11.A).

Dizygotic twins arise when, through superovulation, two eggs are present in the oviduct and both are fertilized. The genetic relationship between these fraternal twins is no closer than that between ordinary sibs. Unlike normal monozygotic twins, dizygotics can be of different sexes. Indeed, one way of estimating the incidence of monozygotic twinning in the population uses the fact that approximately equal numbers of males and females are produced throughout a group of dizygotic twins. Suppose that in a group of twins (of both kinds) the distribution of sexes were found to be 120 pairs ♀ ♀ : 140 pairs ♀ ♂ : 120 pairs ♂ ♂. The distribution among dizygotics would be expected to

were united by a band of tissue. It was very short at first but gradually expanded as Chang and Eng began walking. Despite the fact that conjoined twins are thought to be monozygotic, the Bunker brothers displayed many differences. Mark Twain made the most of this in his famous short story on the Siamese twins. Chang, at maturity, was about an inch shorter, was somewhat deaf, and had an irritable temper. Eng was always healthier and stronger, and was known for his amiable disposition.

After making a considerable fortune with the help of P. T. Barnum by exhibiting themselves, the two brothers retired to raise tobacco. At 42 they married two sisters, and produced a total of 22 children. Eventually, their wives quarreled and the two families set up separate residences, with the twins spending three days in one and then three days in the other. On the whole they got on remarkably well with each other, with only one fight leading to an exchange of blows between them on record. The occasion was precipitated by Chang's heavy drinking, which did not stimulate Eng, who was not an imbiber. At the age of 63, Chang contracted pneumonia (he had had a stroke earlier) and died within four days. Eng immediately became progressively weaker and survived his brother by only two hours, his death being diagnosed as due to fright.

There were other famous conjoined twin pairs. One such twin, Rosa Blazek, gave birth to a normal son.

Siamese Youths.

be $1:2:1$, or $95 ♀ ♀ : 190 ♀ ♂ : 95 ♂ ♂$. The excess of twins of the same sex (50/380) would then lead to an estimate of the porportion of monozygotic pairs in this group of about 13 percent.

Determination of whether particular pairs of twins of the same sex are monozygotic or dizygotic has not always been easy. Because dizygotic twins share the same intrauterine environment and because after birth most twins come closer to receiving exactly the same treatment than siblings born at different times do, additional resemblances between them may be generated. However, discrimination between the two kinds of twins is made much easier by information now available about blood-group and serum protein differences between organisms with given genetic relationships. The best test is provided by grafting of tissues: identical twins, being of the same genotype, will accept grafts from each other; fraternal twins, each having some antigens foreign to the other, will reject them.

This is not entirely true in cattle. It may be recalled from the discussion of the freemartin in Section 8.2 that cattle twins share foetal circulation. Apparently, early exposure to foreign antigens induces a degree of tolerance that makes grafts from one fraternal twin to the other in cattle possible. This discovery is paving the way for the development of methods of overcoming immunogenetic incompatibilities in man (Section 18.3).

Cattle twins have been used extensively in heritability determinations of traits that are of economic importance to breeders. One advantage that identical heifers have for such studies is that if they are mated to the same bull, the offspring they produce are genetically full sibs. Yet these sibs are not subject to the identical maternal effects that often complicate h^2 determinations. They develop in different uteri, and thus give an opportunity for estimating the degree of nongenetic maternal contribution to phenotypic variance.

Multiple births, of course, include triplets, quadruplets, and larger groups. The frequency of such births decreases as the number born at the same time rises. Recently, there appears to have been a rise in the number of human multiple births owing to the extended use of ovulation-inducing drugs or hormones to combat sterility. Children produced in this way are of polyzygotic

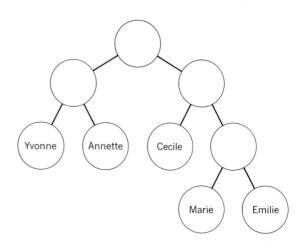

Figure 11.2.
Probable origin of the
Dionne quintuplets
from a single zygote.

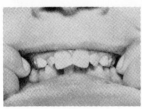
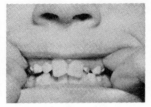
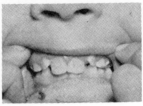

Figure 11.3.
A set of triplets. Note concordance in appearance, tooth shape, and dress.
(The lower photographs are from *Acta Genet. Med. Gemell.*, April 1966.
All are reproduced by courtesy of L. Gedda.)

origin. The Dionne quintuplets, however, were monozygotic. Figure 11.2 diagrams their probable origin by successive divisions and separations.

The frequency of births of monozygotic twins does not show much variation between different populations, but that of dizygotics does. For instance, the frequency per 1,000 births in three groups has been reported as follows:

Population	Monozygotic	Dizygotic
U.S., white	3.85	7.44
U.S., Negro	4.08	10.01
Japan	4.25	2.72

The range of differences in the frequency of dizygotic twins is even higher than indicated here: in one study of African Negroes, the incidence per 1,000 births was found to be 20.0.

These differences may, perhaps, be interpreted to indicate that there is no genetic component for monozygotic twinning. Such twins are produced by developmental accidents. The tendency for dizygotic twinning may have a hereditary component, possibly mediating through the hormones controlling ovulation.

Twins provide a very convenient tool in genetic research, although its use is beset by many difficulties. Since identical twins have all of their genes in common, and fraternal twins only one-half, comparison of intrapair differences might be thought to provide an accurate way of determining heritabilities. Unfortunately for genetic research, the environment of monozygotic twins,

BOX 11.B A TWIN MISCELLANY

A great deal of information has accumulated on resemblances between twins. It is given as percentages of concordance and discordance, as correlation coefficients, or as estimates of heritability (which may have a different definition from that given in Chapter 10). The following data are a sampling, compiled from a variety of sources.

Percentage concordance

	Monozygotic twins	Dizygotic twins
Incidence of schizophrenia	69	10
Tuberculosis	54	16
Cancer	10	5
Clubfoot	32	3
Measles	95	87
Scarlet fever	64	47
Rickets	88	22
Electrocardiogram	39	25
Shape of stomach	24	19
Type of body sway	45	34
Blood pressure	63	36
Pulse rate	56	34

Correlation coefficients for finger ridge counts

	Expected from genetic correlation with $h^2 = 1.0$	Observed
Monozygotic twins	1.00	0.95
Dizygotic twins	0.50	0.49
Sibs	0.50	0.50
Parent-offspring	0.50	0.48
Parent-parent	0	0.05

Differences in age at death (60–69 year old group)

	Monozygotic twins	Dizygotic twins
Males	4 years, 2 months	6 years, 3 months
Females	9 years, 6 months	10 years, 7½ mos.

Intra-pair correlation coefficients

	Monozygotic twins Reared together	Monozygotic twins Reared apart	Dizygotic twins
Binet I.Q. test	0.97	0.67	0.64
Otis intelligence test	0.92	0.73	0.62
Stanford achievement test[1]	0.96	0.51	0.88
Height	0.93	0.97	0.65
Weight	0.92	0.87	0.63
Intelligence quotient[2]	0.87	0.75	0.53
Vocabulary test	0.77	0.76	0.51
Introversion-extraversion[3]	0.42	0.61	
Neurotic tendency[3]	0.38	0.53	
Strabismus (an eye defect)	0.94		0.26
Composite intelligence score[4]	0.87		0.62
English usage	0.71		0.64
Mathematical ability	0.74		0.42
Natural sciences aptitude	0.69		0.51

[1] A higher *G* component than in the other tests is indicated here.

[2] Compare these values with 0.49 for sibs who are not twins and 0.23 for the control correlation between unrelated children.

[3] In these instances, apparently an interaction between twins raised together makes them more dissimilar than when they are raised apart.

[4] These values can be converted to heritability estimates for the four tests, respectively of 0.72, 0.27, 0.80, and 0.51.

tends to be more similar than that of dizygotic twins (partly, it is true, for genetic reasons), so that observed resemblances between them might be greater than dictated by the identity of genotype alone.

Improved h^2 estimation would be possible if identical twins reared apart could be found. Several studies have been done on such pairs, but the total number of such twins investigated is still pitifully small. Surprisingly, the differences between identical twins in such measurable traits as the intelligence quotient, are greater in pairs separated after one year of age than between those separated earlier.

Besides estimations of heritability, other methods may be used to partition the effects of nature and nuture. Comparison of intrapair twins correlation is one, and **concordance** *vs* **discordance** within a pair is another. When both twins show a given character, they are said to be concordant; if only one does, they are discordant. Figure 11.3 shows an example of concordance in a number of features.

Box 11.B gives a miscellany of findings on resemblances between twins, and further examples will be given in the next section. Particular note should be made of the instances in which, contrary to expectation, twins reared apart resemble each other more than twins reared together. This could be due to interaction or competition between twins reared together—another kind of environmental influence on expression of genotype. Such a phenomenon is known in horses: one of a pair of horse twins is usually born as a runt. The equine uterus apparently is not equipped to handle two foetuses, with the result that the twin getting a headstart in its development inhibits the growth of the other by winning the competition for available nutrients.

11.2 INTELLIGENCE

The role of nature and nurture in the determination of intelligence is an exceedingly controversial subject among both psychologists and geneticists. Because political, socioeconomic, and ethical considerations regarding the treatment of minorities and other disadvantaged segments of the population impinge so closely on this problem, it has generated a great deal of emotion. Psychometric literature is bewildering in its scope. The difficulties in drawing conclusions from it lie in the kind of data available, the selectivity with which proponents of one or another view use them, and the interpretation of what various tests measure.

Furthermore, there are philosophic positions that inhibit impartial evaluation of psychometric data. Proponents of what may be termed **educational**, or **psychological engineering**, the neobehaviorists of the school of the American psychologist B. F. Skinner, assume, possibly without warrant, that nearly anyone can, given proper teaching methods, learn anything. Even if there are genetic differences in ability, the invention of appropriate techniques chosen to fit each particular genotype and leading to the desired phenotype makes them irrelevant, according to this view.

At the other end of the spectrum of current ideas, extreme hereditary determinists mistakenly believe that the phenotypic expression of the genotype is fixed at fertilization and is forever unmodifiable. We have already seen many examples which showed that this is not so, including cases of hereditary mental retardation. Perhaps in the remote future, genetical engineering will allow man to modify not only his phenotype but the genotype itself (Chapter 20 continues the discussion of these matters). Although some definite statements about the degree of heritability of intelligence can be made, it is impossible to make unequivocal estimates of its variation. Such estimates may have some validity for an ethnically and socioeconomically homogeneous group, but not for differences between such groups as, let us say, Negroes and whites in the United States.

The first problem is to define what is meant by intelligence. Psychometricians can be divided into two groups, polarizing at one extreme on the view that in the organization of a human being there is a single factor for general intellectual ability, a position held by most British schools of psychology. At the other extreme, more common among American psychologists, is the opinion that various aspects of the intellect are under the control of independent factors. There are also differences about what the term "intelligence" should be applied to: the ability to learn, the ceiling of what an individual can learn, the rate of learning, the motivational drive to learn, or any number of other attributes.

The second problem centers on the question of what the great variety of tests that are intended to measure mental ability really do measure. It would be generally agreed that a test devised to measure intelligence in Boston Brahmans may not be suitable for Calcutta Brahmans. More controversial is the question whether any test can be free of bias that will favor certain cultural groups, even within a given country, a question that is relevant to I.Q. comparisons between whites and Negroes or upper and lower socioeconomic classes. The prevalent opinion (to which many take exception) seems to be that tests that take account of cultural differences do not exist. Such tests as we have measure not native intelligence, pure and unadorned, but a conglomerate combination of innate and learned factors. This seems to be the most reasonable position to take at present. The insistence of some psychometricians that culture-free tests can not ever be prepared—at least not until innate intelligence can be tested on the molecular level—may well be justified.

What are the statements that we can make about the genetics of intellectual ability? Drawing on a small number of sources from the jungle of literature on the subject, we can first say that whatever it is that the various tests measure, it has a strong underlying genetic component. One line of evidence is provided by Figure 11.4. The average r values increase steadily as the genetic relationship between the individuals compared increases. A similar, but apparently smaller, effect is shown for increasing similarities in environment. This factor is also strongly brought out by the correlation noted between the score achieved in an army intelligence test by World War I soldiers grouped according to the states in which they were educated, and the average amount of school expenditure per child in the various states. In these tests, whites rated consistently higher than Negroes from the same state if the schools of that state were segregated and those for Negroes received less support than those for whites. The correlation of educational expenditure and high scores for the test was further supported by the fact that Negroes from Ohio and Illinois

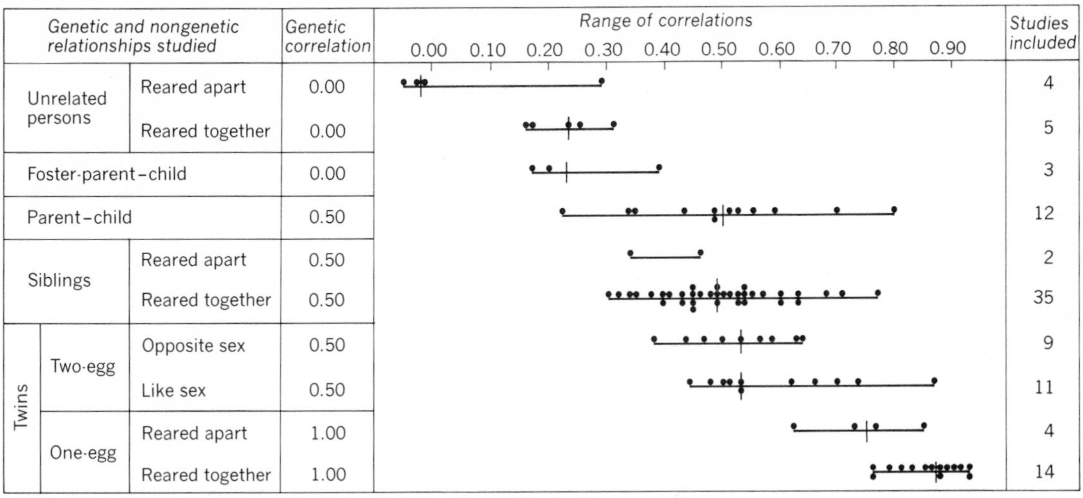

Genetic and nongenetic relationships studied		Genetic correlation	Range of correlations	Studies included
Unrelated persons	Reared apart	0.00		4
	Reared together	0.00		5
Foster-parent–child		0.00		3
Parent–child		0.50		12
Siblings	Reared apart	0.50		2
	Reared together	0.50		35
Twins — Two-egg	Opposite sex	0.50		9
	Like sex	0.50		11
Twins — One-egg	Reared apart	1.00		4
	Reared together	1.00		14

Figure 11.4.
A summary of correlation coefficients compiled by L. Erlenmeyer-Kimling and L. F. Jarvik from various sources. The horizontal lines show the range of correlation coefficients in "intelligence" between individuals of various degrees of genetic and environmental relationship. The vertical lines show the averages.

outscored whites from Mississippi and North Carolina: in the latter states school expenditures for white children was less than those for Negroes who attended unsegregated schools in the Midwest. The only exception was Virginia, where Negroes attained relatively high scores despite a low level of support for schools. There is also evidence that, among Negro children who move from the South to the North, the number of years of schooling obtained in the North is correlated with the intelligence quotient. For example, Negro children from the South who entered Philadelphia schools in grade 1A scored a mean I.Q. of 93.3 in grade 6B, while their classmates who entered in grades 5A to 6B tested only 88.2. Figures from other grades were also consistent with the notion that each grade of schooling in the North raised the I.Q. by one point.

Evidence from adopted children indicates the existence of a high genetic component. Thus, Figure 11.5 shows that the education of the real father and mother correlates with the I.Q. of a child, whether he is reared by his own or by foster parents. On the contrary, the education of the foster parents has no bearing on the adopted child's I.Q.

Even with such information, it is still difficult to make a meaningful estimate of the h^2 of traits measured by intelligence tests. In culturally homogenous groups, values of 0.4, 0.6, and higher have been suggested—all on reasonable grounds. But these values clearly apply only within, and not between, ethnic and economic classes. No extrapolation to the partitioning of variation existing between classes or ethnically different groups can be made from the material reported. This is a point of utmost importance, to be returned to in Section 16.4.

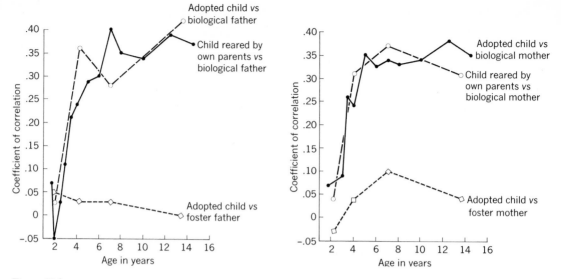

Figure 11.5.
Correlation between the I.Q. of children and the educational level of real and foster parents.
(From M. Honzik, and M. Skodak and B. M. Skeels.)

How much more can be learned about the inheritance of intelligence from the kinds of study described is difficult to say. Perhaps tests on successive generations might be helpful, but they too would present difficulties of separating cultural from genetic influences because the cultural milieu of successive generations is not the same. For example, the massive exposure to television of American children today would very likely make it impossible to compare their scores on a given test with the childhood scores of their parents on the same test. The optimists might suggest that the I.Q. of the children would go up because of exposure to television; the more realistic pessimists would take the contrary view.

In general, both in the past and at the present time, fears have been expressed that the inequality in birth rates among people in different occupational classes together with the differences in the average I.Q. of families of different sizes may erode the level of intelligence in the human population. This argument is based on the kind of information shown in Box 11.C.

It has been argued that—whatever the proportion of the genetic component is for socioeconomic status, so long as it is not zero—the fact that people of low economic status produce more children than those of higher status may have a selective effect in the direction of decreased intelligence. This is reinforced by the finding that, irrespective of status, children of larger families tend to have lower I.Q.'s. In one Scottish study, a negative correlation between family size and average I.Q. of −0.28 has been reported; the mean Stanford-Binet score of single children was 113, that in sibships of six, 91. But as it happens, the information available does not support the pessimistic prognosis that we are on the way towards becoming a species of morons.

Data from the Scottish study noted provides one link in the chain of evidence on this point. Some 87,000 eleven-year-old children in Edinburgh were given I.Q. tests in 1932, and the same tests were given to 71,000 children of the same age in 1947. From the correlation between I.Q. and sibship size, a significant drop was expected from the first to the second group. Instead, if anything, the average performance improved. Somewhat similar results covering I.Q. differences between successive generations have been obtained in England, New Zealand, and the United States.

One possible reason for this apparent paradox has already been mentioned: because the tests are culture-bound, the inevitable changes in the social, educational, and other environmental influences affecting the two generations tested would obscure any genetic trends that might exist.

Another reason may be that the drop in the I.Q. among large sibships is due to the less satisfactory environment provided by large families. In other words, the expressed genetic correlation between parents and offspring is greatly reduced by interaction with the environment so that the phenotype of the offspring reflects less of the genetic contribution of the parents than might be otherwise expected. Still another reason may be found in the statistics on reproduction that have been collected in the past. That is, data on family size usually excluded unmarried or infertile adults. When they were included, the

---

BOX 11.C OCCUPATION, I.Q., AND FAMILY SIZE

Demographic statistics relating socioeconomic class, I.Q., and family sizes are abundant. Here, we shall give a composite picture from several sources. The data are not strictly comparable, and for the sake of compactness, some of the occupational categories are not described in the original terms. They are however, sufficiently accurate to make the general picture emerging reliable.

The trend of decreasing intelligence quotients with a decrease in socioeconomic status is remarkably uniform in the three countries.

Occupational status of parents	Average I.Q. of Children			Average size of English family
	U.S.	USSR	England	
Professional	116	117	115	1.73
Semiprofessional	112	109	113	1.60
Clerical and retail business	107	105	106	1.54
Skilled	105	101	102	1.85
Semiskilled	98	97	97	2.03
Unskilled	96	92	95	2.12

correlation between I.Q. and the average number of children disappeared, at least in one investigation carried out in Minnesota:

I.Q. of sibs	Number of sibs studied	Average number of children in family produced by the sibs
55 and below	29	1.38
56–70	74	2.46
71–85	208	2.39
86–100	583	2.16
101–115	778	2.26
116–130	269	2.45
131 and above	25	2.96
Total	1966	2.27

Although this table does not show it, it is not impossible that there is a stabilizing selection for intelligence, based on a reproductive disadvantage for both high and low I.Q., with the persons in the middle having the highest fitness. This is known to occur with birth weight. In one investigation, the average 28-day survival of newborn babies was found to be 95.9 percent. But only 41.4 percent of babies weighing less than 4.5 pounds and only 90.5 percent of those weighing more than 10 pounds survived, the optimal weight being intermediate (7.5–8.5 pounds), with a survival rate of 98.5 percent. Birth weight and I.Q. are not entirely independent (see Chapter 20). Hence, a stabilizing form of selection may also play a role in the total picture.

Results similar to those from Minnesota emerge from a study of 979 people in Indiana born in 1916:

I.Q.	Average number of offspring produced	Relative fitness	Percent without issue
69–79	1.50	0.58	30.0
80–94	2.46	0.95	22.5
95–104	2.02	0.78	22.0
105–119	2.24	0.86	17.0
120+	2.60	1.00	13.4

There are other causes for optimism with regard to lack of erosion of intelligence. A recent study of a population in Ann Arbor, Michigan, seems to indicate that there may be a reversal in the reproductive pattern, in that individuals with higher I.Q.'s now produce more children than individuals of middle or low I.Q.'s, as in the above table. This trend is also indicated by the fact that when the percentage change in family size from 1940 to 1950 is computed for the U.S. urban population, they are respectively (from high to low socioeconomic status) found to be 12, 8, 7, −5, −6 and −6, showing increases in the upper and decreases in the lower status groups.

Similarly, in a study of replacement rates of scholars at Winchester College, an economically highly privileged group in English society, a steady increase in average family size over a period of about thirty years has been found. Those born between 1893 and 1897 produced an average of 1.96 children; those born between 1923–1927 had families averaging 2.92 children in 1966. Some demographers nevertheless consider that the possibility of a complete reversal of the previously observed correlations between sizes of families and their social status is a matter of wishful thinking.

So far, we have been addressing ourselves to the inheritance of intelligence, which we have regarded as a polygenic trait with a quasi-normal distribution. In reality, there is a component of the human population that, although appearing to be part of a continuum of phenotypes for intelligence, is genotypically discontinuous from the rest of the population. Whether there is such an element at the upper end of the distribution, that is, whether there exists a class of geniuses discontinuous from the distribution of the rest of us is not known. But at the lower end, such a class of genotypes, which express themselves in the form of mental retardation, undoubtedly exists.

Diseases caused by metabolic blocks produced by single defective genes fall into this category. PKU provided us with one such example, and the disease **galactosemia** is another. The defect causing this disease is failure of the body to produce an enzyme needed to metabolize galactose, the sugar of milk, and is produced by a recessive autosomal gene. As in PKU, there is a toxic accumulation of an intermediate metabolite, galactose-l-phosphate, in the pathway from galactose to glucose, the sugar that is the chief form of cellular energy. Galactosemia produces a variety of severe symptoms and may cause an early death; the inflicted individuals who survive are severely retarded physically and mentally. Treatment, like that for PKU, is dietary, and involves replacement of milk by galactose-free substitutes.

Heterozygous carriers of this gene are identifiable, because they have intermediate levels of the enzyme involved, which can be directly measured. In PKU only the amount of the accumulating substances can be measured; hence recognition of heterozygotes is not as yet completely accurate. There are, incidentally, other metabolic diseases produced by single genes for which heterozygotes can be recognized. For instance, in one form of diabetes (nephrogenic diabetes insipidus) caused by a sex-linked recessive gene, heterozygotes are identifiable by the specific gravity of their urine.

There are many other biochemically determined mental defects, some of which involve lipid metabolism (e.g., amaurotic idiocy and gargoylism); others, like PKU, the metabolism of proteins (oligophrenia is an example of a deficiency rather than an absence of an enzyme); and still others, carbohydrate biochemistry (glycogenesis is an example).

Furthermore, there are also forms of mental retardation of which neither the biochemistry nor the genetics is known. But indications that a genetic component exists in mental retardation is provided by such studies as the Minnesota investigation already cited. That investigation found that among first-degree relatives (parents and children, sibs) of mentally retarded persons, 28.0 percent were also mentally retarded; among second-degree relatives, such as cousins, 7.1 percent; and among individuals of still more distant kinship, only 3.1 percent.

Beyond citing such data little can be said at this point, except to emphasize our ignorance of the details of the genetics of mental retardation. To a degree, this is also true of mental defects other than retardation, that is, psychoses and personality disturbances. As with intelligence, the literature is vast, the hypotheses offered in explanation numerous, and the controversies heated, thus making it difficult, if not impossible, for individual geneticists or psychiatrists to make consistent sense of the information available.

Among the debatable topics in this area is the genetic basis of **schizophrenia**, a mental illness that hospitalizes more than a quarter of a million persons in the United States alone, accounting for about half the patients in public mental hospitals. Schizophrenia is a behavioral disease with a great variety of expression among different individuals. Some investigators even believe that it includes several different diseases. Affected individuals tend to display abnormal responses (or no responses at all) to environmental stimuli and particularly to other people. They are withdrawn from reality, and may have delusions or persecution complexes and manic-depressive fluctuations in mood. They show symptoms of what has been referred to as split personality: in fact, the name of the disease derives from the Greek words for split mind. They also exhibit an increased frequency of overt or latent homosexuality, and a variety of emotional disturbances.

In spite of tremendous effort on the part of psychiatrists, no generally successful treatment has been discovered, although drug therapy appears to be

BOX 11.D SCHIZOPHRENIA

If schizophrenia is a polygenically determined character and has a continuous phenotypic distribution, the concordance-discordance method of analysis is not necessarily the appropriate one. In the past, however, it was viewed as an all-or-none trait, and data on twins have been collected on that basis. The figures in the table at the bottom of the box represent an extract from material gathered by I. I. Gottesman and J. Shields from many sources.

Another way of expressing the degree of heritability of a character is to compute *recurrence risks*; that is, the likelihood of a trait being manifested in relatives of a known individual. For instance, in the simplest situation, if a child shows a recessive phenotype the probability that a sib will also show it is one out of four. For situations in which the exact mode of inheritance is not known, such risks are computed from empirical observation. F. J. Kallman has estimated that the

rates (per 1,000) of occurrence of schizophrenia among relatives of twins, one of which is known to be affected, are:

Parents	9.2	Dizygotic	
Spouse	2.1	co-twin	14.7
Step-sib	1.8	Monozygotic	
Half-sib	7.0	co-twin	85.8
Sib	14.3		

One more figure may be added to this table from a study by L. L. Heston on psychiatric disorders in children separated from schizophrenic mothers when not more than two weeks old, and raised in foster homes. He found that 166 per 1,000 had such disorders, thus indicating either a high heritability or the possibility that the mothers supplied their children with a toxic intra-uterine environment. Among other attributes of these children, Heston found a greater than average incidence of mental deficiency, neurotic personality disorders, and criminal behavior.

Country	Year	Monozygotic twins		Dizygotic twins	
		Number of pairs studied	Percent concordance	Number of pairs studied	Percent concordance
Denmark	1965	7	29	31	6
Germany	1928	19	58	13	0
Great Britain	1953	26	65	35	11
Japan	1961	55	60	11	18
Norway	1964	8	25	12	17
U.S.A.	1946	174	69	296	11

promising. There is a wide range of opinions about the causes of the disease. One school of thought is that schizophrenia stems entirely from up-bringing and early social environment that produces disturbances in interpersonal relations. One study of discordant twins suggests the existence of a competition effect, such as that noted in Box 11.B. Another viewpoint seeks the explanation in biochemistry and metabolic blocks. Some biochemical differences between the excretions of schizophrenics and those of normal people have been reported, but it is not clear if these abnormal excretions are manifestations of the cause or the effect. Other theories are based on the idea that schizophrenia is caused primarily by hereditary factors that operate either directly on metabolism or follow a more complex developmental pathway, in which social situations may trigger the appearance of schizophrenic symptoms.

Some upholders of the genetic viewpoint believe that a single major dominant gene with a low penetrance (25 percent) can account for the observed patterns of incidence in the population. But since the reproductive rate of expressed schizophrenics was considerably below normal before the introduction of modern drug therapy—one report showing only 0.5 children per schizophrenic male and 0.7 per female, whereas 2.2 children per woman is the required-replacement rate—a selective advantage for the gene operating on the nonexpressed cases must therefore be postulated in this hypothesis. Indeed, sibs of schizophrenics show, in some studies, a higher number of children than the average for the general population. This advantage has been suggested as being due to increased resistance to surgical and wound shock, freedom from allergies, and to other factors.

A contrasting genetic theory proposes that liability to schizophrenia is polygenically controlled, and has a rather high heritability. The clinical manifestation of the disease may be of a *threshold* type, a form of inheritance, also known as *all-or-none*, which has been extensively explored in experimental animals. Assuming a polygenic basis of inheritance and a normal distribution of genotypes, such as would be given by Pascal's triangle (Box 10.A) for many genes, at some point of gene dosage there would be a threshold beyond which the trait would be expressed. Environmental thresholds can, of course, also exist: some quantitative component of the environment may also have a normal distribution so that for each given genotype there may be a particular threshold. Box 11.D gives a sampling of data supporting the genetic interpretation of schizophrenia.

Other personality disorders with a genetic basis have also been described. Thus, significantly large heritability indexes have been reported for tendencies described by such terms as depression, psychopathic deviation, paranoia, and anxiety reactions, all of which form, perhaps, part of the total range of inherent attributes entering into the determination of temperament and personality.

11.4 PERSONALITY AND BEHAVIOR

Although there are still psychologists who deny genetic influences on the development of personality and on behavioral characters, the accumulation of vast amounts of data in recent years leaves no doubt that they exist. The exact degree to which phenotypic variance of psychological traits depends on genetic variance among individuals is difficult to establish for reasons already noted, but many current investigations are directed to its determination. Some of the studies are summarized in Box 11.E.

The intracellular products of the genes which find phenotypic expression in behavioral differences between men are known for only a few major metabolic defects. But pleiotropic pathways of gene action that eventually affect person-

---

BOX 11.E HERITABILITY OF PERSONALITY TRAITS

Of the numerous studies on the inheritance of personality traits, two by the American psychologist I. I. Gottesman have been chosen to illustrate the kind of results that have been obtained. From these studies, based on comparisons of correlations between monozygotic twins on the one hand and dizygotics of like sex on the other, he has devised indices of heritability. His method for determining them is not exactly equivalent to those given in Section 10.2, but his indices do provide an estimate of the proportion that genetic variation forms of the total phenotypic variation, even though they do not correct for the probability that there is greater similarity in the environment of identical twins than there is in that of fraternal twins. (The statistical significance of his estimates was determined by appropriate tests, which need not concern us here.)

The first study is based on 34 pairs each of one-egg and two-egg twins from Minnesota, who were administered a battery of tests used by psychologists to measure differences in personality. The table shows some selected results from the standard Minnesota Multiphasic Personality Inventory (also scored on certain experimental scales): three significant heritabilities and four which were not statistically significant are shown.

		Correlation between twins		
	Scale of test	Monozygotic	Dizygotic	Heritability Index
Significant	Social introversion	0.55	0.08	0.71
	Psychopathic deviation	0.57	0.18	0.50
	Depression	0.47	0.07	0.45
Not significant	Dominance	0.46	0.21	0.24
	Anxiety	0.45	0.04	0.21
	Dependency	0.52	0.25	0
	Ego strength	0.25	0.47	0

ality are not too difficult to imagine for at least some characteristics: being an albino in Nigeria must affect a person's behavior. Similarly, genes for excessive stature or dwarfism, or those producing metabolic disorders leading to obesity, could readily be reflected in the temperament of their possessors, as are the sex chromosome abnormalities noted in Section 8.4. For instance Turner females are not very good at abstract thinking, or finding their way about, or doing mathematical problems.

The same twins were also given another series of tests, known as the High School Personality Questionnaire. Here the children were rated on a series of scales for different attributes, as shown in the following tables. Once more, significant and nonsignificant heritabilities are given.

	Low score	High score	Heritability index
Significant	Sober, serious	Enthusiastic	0.56
	Group dependent	Self-sufficient	0.56
	Confident, adequate	Guilt prone	0.46
Not significant	Stiff, aloof	Warm, sociable	0.10
	Tough, realistic	Esthetically sensitive	0.06
	Phlegmatic temperament	Excitability	0
	Relaxed composure	Tense, excitable	0

Gottesman's second study, of children in the Boston area, involved 79 pairs of identical and 68 pairs of fraternal like-sexed twins. The test used was the California Psychological Inventory, and once more selected results are presented. Two categories of traits are shown with examples of both significant and nonsignificant heritability estimates.

Personality aspect and scale of test			Heritability index
Introversion–extroversion	Significant	Sociability	0.49
		Dominance	0.49
		Self-acceptance	0.46
		Social presence	0.35
	Not significant	Capacity for status	0.25
		Sense of well-being	0.13
Dependability–undependability	Significant	Good impression	0.38
		Socialization	0.32
	Not significant	Tolerance	0.27
		Self-control	0.27
		Responsibility	0.26

Figure 11.6.
The upper row depicts eggs of a variety of species, and the lower, the eggs of
cuckoos that parasitize them. (From a Russian journal.)

Certain other forms of psychological variability, falling within the normal range of expression, may involve subtler developmental effects. It is difficult, for example, to see how differences in the so-called *personal tempo* arise, even though this attribute is undoubtedly under genetic control. It has been found that if a person is asked to rap repeatedly on a table, he will do so at a tempo characteristic for him. The tempi of identical twins resemble each other more than do those of fraternal ones, the similarities within pairs of the latter being of the same order as those among sibs. Musical ability as tested by pitch and loudness discrimination, musical memory, speed of learning music, and even preference for a given composer, has also been found to be heritable on the basis of studies of dizygotic twins and monozygotic twins reared together and apart. Although it is obvious that development of musical ability must depend to a great degree on exposure and environment, it appears likely that the genetic endowment imposes the upper limit to possible achievement.

Somewhat more is known about the genetics of behavior of experimental animals than about the genetics of human behavior. Indeed, the field of behavior genetics, though relatively young, is already a vast one and includes investigations of animals of nearly all degrees of complexity and organization. Most of the information comes from selection experiments and from observation of differences between inbred lines, that is, lines produced by continued mating between close relatives. As we shall see in Chapter 19, different lines that have been produced by inbreeding can be expected to differ in the contents of their gene pools. Differences in phenotypic expression in standardized environments are interpreted as evidence that genetic variation existed in the original gene pool from which the inbreds were derived. An extension of this method of investigation involves crosses between different lines or breeds of animals.

Only a small sampling of what has been learned about different characters in different animals is possible here. In all the examples cited, such expressions as "genetically determined" or "inherited" do not imply absence of the environmental component of variation, but merely presence of a genetic one. The inheritance of temperamental differences in crosses between dogs has been extensively studied, and such traits as wildness *vs* tameness, the tendency to bite, barking capacity, and differences in degree of obedience to commands, have been found to have genetic components.

In rats, the ability to learn to run through a maze has been established as genetically determined. Selection for susceptibility to morphine addiction in the same species was also successful, indicating a genetic basis for this trait. Similarly, differences in preferences for alcohol have been found in mice—a behavioral phenotype that may in part be based on genetic differences affecting the level of activity of alcohol dehydrogenase, a liver enzyme that takes part in the metabolic breakdown of alcohol.

Among birds, aggressive behavior in chickens was found to be inherited, and cuckoos show a complex behavioral pattern, also apparently inherited. Cuckoos deposit their eggs in nests of other species of birds, who unwittingly incubate them and, raise the young. By natural selection, each variety of cuckoo has "learned" to recognize nests of species that lay eggs similar in color and size to those laid by the cuckoo (Figure 11.6) and thus accept the cuckoo's eggs as their own. Beyond that, cuckoos lay their eggs at a time that permits their young to hatch earlier than those of the host and thereby acquire a selective advantage over their foster sibs. Young cuckoos have even been known to push the unhatched eggs of their foster parents out of the nest.

Many genetically determined behavioral characters of insects have been studied. In Drosophila, strains differing in mating activity, in duration of copulation, in geotaxis (tendency to fly up or down when offered a choice in a vertical maze-like apparatus), and in phototaxis (tendency to travel towards a light) have been established by selective breeding. Figure 11.7 shows the results of one such experiment.

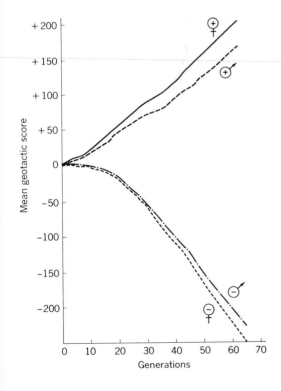

Figure 11.7.

Over sixty generations of selection for positive and negative geotaxis in *Drosophila melanogaster* has not exhausted the genetic variation for this property in the original gene pool, since responses to selection continue. (From L. Erlenmeyer-Kimling, et al.)

Figure 11.8.

Selection progress for speed of running through a T-shaped maze by flour beetles of the species *Tribolium castaneum*. The ordinate shows the percentage of beetles completing the run within a two-hour period in each generation of selection. (From I. M. Lerner and N. Inouye.)

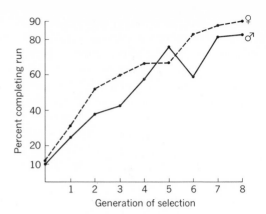

There is a disease of honey bees, American foulbrood, which usually destroys infected colonies. Certain strains, however, are resistant to the disease. In such strains, workers uncap the wax cells containing infected larvae and remove them from the hive. This behavior appears to be controlled by two recessive genes, one for uncapping and the other for removing. Hence, it is possible to have four kinds of genotypes, one resistant (both genes present) and three susceptible (only one or neither of the genes present).

Two behavioral characteristics have been selectively bred into strains of the flour beetle Tribolium. One of these is flying ability. Normally these beetles crawl, but when starved some will undertake short hops, or flights. By using as parents of successive generations beetles who were the first of a group to engage in this activity, the percentage of fliers—defined as those who hop within a 24-hour test period—was raised from one or two to 50 in just 6 generations. In the same experiment, the percentage who hopped in a test period of 104 hours rose from 6 or 7 to about 75.

The second Tribolium characteristic studied is the ability of the insect to complete a run through a maze-like apparatus in a short period of time. Figure 11.8 shows selection progress for this characteristic. Its biological basis is not fully understood, but it is probably the behavioral manifestation of a physiological trait. Tribolium normally have a pair of glands that excrete a mixture of highly obnoxious substances when the insects are excited, starved, or crowded. These substances act as predator repellents and also serve as a population-control device by causing the beetles to disperse, thus decreasing mating frequency. Although the insects bred in the selection experiment were chosen because of their speed, there is evidence that the basic physiological trait selected was for sensitivity to the unpleasant excretions. In the maze beetles were starved and crowded, and the fast runners were merely those trying hardest to get away from the crowd. It is suggestive that beetles from the fast strain do not bother to run at all if placed singly in the maze, and only show their speed when other beetles are present.

Most of the discussion thus far in the book has dealt with the inheritance of differences between individuals, although the concept of heritability is one applicable to the population level. We are now ready to extend the discussion to genetic properties of interbreeding groups of individuals, the subject matter of population genetics.

12

POPULATION GENETICS

12.1 THE HARDY-WEINBERG EQUILIBRIUM

In Section 7.1 we referred to random fertilization, the union, governed by chance, in a given mating of any of the different kinds of sperm with any of the different kinds of eggs. A similar concept refers to matings at random between individuals having the different kinds of genotypes. If the matings are entirely governed by chance, the mating system is described as **random mating** or *panmixia*.

In such a system the probability of mating between two carriers of given genotypes in a population is proportional to the product of the frequencies of those genotypes in that population.

Thus, if we take an ordinary F_2 ratio of $1AA:2Aa:1aa$, and postulate random mating for the production of the F_3, the proportions of the different types of unions will be

$$
\begin{array}{lll}
\text{♀} & \text{♂} & \\
\hline
AA \times AA & = \frac{1}{4} \times \frac{1}{4} & = \frac{1}{16} \\
AA \times Aa & = \frac{1}{4} \times \frac{1}{2} & = \frac{1}{8} \\
AA \times aa & = \frac{1}{4} \times \frac{1}{4} & = \frac{1}{16} \\
Aa \times AA & = \frac{1}{2} \times \frac{1}{4} & = \frac{1}{8} \\
Aa \times Aa & = \frac{1}{2} \times \frac{1}{2} & = \frac{1}{4} \\
Aa \times aa & = \frac{1}{2} \times \frac{1}{4} & = \frac{1}{8} \\
aa \times AA & = \frac{1}{4} \times \frac{1}{4} & = \frac{1}{16} \\
aa \times Aa & = \frac{1}{4} \times \frac{1}{2} & = \frac{1}{8} \\
aa \times aa & = \frac{1}{4} \times \frac{1}{4} & = \frac{1}{16} \\
\end{array}
$$

Putting together combinations of genotypes that were broken down according to sex in the tabulation just given, we have

$$AA \times AA = \tfrac{1}{16} \qquad\qquad Aa \times Aa = \tfrac{1}{4}$$
$$AA \times Aa = \tfrac{1}{4} \qquad\qquad Aa \times aa = \tfrac{1}{4}$$
$$AA \times aa = \tfrac{1}{8} \qquad\qquad aa \times aa = \tfrac{1}{16}$$

Random mating is an idealized situation, convenient to assume for purposes of computation. Actually, there are often departures from it, particularly among human populations. These departures have been classified into four types that may occur in different populations, sometimes in combination with each other.

In **assortative mating** like phenotypes tend to mate together in more instances than would be expected from their frequencies.

In **disassortative mating** the opposite is true, that is, more matings between unlike phenotypes happen than expected under random occurrence.

In **inbreeding** or **consanguineous mating** there are more matings between relatives than under random mating; this departure might be described as genotypic assortative mating, or just **genotypic assortment**.

In **outbreeding**, or **crossbreeding**, a common technique in animal breeding, individuals of different breeds are mated to produce **hybrids**. This is **genotypic disassortment**.

In the subsequent discussion of mating, random mating will often be postulated for the sake of simplicity, but the important consequences of deviation from randomness will be noted.

Another concept previously mentioned is that of gene frequency, the fraction of the total loci for a given gene in a population occupied by a specific allele. Different populations have different characteristic gene frequencies. For example, in Israel, which is now populated by many immigrant groups previously isolated from each other, examination of the glucose-6-phosphate dehydrogenase (G6PD) locus shows the following frequencies of the sex-linked recessive allele causing deficiency of this enzyme among Israeli males differing in origin:

Kurdish, 0.60   Yemenite, 0.05
Persian and Iraqui, 0.25   North African, 0.02
Turkish, 0.05   European, 0.002

In the usual notation, frequencies of recessive alleles are designated by q, and dominants by p. It should be noted that in a two-allele situation, $p + q = 1$, and $p = 1 - q$. For the Israelis of Turkish origin, q of the G6DP gene is 0.05 and p, 0.95.

The notation can be extended to multiple-allele situations. Thus, if we consider that at the ABO locus there are three alleles (an oversimplification to be corrected in Chapter 18) A, B, and O, it is found, for example, that Germans in Berlin have the frequencies:

$$A = 0.29, \qquad B = 0.11, \qquad O = 0.60,$$
$$p_A + q_B + r_O = 1,$$
$$0.29 + 0.11 + 0.60 = 1.$$

Next we may consider the concept of **genetic equilibrium**. An equilibrium, as the name implies, refers to a state of balance. We may, however, distinguish

BOX 12.A CONSTANCY OF GENE AND GENOTYPIC FREQUENCIES

Consider a two-allele gene pool, in which the gene frequencies are given as $p + q = 1$. The genotypic frequencies can be obtained by expansion of the square of this binomial,$(p + q)^2 = p^2 + 2pq + q^2$. For example, in an F_1 population consisting entirely of Aa individuals, p and q are both equal to $\frac{1}{2}$. The F_2 will also have the same frequencies, and $(\frac{1}{2} + \frac{1}{2})^2 = \frac{1}{4} + \frac{1}{2} + \frac{1}{4}$, which are the frequencies of the three possible genotypes. The formula can be expanded to any number of alleles, for example,

$$(p + q + r)^2 = p^2 + 2pq + 2pr + q^2 + 2qr + r^2.$$

Now let us examine a gene pool in which the gene frequencies are $p_A = 0.8$ and $q_a = 0.2$. These, in the absence of selective advantage of one genotype over another and of mutation, are also the gametic frequencies. The genotypic frequencies are readily obtained from the following square:

Eggs

	$A = 0.8$	$a = 0.2$
$A = 0.8$ Sperm	AA 0.64	Aa 0.16
$a = 0.2$	Aa 0.16	aa 0.04

The population thus consists of 64 percent AA's, 32 percent Aa's, and 4 percent aa's.

In the next generation six different types of matings are possible, as shown by the next square, in which like combinations are assigned like letters.

Maternal genotypes

	AA 0.64	Aa 0.32	aa 0.04
AA 0.64 (Paternal genotypes)	a	b	c
Aa 0.32	b	d	e
aa 0.04	c	e	f

By multiplying we obtain the proportions of the various kinds of matings, and the frequencies of the offspring of the next generation. Two sets of figures appearing for a mating in the table below represent reciprocal crosses.

Under departures from random mating, gene frequency is in equilibrium, but the genotypic frequencies change from generation to generation. If we consider, for instance, complete assortment, so that only three kinds of mating occur: $AA \times AA$, $Aa \times Aa$, $aa \times aa$, we can see that because of segregation of AA and aa genotypes in the $Aa \times Aa$ matings, the number of Aa individuals will be reduced by half in every generation. In the limit, the population will consist entirely of AA's and aa's, and their frequencies, and clearly those of the alleles, will be 0.8 and 0.2 respectively.

Mating	Frequency	Offspring		
		AA	Aa	aa
$AA \times AA$	$0.64 \times 0.64 = 0.4096$	0.4096		
$AA \times Aa$	$\left.\begin{matrix}0.64 \times 0.32 \\ 0.32 \times 0.64\end{matrix}\right\} = 0.4096$	0.2048	0.2048	
$AA \times aa$	$\left.\begin{matrix}0.64 \times 0.04 \\ 0.04 \times 0.64\end{matrix}\right\} = 0.0512$		0.0512	
$Aa \times Aa$	$0.32 \times 0.32 = 0.1024$	0.0256	0.0512	0.0256
$Aa \times aa$	$\left.\begin{matrix}0.32 \times 0.04 \\ 0.04 \times 0.32\end{matrix}\right\} = 0.0256$		0.0128	0.0128
$aa \times aa$	$0.04 \times 0.04 = 0.0016$			0.0016
	Total	0.64 p^2	0.32 $2pq$	0.04 q^2

Figure 12.1.

The first sphere is rolling downhill and will be in equilibrium only when it reaches bottom. Sphere 2 is in unstable equilibrium; it is resting on top only precariously, and may proceed downwards in either direction. Sphere 3 is in stable equilibrium.

between *stable* and *unstable* equilibria, as illustrated in Figure 12.1. Gene frequencies are said to be in equilibrium when they remain constant from generation to generation. *Such equilibrium under random mating and free from disturbing forces implies that genotypic frequencies will also be constant in successive generations.*

This generalization was independently arrived at in 1908 by an English mathematician, **G. H. Hardy** (1877–1947), and a German physician, **W. Weinberg** (1862–1937). It has been formulated in a variety of ways, and is known as the **Hardy-Weinberg law.** Box 12.A illustrates the operation of the law.

12.2 DISTURBING FORCES

The equilibrium will prevail, as has been stated, only if disturbing forces do not act on the population. We already know from Section 4.3 what these forces may be: selection, mutation, immigration, and drift. Since selection has been defined as the differential reproduction of genotypes, different genotypes contribute genes to the gene pool of each successive generation not precisely in porportion to their number but relative to the degree of selective advantage they enjoy. If selection is of the stabilizing kind, an equilibrium may still persist. For example, if only the heterozygotes from a population in which the initial frequencies were $p_A = q_a = 0.5$ reproduced, the gene frequencies would still remain constant. So would the genotypic frequencies of 0.25, 0.50, and 0.25.

Under directional selection, this would not be the case. The frequency of the allele that conferred a selective advantage on its carrier would increase, until it would be the sole component of the gene pool. The rate of this process would depend on whether the allele selected was dominant or recessive, and on the degree of the advantage. Box 12.B illustrates these points.

Situations can arise in which there is a combination of directional and stabilizing forms. Figure 12.2 shows the results of an experiment, begun in 1940, in which selection was directed to increase the number of blades on a chicken comb. The original population consisted of a mixture of birds with one, two, and three blades. By 1944, birds with five blades had made their appearance; by 1946, the flock had become a stable mixture of three-, four-, and five-bladed individuals. Apparently, the directional force of artificial selection was being defeated by the stabilizing force of natural selection. What happened may be described as resulting from **genetic homeostasis**, the property of a population to regulate or stabilize its gene pool contents. Various examples of this property in laboratory and natural populations are available.

Mutation is the second of the forces that may interfere with the maintenance of the genetic equilibrium. If the rate of mutation from A to a is m per generation, then the frequency of A will drop from p in the foundation population to $p - mp$, while that of a will increase from q to $q + mp$. If this process is recurrent and continues indefinitely, eventually all A's will mutate to a, which will become fixed at the frequency of 1.

Mutation pressure, however, can operate in both directions: a may show **reverse mutation** to A with a frequency of n. This will produce, in a single generation, frequencies of

$$p - mp + nq \qquad \text{for } A$$

and

$$q + mp = nq \qquad \text{for } a.$$

Under these circumstances an equilibrium will be reached if the losses in the numbers of A by mutation to a are balanced by the gains from reverse mutations. Because, however, these usually occur in a very much lower frequency than **direct mutations**, mutation pressure can lead to near fixation. Degeneration of organs that have lost their adaptive value, for instance, the evolution of blindness in cave-dwelling fish, can be accounted for by this process.

Immigration and drift, already discussed in Section 4.3, have mathematical properties that are somewhat complex, and, in fact, have not been fully analyzed. But the important point is that whatever new genes are brought in by immigration, and whatever changes arise from drift, they are then subject to mutation and selection pressures that determine the ultimate composition of the gene pool. We shall consider next the joint effect of these two forces.

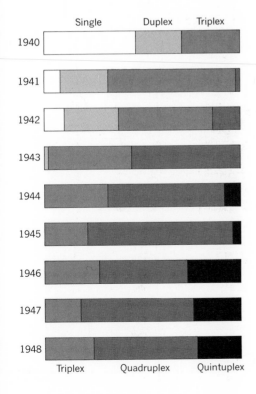

Figure 12.2.

Directional and stabilizing selection for the number of blades on the comb of chickens. (Based on the data of L. W. Taylor.)

BOX 12.B RATE OF SELECTION PROGRESS

Natural selection usually operates in such a way that different genotypes have *on the average* different numbers of offspring. In artificial selection used in plant and animal improvement, certain genotypes (or phenotypes) are prevented from reproducing, which is selection by **truncation**. For polygenically determined characters, the distribution is truncated; all individuals falling on one side of the demarcation are discarded, and those on the other become parents of the next generation. Among the selected group, however, natural selection can still operate. To help visualize the changes under selection in the gene frequencies of the gene pool, some examples of truncated selection are shown.

In each of the three graphs, two situations are represented. In one, the **selection intensity** is 5 percent for each sex, meaning that each selected couple is allowed to produce 20 offspring to maintain a constant population size. This value is unrealistic for humans, but common among chickens. In the other, a *lower* intensity of 25 percent is applied, with each couple giving rise to four descendants.

The graph below depicts the situation when the recessive homozygote is the desired genotype. When its frequency is very low at the start, selection progress is exceedingly slow, because to keep the size of the population constant, heterozygotes and dominant homozygotes must be permitted to reproduce. However, once enough recessive homozygotes are available for use as breeders, progress is exceedingly rapid. The gene pool then proceeds to **fixation**, that is, finally only one allele is represented in it. The frequency of this allele becomes 100 percent; that of the extinct allele, 0.

Selection for a dominant homozygote, shown in the middle graph, has a different pattern. Progress is reasonably rapid at first because even at a low frequency of A, there are enough heterozygotes available to use as parents. When the frequency of A becomes high, selection slows down. With complete dominance, AA and Aa are undistinguishable, and aa individuals thus keep appearing in the population for a long time. For instance, in black breeds of cattle, recessive red-colored animals are still occasionally found after many

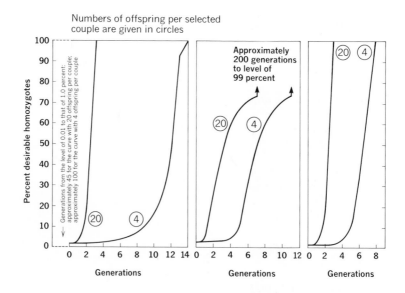

Numbers of offspring per selected couple are given in circles

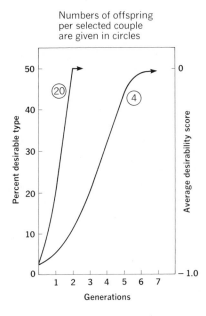

Numbers of offspring per selected couple are given in circles

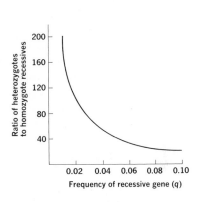

generations of selection against them. Animal breeders, who want to fix a desired genotype in as few generations as possible, must resort to progeny testing to distinguish AA from Aa individuals. Those offspring identified as AA are then used to produce the succeeding generation.

When there is no dominance, selection progress is fairly rapid as shown in the above right graph, because all three classes are distinguishable.

Selection for the heterozygote, for example, the Palomino horse, is considered next.

Fixation for the heterozygote is impossible since $Aa \times Aa$ matings will always produce AA and aa segregants. Hence, the frequency of the desirable type cannot rise above 50 percent. In animal breeding this difficulty can be alleviated to a degree by combining selection with disassortative mating in part of the parental population. Aa's are mated with Aa's. but AA's are always mated with aa's to produce the desirable heterozygous genotype.

The following table (from W. C. Boyd) illustrates the more general type of selection (not truncation) in which computations are based on one or the other homozygote having only a one

percent increase in fitness relative to the other. The outside columns show the changes in gene frequency. The one on the right should be read upwards.

Selection for a dominant	Number of generations required	Selection for a recessive
0.01 → 0.1	900,230	99.9 → 99.99
0.1 → 1.0	90,231	99.0 → 99.9
1.0 → 50.0	6,779	50.0 → 99.0
50.0 → 97.0	3,481	3.0 → 50.0
97.0 → 99.0	559	1.0 → 3.0
99.0 → 99.9	231	0.1 → 1.0
99.9 → 99.99	30	0.01 → 0.1

Finally, in connection with the ineffectiveness of selection against recessives discussed in Section 12.3, the graph shows the proportion of heterozygotes in a population as a function of gene frequency. The ordinate gives the ratio of the number of heterozygotes to that of recessive homozygotes at various low values of q. After q becomes large enough, the ratio drops rapidly. At 0.5 it is 2.0, and at 0.9 it is 0.2.

12.3 POPULATION STRUCTURE

Most recurrent mutations in reasonably adapted populations are deleterious, since favorable ones would already have been incorporated into the gene pool. However, in the process of evolution, because of changes in either external or genetic environments, a disadvantageous mutant gene may become advantageous. An example in economic practice is the gene for hornlessness in cattle. In natural populations horns originally served a useful function, perhaps in fighting and defense. But after cattle were domesticated, horns led to economic losses by causing injuries to animals kept in close confinement. The breeders then took advantage of the presence of a dominant mutant gene for hornlessness in the gene pool and, reversing the direction of selective advantage, produced polled breeds. Similar situations, of course, occur in nature.

The reserve of mutations in populations is an important factor in evolutionary change and, despite the deleterious effects that mutant genes tend to produce, bestows an overall advantage for the species in the process of adapting to changed conditions. Furthermore, mutation pressure is balanced by selection against the currently disadvantageous alleles. Box 12.C illustrates how the two counteracting forces can produce an equilibrium.

The results of the mathematical relationships described in Box 12.C lead to the conclusion, surprising at first sight, that even extreme selection, such as against a lethal allele, can be an ineffective process. Let us consider as an example PKU and use approximate figures, to be viewed only in terms of orders of magnitude. If we assume that the white population of the United States is in equilibrium with respect to this locus, and that the incidence of the disease is 1 in 10,000 then, $q^2 = 0.0001$, $q = 0.01$, and $2pq$, or the proportion of heterozygotes, is $2 \times 0.01 \times 0.99 = 0.0198$. The mutation rate, assuming complete lethality, is equal to q^2 or 100 per million gametes in each generation. Taking the population at 180 million and assuming that there are 5 million births a year, we arrive at the numbers:

number of PKU babies born annually   = 500,

number of carriers of newly
arisen mutations in ten million
gametes (double the number of zygotes) = 1,000,

number of heterozygotes in the
population accumulated from
previous mutations   = 3,564,000.

Thus a vast majority of the deleterious alleles is carried by heterozygotes. Preventing the recessive homozygotes from reproducing themselves would remove only 1,000 alleles of the three-and-one-half million. The folly of any program to purge mankind's gene pool of detrimental alleles by sterilizing such homozygotes (or in any other way preventing them from producing offspring) becomes immediately apparent from these computations.

If heterozygotes could be identified and removed from the breeding population such programs (negative eugenics) could work, except for the fact that all of us are carriers of, on the average, several detrimental mutations. Thus, eugenics based on heterozygous screening on a scale large enough to be of significance would not lead to improvement but rather to termination of mankind on earth. Comparison of eugenic proposals with other methods of management of human genetic resources will be made in Chapter 20.

Another class of deleterious mutant genes is kept in the gene pool not by virtue of mutation pressure, but because of overdominance, or pseudo-overdominance, which might result from the close linkage with a favorable allele or alleles at neighboring loci. This is the situation already described in Section 7.4 for the defective hemoglobin alleles. If the selective disadvantage

---

BOX 12.C MUTATION-SELECTION BALANCE

For illustrative purposes we shall consider an extreme case, that of a recessive lethal gene, which in a homozygous state is lethal or renders the carrier sterile. Let us indicate the relative fitness of three possible genotypes as

AA	Aa	aa
1	1	$1-s$

where s, the selective disadvantage, is equal to 1. In other words, the fitness of AA is equal to that of Aa, and the fitness of aa is zero. For convenience, we shall use here $1-q$ instead of p as the notation for the gene frequency of A.

At birth the respective genotypic frequencies are

AA	Aa	aa	Total
$(1-q)^2$	$2q(1-q)$	q^2	1

To obtain the proportions of each genotype after selection, we can multiply these by the respective fitnesses to obtain

AA	Aa	aa	Total
$(1-q)^2$	$2q(1-q)$	0	$(1-q)(1+q)$.

The frequency of A (we are dealing with diploids) is

$$\frac{2(1-q)^2 + 2q(1-q)}{2(1-q)(1+q)} = \frac{1}{1+q}.$$

The frequency of a can be similarly computed to be

$$\frac{2q(1-q)}{2(1-q)(1+q)} = \frac{q}{1+q}.$$

A would have then gained by selection

$$\frac{1}{1+q} - (1-q) = \frac{q^2}{1+q}$$

alleles, and a lost as many.

Now if we assume that an m fraction of A mutates to a (we shall ignore reverse mutation), then in every generation A will lose and a will gain $m/(1-q)$ alleles. An equilibrium will be established when losses are balanced by gains, i.e., when

$$\frac{m}{1+q} = \frac{q^2}{1+q}, \text{ or } m = q^2$$

The more general expression is

$$\frac{m}{s} = q^2$$

Thus the equilibrium value of q for a is $\sqrt{\dfrac{m}{s}}$, or for a recessive lethal gene in which $s = 1$, $\sqrt{m}$.

The remarkable property of this relation is that it permits the computation of the rate of mutation. When a population is in genetic equilibrium the rate of mutation of a recessive lethal is equal to the proportion of homozygous recessive genotypes found in a given generation. In practice, of course, determination of mutation rates is not so simple, because among other difficulties it is not always possible to determine whether or not a population is, indeed, in equilibrium. Nevertheless this method has been used to estimate human mutation races (Chapter 14).

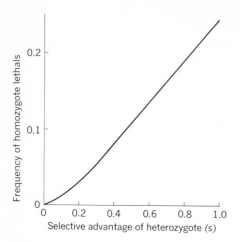

Figure 12.3.
Maintenance of lethal alleles in a
population by heterozygote superiority.

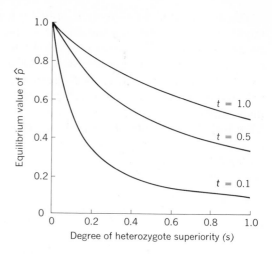

Figure 12.4.
Equilibrium values of *A* under various degrees of
heterozygous selective advantages.

of one homozygote, relative to the heterozygote, is indicated by *s*, and of the
other by *t*, so that the relative fitnesses of the three genotypes are

AA	*Aa*	*aa*
1–*s*	1	1–*t*,

it is readily demonstrable that the equilibrium values are $p = t/(s + t)$ and $q = s/(s + t)$. If both kinds of homozygotes died before reaching maturity, or were sterile, or for any other reason produced no offspring ($s = t = 1$), the gene frequencies of *A* and *a* would be 0.5, as noted in the first paragraph of Section 12.2. The more common equilibrium, in which only the homozygous recessive state is lethal, is illustrated in Figure 12.3, which shows that a lethal allele can be maintained in a population at high frequency when the heterozygote exceeds both homozygotes in fitness. Figure 12.4 is a more generalized graph for different values of *s* and *t*.

The genetic structure of populations exhibiting this type of mechanism is **balanced polymorphism**, that is, a structure containing many alleles in various frequencies depending on the *s* and *t* values. **Transient polymorphism** is also known, in which this structure is only a temporary one. For instance, many African populations are polymorphic with respect to hemoglobin C and hemoglobin S. The former, as judged from geographical distribution, arose as a mutation, perhaps only once in the last 1,500–2,000 years, and spread into malarial areas. Upon reaching places where hemoglobin S provided a defense mechanism against malaria, the *Hb^c* allele, as already noted, began to displace the *Hb^s* allele. If this process were to continue, the present-day polymorphism for the two alleles would disappear when the replacement was completed. Chances are that now, when malaria is being brought under control, *Hb^A* may replace both.

The discovery of the two mechanisms for maintaining genetic variability—mutation pressure and the balance between the reproductive rates of heterozygotes and homozygotes—dealt a death blow to a typological view of the evolutionary species. In the presence of polymorphism at a great number of loci the notion that there is a type for each given species became entirely untenable and gave way to the statistical approach to evolution. Mechanisms other than heterozygote superiority for maintaining polymorphisms are also known. They include alternation of selective advantage between alleles in the course of a life cycle or from generation to generation, differences in preference for ecological sub-niches between the different genotypes, and frequency-dependent selection.

One of the first to recognize the existence and the significance of the stores of expressed and concealed genetic variability in natural populations was the Russian naturalist and geneticist **S. S. Chetverikov** (1880–1959). He may be considered the founder of experimental population genetics (see Box 12.D). Ever since his 1926 experiment, evidence is growing that the capacity of populations for storage of direct genetic messages and messages concealed by dominance and epistasis is tremendous. For some characters, it has even been claimed that the total variability of a deme could be reconstructed by a population derived from very few individuals (but see the founder principle mentioned in Sections 4.3 and 17.3). Recently, a great spurt of activity in the study of population structure has been initiated by the discovery of many biochemical polymorphisms in Drosophila by the American geneticists R. C. Lewontin and J. L. Hubby. The polymorphisms appear to exist at a high proportion of loci producing particular proteins and specific enzymes in both wild and laboratory populations. Biochemical polymorphisms appear also to be widespread in human populations. Thus the English geneticist H. Harris recently found that three out of ten arbitrarily chosen enzymes were polymorphic. At least seven such enzymes have been discovered within the last few years in England alone, and some 26 loci for specific proteins (with nearly 200 alleles between them) altogether are known to be polymorphic in man. It has been computed from blood-group data that an average individual is heterozygous for 16 percent of his loci, a figure remarkably close to one found experimentally in Drosophila.

In addition to balancing mechanisms affecting characters controlled at a single locus, there are others, perhaps more complex, that deal with polygenically determined traits. Their complexity lies not only in the fact that many loci are involved, but also in their usual remoteness in the developmental pathway from the original gene products. This means that whatever balance is attained, it involves a great many intermediate biochemical and physiological interactions. Nevertheless, genetic homeostasis has also been demonstrated for some metric properties of organisms. One very schematically presented example will suffice here.

In the selection of chickens for egg production, large egg size is one of several economically desirable objectives. Hence, breeders exercise artificial selection to obtain more hens that lay larger eggs. But the biologically balanced phenotype, as a result of prolonged natural selection, is represented by a smaller egg than the breeder wants. The highest reproductive fitness, then, is found among hens laying smaller than average-sized eggs, the flock's average

BOX 12.D S. S. CHETVERIKOV

After the rediscovery of Mendel's laws, Darwinism suffered a temporary eclipse; natural selection was relegated to a secondary role in evolution, and, at least according to one school of thought, mutation assumed the principal role among evolutionary forces. R. A. Fisher, Sewall Wright, and J. B. S. Haldane, independently of each other, formulated the basic tenets underlying the synthesis of Darwinism and Mendelism, for which they also provided a quantitative basis. Only recently has the fourth of the co-founders of the current synthetic theory of evolution, the Russian naturalist S. S. Chetverikov, been given credit for his role in its formulation.

There are two reasons why Chetverikov was so long neglected. First, his now classical 1927 essay on evolution from the genetic standpoint was originally published in Russian and did not become fully available in English until 1961. And, second, the bizarre and tragic period in the history of Soviet genetics under Stalin, which is described in Chapter 21, not only robbed Chetverikov of honor, but led to his demotion, dismissal, and exile, and barred him until just before his death from any possibility of further intellectual or experimental contribution to science.

Chetverikov's essay included most of the basic ideas on which current evolutionary theory rests. He recognized the existence of the great store of genetic variability supplied by mutation in natural populations; he understood clearly how particulate Mendelian inheritance makes it possible to maintain this variation; he visualized the concepts of gene frequency and the gene pool; he realized the roles of such evolutionary forces as isolation and drift; he emphasized the importance of such phenomena as pleiotropy of gene action and of polymorphisms in populations.

Many of his notions were in the air at the time. Thus, in America, F. B. Sumner studied variation in wild mice, and G. H. Shull and E. M. East in corn. But it was Chetverikov's simple Drosophila experiment that was probably the first one based on strict Mendelian considerations. Capturing inseminated females in the wild, he inbred their offspring to find a great reservoir of recessive

alleles carried by them. Chetverikov laid the foundations of a great school of Russian population geneticists, in which his students, N. Timofeev-Resovsky, B. L. Astaurov, N. P. Dubinin, and others, played a prominent role until the government fiat practically extinguished genetic research in the USSR.

His personal biography was tragic. Dismissed from his university position, he was successively a consultant to a zoo in the Ural mountains and a mathematics teacher in a junior college. Reprieved for a while, he was able to do some work on selection in a species of silkworm, but when genetics was formally outlawed in 1948, he lost his post again. He ended his days blind and in poverty, and it was only just before he died in 1959 that relaxation of the attitude of the Soviet government towards genetics brought him some measure of recognition. The photograph is by courtesy of B. L. Astaurov.

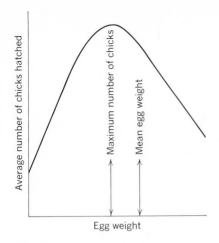

Figure 12.5.
The curve shows the relationship between the size of eggs laid by pullets and the relative fitness of the pullets as judged by the number of chicks they produce on the average.

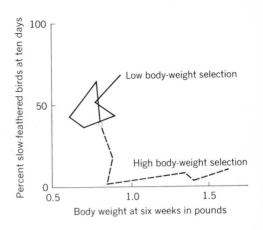

Figure 12.6.
Correlated response in feathering rate to selection for low body weight. (Based on the data of G. F. Godfrey and B. L. Goodman.)

egg size being maintained by the pressure of artificial selection. If the breeder suspends artificial selection for this trait, it reverts to a lower average egg size by natural selection (Figure 12.5).

The final point that needs to be made about balance regards **correlated response.** Darwin recognized that selection exercising its pressure on some character unavoidably modifies others. He was viewing this phenomenon on a phenotypic basis and assumed, entirely correctly, that there is an interdependence of structures and functions in a harmonious living being. Today we can also understand this phenomenon both on the level of the genotype because of pleiotropy and linkage, and on the level of the gene pool as a form of coadaptation.

We refer often to chickens which provide many useful illustrative examples because the genetics of the fowl has been intensively studied, in part for economic reasons. Figure 12.6 shows selection progress for high and low body weight in an experiment in which the rate of feathering of the chicks was not used as a criterion of selection. In the line selected for high weight, feathering rate remained rapid. But in selection for low weight, which was not very successful, since the modification was "anti-adaptive," a correlated response of slowing down the rate of feathering was observed. Evidently, the small birds could not support metabolic activities necessary for rapid feathering. It might be noted that a common form of correlated response to prolonged artificial selection of metrical traits is a drop in reproductive fitness. This is to be expected if coadaptation cannot keep pace with extreme changes induced by selection, because natural selection operates on the totality of fitness components and sudden or rapid changes in one of them unbalances the rest.

13

SELECTION

13.1 NATURAL SELECTION IN MAN

We have already examined a number of instances of natural selection, such as for industrial melanism in moths and for hemoglobin variants in man. Much evidence has been compiled that natural selection is operating on a number of traits in various organisms including our own species. An example of a dynamic interaction between selective forces is provided by the Australian experience in attempting to control the rabbit population. In 1859 a gentleman farmer in southern Australia imported twelve pairs of wild rabbits from England in order to be able to satisfy his passion for hunting. Within a few years, the rabbit became a major agricultural pest on the whole continent. Many ways of eradication were tried without success. In 1950 a virus producing myxomatosis, a disease fatal to rabbits, was deliberately released in the countryside and rapidly spread throughout Australia. It caused such a widespread epizootic, that in some areas the census numbers of rabbits went down from 5,000 to 50 in a matter of six weeks. However, year after year, fewer and fewer rabbits died, so that this solution did not turn out to be a permanent one. What happened was that the epizootic became a powerful selective force for resistance of the rabbits to the disease. At the same time, the virus itself mutated and was being naturally selected for lowered virulence, permitting it to multiply without killing the hosts. Survival of the more resistant rabbits was advantageous not only to them but to the parasite as well. This is an example of the general phenomenon of interspecific coadaptation (if viruses can be considered to represent species), characteristic of host-parasite relations.

Another example is provided by natural selection for resistance to bubonic plague in rats. Rats, in India, taken from areas where plague epidemics had recently occurred, showed only a 10 percent mortality when infected with the disease in the laboratory. Rats taken from cities free of plague, however, had a mortality of 90 percent. Other instances of natural selection are the rising resistance of insects to DDT and increased resistance of various bacteria to antibiotics. Indications that transduction (Section 6.5) plays a role in the latter example have recently been found.

In man, evidence for natural selection at various loci is more tenuous and speculative, largely because of difficulty in obtaining data. Nevertheless, many signs suggest that much of human polymorphism is maintained in populations by a variety of selective processes, including that of heterozygote advantage, which seems probable at the locus controlling the MN blood group. Also of interest is the more commonly known ABO blood-group polymorphism (see Chapter 18).

It has been found that people differing in genotype at this locus show different incidences of a number of diseases. Relative susceptibilities of individuals differing in blood type have been reported as follows:

Disease	Blood group	Ratio of incidence
Duodenal ulcer	O/(A + B + AB)	1.38
Gastric ulcer	O/(A + B + AB)	1.19
Stomach cancer	A/(O + B)	1.19
Pernicious anemia	A/O	1.26
Diabetes mellitus*	A/O	1.16

A connection has also been suggested between the geographical distribution of the ABO genes and the previous epidemiological history of the various areas. Where plague was once common, there seems to be a relative shortage of O individuals, whereas areas known to have had severe outbreaks of smallpox show a similar deficiency of people belonging to the A group. A possible explanation, by no means agreed upon by all immunologists, is that in these cases the causative agents of the disease (the bacterium *Pasteurella pestis* for plague, and the *Variola* virus for smallpox) have immunological properties similar to the respective blood group antigens. Those O individuals having the one disease, and the A having the other, are not able to recognize the infective agent as a foreign antigen and to produce sufficient antibodies to combat it. A study in India supported this explanation for one of the diseases: the severity of smallpox was found to be higher in patients carrying the allele for the A group than in those lacking it.

---

*The type produced by insulin deficiency, rather than by failure of pituitary hormone production, which is known as diabetes insipidus and for which both sex-linked and autosomal dominant genes are known.

Still another example of possible natural selection, this one probably operating on more than a single locus, may be found in heart disease. The genetic basis of coronary artery disease is not understood as yet, but the disease is known to be common in families with a history of defective lipid metabolism and among diabetics. At the present the incidence of the disease seems to be increasing. In part this may be explained by increased longevity. More people are now surviving to the age when arteriosclerosis tends to occur. And in part this may be connected with eating habits. There is a correlation between incidence of the disease and amount of animal fats in the diet.

A New Zealand physician has suggested that susceptibility to heart disease may have had a selective advantage at one stage of human society, because groups not having to support individuals past their reproductive age would have an advantage in periods of food scarcity. Haldane had earlier proposed the existence of such selection for liability to cancer and other diseases of old age, although such intergroup selection is generally not very efficient. When tools and fire were invented man became largely carnivorous. A rich reservoir of previously unexploited food resources was opened for the hunting societies of the Stone Age and with the change in diet, selective forces for heart disease susceptibility came into operation. With the invention of agriculture, the diet once more became predominantly vegetarian, as it still is in many primitive societies or in underdeveloped areas. In recent years the animal-fat consumption in the more prosperous countries has again been rising, with a consequent increase in incidence of the disease among genotypes predisposed to it by Stone Age selection. Speculative and unsupported by concrete evidence as this hypothesis is, it is worth mentioning as another possible instance of interaction between man's biological and cultural evolution.

In general, in spite of man's increased life-span (Box 5.C), considerable opportunity doubtless still exists for natural selection to occur in man. Statistical studies verifying this fact have been carried out. In the past, much of selection operated by eliminating disadvantageous genotypes in the intrauterine, early postnatal, and adolescent stages in life. There also was and still is some prezygotic selection produced either by segregation distortion, in which heterozygotes produce unequal numbers of the two kinds of gametes, or by competition between sperm, or by sperm-egg incompatibility. Today

Figure 13.1.

An experiment on selection for the incidence of crooked toes in baby chicks. The selected line essentially showed fixation for this trait, but part-way along, selection in the reversed direction was capable of bringing down the level of the defect to that of the control.

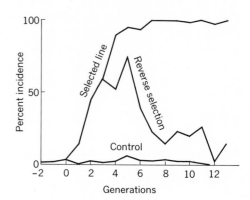

selection pressure is largely directed towards fertility. On the average about one-third of the individuals of one generation contribute two-thirds of the genes in the gene pool of their great grandchildren's generation. Even more extreme selection opportunities exist in certain populations. In one study on Navajo Indians in New Mexico, one of the founders of the population was found to have, after eight generations, 411 descendants, forming 14 percent of the total group living today. Indeed, six individuals among the founders accounted for more than half of all descendants. Clearly, considerable natural selection can be accommodated with reproductive patterns of this type.

13.2 RELAXATION OF SELECTION

With the changing environment in the history of man, obviously the direction of selection and the characters selected for also have changed. When tuberculosis was a major cause of mortality, resistance to it had a selective advantage. Today, this selection pressure no longer exists over the larger part of the world. If the genes for resistance have no other effect, their frequencies may be expected to drift. If they are disadvantageous for some reason, they would tend to be eliminated under the changed conditions. But in some populations fixation may already have occurred, although this is unlikely for tuberculosis resistance. Hence, barring new mutations, selection in such populations would not be a reversible process.

Figure 13.1 shows a selection experiment on chickens, in which defective toes, in the extreme form producing club feet, were selected for. As may be readily seen, after three generations of selection it was still possible to reverse the pressure and return a sub-line to the initial level. But after eight generations, the direct selection line had 100 percent incidence of the defect, and reversal would be impossible.

The question has often been raised whether the various preventive and therapeutic measures now available have a **dysgenic** (that is, opposite to eugenic) effect. The formal mathematical answer is different for recessive genes from that for dominant genes. Using crude approximations for illustrations, and assuming that q for PKU is 0.01 and that the fitness of the homozygote recessives was zero before treatment was discovered, J. F. Crow computed the effect of restoring normal reproductive capacity (fitness of 1) to all PKU patients. It turns out that permitting the previously eliminated q^2 individuals to contribute to the gene pool of the next generation increases the incidence of the disease at a rate of 2 percent per generation, a rate that doubles the incidence over 40 generations, or some 1,200 years. For rare dominant genes, the situation is different: the incidence of the defect produced by them may be expected to double in each generation.

Too little is known as yet about human gene frequencies in different generations to estimate accurately the actual effects of reversal, suspension, or relaxation of selection on various traits. Several attempts, however, have been undertaken to gauge the effects, by comparing incidence of various defects in primitive societies, in which they might be expected to have selective disadvantages, with that in more advanced societies in which selection has been relaxed. The frequency of red-green color blindness in populations of Eskimos, Australian aborigines, and other hunters and gatherers is found to be 2.0 percent among the males. Groups somewhat removed from hunting and gathering, such as some American Indians and African Negroes, have an incidence of 3.3 percent. Populations still farther removed from hunters in time or mode of existence, including Europeans, Filipinos, and some Arabs, show a frequency of 5.1 percent. These statistics, as well as similar ones on visual acuity, indeed suggest that selection no longer operates against such eye defects in modern urban societies. The need to have glasses confers no reproductive disadvantage on males, and contact lenses may correct the passless situation of females wearing them, although, of course, color blindness is not yet correctable.

Deformities of the nasal septa (the bony membranes of the nose) have also been studied. They can occur in three different areas, the cartilagenous region, and the lower and upper bone regions. Their heritability is estimated, on basis of concordance rates in monozygotic and dizygotic twins, at about 60 percent. They range in expression from a mild form, in which they interfere with nasal breathing only during exercise, to severe ones that make the possessor liable to catarrh and infection, and also, perhaps, affect the sense of smell. It is highly likely that among hunters the need for oral instead of nasal breathing would be a disadvantage. But in agricultural societies the defect would not present as much of a handicap. And, as would be expected from this line of reasoning, there are interpopulational differences in the incidence of these deformities, as the following selected statistics demonstrate.

| | *Percentage incidence of abnormal septa* | | |
| | | | |
Population	*In the cartilage region*	*In the lower bone region*	*In the upper bone region*
Chinese	67	30	13
Europeans	62	32	23
Egyptians	47	37	14
Algonquin Indians	42	10	14
Papuans	33	9	12
Alaskan Indians	25	4	15
Eskimos	10	10	17

Increases in deleterious-gene frequencies, such as those we may observe if we move from the data on the most primitive people in the tabulation just given to those on people whose technology and medical science compensate for genetic disadvantage, have alarmed some geneticists. Some even find them a threat to mankind's continued existence. But, as has already been shown in Section 12.3, negative eugenic measures can do but little to control the frequency of genetic defects in the face of mutation pressure since ten or more percent of all human zygotes carry a new mutation. Relaxation of selection pressures for various traits occurred long before *Homo sapiens* emerged. Every cultural invention, including tools, fire, clothing, and housing, changed the adaptive values of some genes in one direction and some in another. This process should continue so long as an opportunity for selection to operate is provided by our pattern of reproduction.

As already noted, genes kept in low frequency in a population by selection against them might be expected to spread when selection is suspended. Genes that lose their selective value without becoming disadvantageous will drift or be lost by mutation pressure. This does, in a sense, mean a tug-of-war between biology, which is responsible for increases in what may be considered at some stage of human history a defect, and culture, which provides corrective devices. We are already accustomed to glasses for near- or far-sightedness. Surgical intervention for such abnormalities as a harelip or polydactyly (extra digits) is commonplace. Replacement therapy, by hormones in diabetes, or by other substances in anemia, is available. Dietary control for some metabolic blocks has already been discussed, and a variety of other **euphenic** (that is, improving the phenotype) measures are being developed for the various genetic ills to which man is subject.

It has been suggested that the cost to society of such measures may become an intolerable burden. But because cultural evolution is currently so much more rapid than biological evolution of human populations, we can expect to keep ahead of the game for a long, long time to come. Apart from that, book-keeping of social costs and gains is not a simple matter, and surely cannot be lightly invoked where human welfare is concerned.

Perhaps a more important aspect of negative eugenics is that affecting the individuals themselves and their families. Voluntary restriction of reproduction where recurrences of grave defects are expected to be high is an obvious partial solution of the problem, and one that is considered further in connection with genetic counseling (Chapter 17). The possible role of positive eugenics is discussed in Chapter 20.

13.3 SELECTION IN INDUSTRY

Artificial selection has been a very powerful tool in agriculture and in the pharmaceutical industry. Man learned early in the course of agrarian society that like begets like. He has used this principle ever since for the improvement of domestic plants and animals. Several thousand years after he had begun using the principle, it was considerably refined, owing to Mendelism and studies on the genetics of quantitative traits. At first, *mass selection* was the primary method used, one in which only the most desirable phenotypes were permitted to propagate. This technique of selection, although effective for characters of high heritability, is not an efficient one where heritability is relatively low. Figure 13.2 illustrates the point. When h^2 equals unity as in the lowest graph, the correlation between phenotype and genotype is perfect. Hence, the former is an exact measure of the latter. But when the correlation is zero, as in the uppermost diagram, phenotypic information gives no clue to the merits of the genotype, and selection is unsuccessful (see also Box 10.C). Intermediate heritabilities produce intermediate gains from selection.

In order to increase the accuracy of estimation of genotypic merit, breeders resorted to *family selection*. Under it, in addition to the phenotypic performance of the individual tested, the phenotypes of its sibs or its progeny are also tested and taken into account. With the development of methods of population and biometrical genetics, it has become possible to choose from among

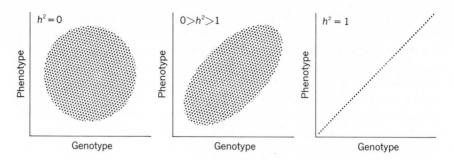

Figure 13.2.
The correlation between phenotype and genotype for heritabilities of zero, one, and an intermediate value. Each dot represents an individual.

different methods of selection (mass, sib test, half-sib test, progeny test, pedigree, or a combination of these), the ones that would produce the most rapid or the most prolonged gains in the objectives sought.

Further complications arise when, rather than a single criterion, multiple criteria of genetic worth have to be used. In selecting for increased milk production, for example, the amount of butterfat and nonfat solids must be considered in addition to the yield of milk. In fact, the requirements of modern food production make efficient selection a complicated matter. Only after the development of high speed computers did it become possible to put into efficient operation *selection by index*, which takes into account the great number of different variables determining the total genetic worth of individuals.

Breeders of egg-laying chickens now have to combine in an index properly weighted heritabilities, genetic correlations and economic values of as many as 16 different traits expressed by the individuals and their relatives: fertility, hatchability, incidence of crippled chicks, chick mortality, pullet mortality, degree of broody behavior, body size, rate of sexual maturity, rate of egg laying, egg size, shell thickness, egg shape, shell texture, internal egg quality, shell color, and frequency of blood spots in the eggs.

Figure 13.3.

Long-term selection for long-legged chickens. Note periods of progress and of stasis. (Data courtesy of D. C. Lowry.)

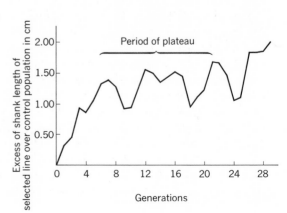

Many problems still remain to be solved in artificial selection practice, and new ones keep arising as higher levels of sophistication in the breeding industry are reached. For instance, in many classes of plants and animals, higher production is obtained from progeny of crosses between lines or strains than from individuals whose gene pools have been kept discrete. This phenomenon of hybrid vigor or **heterosis** requires selection for good combining ability between lines rather than a high performance of the lines themselves. Other complications arise because of genetic homeostasis, which causes a resistance to artificial selection by opposing natural selection pressure. Figure 13.3 shows

---

BOX 13.A SELECTION FOR EGG PRODUCTION IN THE FOWL

The University of California at Berkeley has been carrying on a long-term experiment designed to explore the optimum methods of selection for an economically useful character, the number of eggs laid by a flock of hens. The foundation flock in 1933 averaged a little over 120 eggs per year per pullet, a figure roughly comparable to the level of commercial egg production of the day. A few sires were added from other populations in the early part of the experiment, but after 1941 the flock was *closed*.

The actual methods of selection changed as more information on the theory and empirical results of selection was obtained. Basically, however, selection emphasized the performance of families of sibs and half-sibs. Since egg production is a *sex-limited* character, expressed only in females, sires were selected in the early part of the experiment on the basis of progeny and sister tests. In later years sister tests were used exclusively. One of the shortcuts found in the course of the experiment was that the criterion of selection need not be production for the whole year. Spring-hatched pullets start laying late in the summer or early in thė fall. By using the record of egg production to December 1 or January 1, the interval between generations—and hence the gain per unit of time—could be shortened. Other economic considerations (for example, resistance to specific diseases, egg weight and quality) were also selected for through most of the experiment.

The illustration shows the average egg production of the flock at five-year intervals, and also includes the data for the last full normal year's performance available (pullets hatched in 1965).

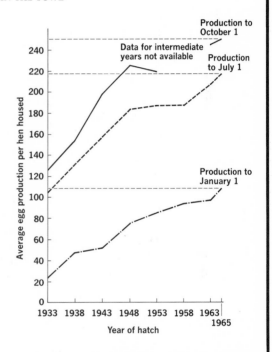

It may be readily seen that selection has been and continues to be extremely effective. The economic significance of doubling the number of eggs laid in a year, from 125.6 in 1933 to 249.6 in 1965, is obvious. Note that by January 1 the birds of the last generation laid as many eggs as the foundation flock took until July 1 to lay. Similarly, production to July 1 in the last generation exceeded the 1943 production figure for the whole year. The early data, taken from I. M. Lerner, have been brought up to date by courtesy of D. C. Lowry.

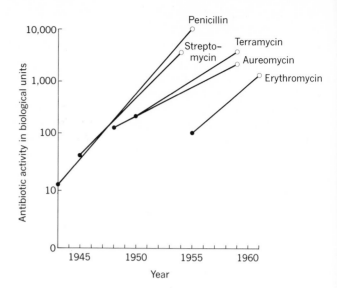

Figure 13.4.

Increased antibiotic activity obtained by selection from initially low-yielding strains of fungi. The scale is geometric. (Data from S. I. Alikhanian.)

an example in a selection experiment for long shanks of chickens. Coadaptation of leg length and genes for reproductive capacity is a slow process. In this example, successful selection for increased length of shank had a setback, because the birds with the longest bones, as a correlated response, lost fitness. After a period without gains, however, a new balance was reached, and gains resumed.

The literature on the use of selection in breeding practice is vast. Here, one example of the economic significance of animal improvement methods is given in Box 13.A. Finally, an example of application of selection principles in the pharmaceutical industry is provided by Figure 13.4.

Having considered the evolutionary force of selection, we now turn to the equally important force of mutation.

14

MUTATION

14.1 THE KINDS OF MUTATION

We have defined germinal mutation as a remembered change in the genetic message from one generation to the next. The variety of such changes is great, and ranges from the mere substitution of one nucleotide in the DNA molecule to the duplication of the entire chromosome complement. All genetic changes may be placed in one or another of four categories: (1) intragenic, or point, mutations; (2) changes in groups of genes on a chromosome; (3) changes in whole chromosomes; and (4) changes in a whole chromosome set. These four kinds of mutation can be correlated only imperfectly with the magnitude of the phenotypic effects they produce.

The molecular basis of the first kind of mutation has already been discussed in Section 6.4. Point mutations supply most of the evolutionary significant genetic variation. The substitution, deletion, or addition of one or more base pairs in the DNA of the chromosome can produce a great variety of alleles at each locus. It has been computed that between a quarter and a half of such changes in instructions for protein manufacture should be detectable. Changes that merely substitute one triplet for another coding for the same amino acid would not be detectable.

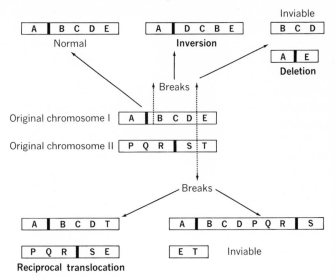

Figure 14.1.

Schematic representation of the
origin of deletions, inversions, and
translocations.

Mutations produced by transduction, which results when DNA from one organism is carried by a virus and incorporated into the DNA of another, may fall into either the first or the second category. Although it is probable that viruses can interfere in one way or another with the informational machinery of the somatic cells of higher organisms (see Sections 6.5 and 8.6 for examples), it is not known whether mutations caused by transduction occur in organisms other than microorganisms.

Several varieties of intrachromosomal change are possible: deletion, duplication, inversion, translocation. A **deletion** consists in the loss of part of the chromosome. All but exceedingly small deletions that involve sequences of several genes are usually lethal in the homozygous state. This is to be expected, since absence of gene products essential for the existence of an organism may result from deletions. Especially damaging are deletions that include the **centromere**, the part of the chromosome that holds together the sister strands in the dividing nucleus. In Figure 14.1 the centromere is represented by black bars. A chromosome without a centromere is usually lost in the course of cell division. Chromosomes with more than two centromeres are similarly inviable.

At least one deletion (probably in chromosome 5) has been described in man. It causes a variety of symptoms, including severe mental deficiency. Babies so affected have a characteristic plaintive cry resembling that of a cat, so that the syndrome is known as *cri du chat*.

Duplication of parts of chromosomes is an important evolutionary phenomenon, because it provides additional possibilities for new mutations to be incorporated into a species. The presence of two genes for the same polypeptide permits one of them to mutate in a new direction without damage to the organism, because the other would still carry on the vital function under its control. The different chains of hemoglobin have very likely evolved from duplicate genes.

Inversion changes the sequence of genes on the chromosome. Consequently, inversion affects the pairing of homologous chromosomes in meiosis of cells heterozygous for them, and crossing over may be suppressed in the region where the order of genes on the two chromosomes is reversed. An example of the evolutionary role of inversions has already been shown in Figure 3.8 for the *Drosophila pseudoobscura* group.

Translocations, as shown in Figure 14.1, are aberrations involving two or more chromosomes. Stern, in the experiment described in Box 9.C, used such aberrations. Translocation heterozygotes produce many incomplete and inviable gametes (Figure 14.2). They have complex chromosomal pairing patterns that can lead to ring-shaped chromosomes and other abnormalities.

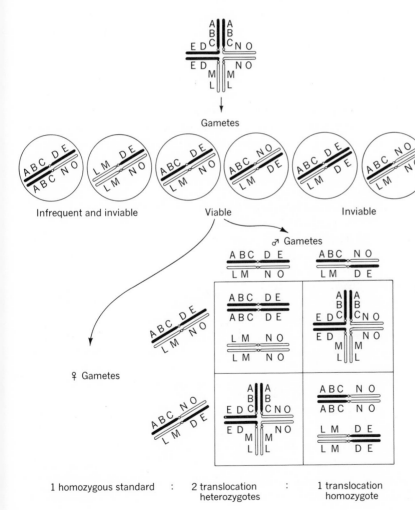

Figure 14.2.
A schematic illustration of the results of self-fertilization in a plant heterozygous for a translocation. (From Adrian M. Srb, Ray D. Owen, and Robert S. Edgar, *General Genetics*, 2nd Ed. San Francisco, W. H. Freeman and Company. Copyright 1965.)

Among such plants as evening primroses and peonies, translocations have played a significant evolutionary role in the formation of strains and sub-species, much as inversions have in Drosophila. Translocations are known to be associated with certain phenotypic defects in man.

Mutations of whole chromosomes may result in **monosomy**, if one of the two chromosomes in a set are lost, or in **trisomy**, if a chromosome is added to a set (at least one case of monosomy has been reported in humans, the individual affected being a mentally retarded four-year-old girl). We have already dealt with trisomics for the X-chromosome, as well as with additions of more than one X- or Y-chromosome (Section 8.4).

In humans, the best-known trisomic mutation is **trisomy 21**, that is, the presence of an extra chromosome 21 (Figure 14.3). It occurs in about one out of 650 births, possibly because of nondisjunction, and leads to gross phenotypic abnormalities. The defect has been designated in the past as mongoloid idiocy, or as the Langdon Down syndrome, after the British neurologist who first described it in the 1860's. The same symptoms have been produced in some individuals by translocations involving chromosome 21.

Trisomics 21 exhibit retardation of growth, a fold on the eyelid (which to Europeans made the patients look Oriental, hence the name "mongolism"), certain changes in finger and palm prints, an apparent increased susceptibility to leukemia, and gross mental retardation. Perhaps as many as 10–15 percent of institutionalized mental defectives are in this category.

The history of the studies of this disease reveals the complexity of interaction between genotype and environment. Before cytological studies established its chromosomal basis, the disease was largely ascribed to environmental causes. Because only a few trisomics 21 have offspring, the majority of which have been described only recently, no thorough genetic study of transmission

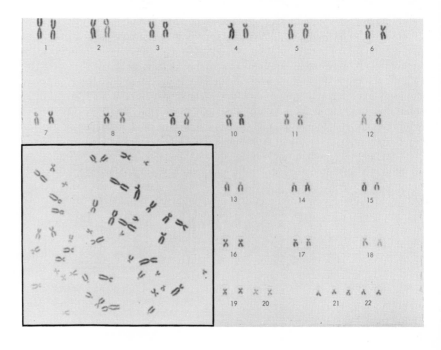

Figure 14.3.
The chromosome set of a male in trisomy 21. (Courtesy of A. G. Bearn and James L. German.)

was possible. The most evident attribute of the disease was its increased incidence with maternal age. The incidence of trisomics born to mothers under 30 was found to be 0.04 percent; for successive 5-year increases in age the incidence increased to 0.11, 0.33, and 1.25 percent, with a sharp increase to 3.15 percent for mothers over 45. For a time it was thought that these figures could be completely explained as a result of the increase in the frequency of nondisjunction with maternal age—a conclusion drawn from studies of Drosophila. Recent studies in Australia, however, have also shown that there have been secular trends in the incidence of the syndrome and that these closely resemble those in epidemics, with a characteristic temporal cycle and a pattern of spread from town to countryside. This finding once more raised the issue of the fundamental causality, since no ordinary genetic explanation would account for it. It seems possible that the chromosomal abnormality might be induced by virus infection. Indeed, there appears to be a relation between the temporal cycle of trisomy 21 and that of infectious hepatitis; thus we apparently have another instance of interplay between genetic and environmental forces.

In addition to trisomy 21, several other trisomics are known in man. They are responsible for a variety of different abnormalities, such as cleft palate, extra digits, deformed fingers, and congenital heart disease.

A great variety of other chromosomal abnormalities are common in man. It has been estimated that some 100,000 miscarriages (one-fifth of the annual number in the U.S.) are caused by them. In addition 15,000 of the babies born each year are deformed, mentally retarded, or sexually abnormal because of chromosomal defects. These aberrations are of considerable medical and social concern. But they are evolutionary dead ends since they lead to great reductions in fitness. However, adaptive changes in chromosome numbers have occurred in past evolutionary history, as we know from the variation in chromosome numbers and in shapes among related species.

Mutations that involve whole sets of chromosomes—that is, those that induce polyploidy, the possession of more than the diploid number of complete sets of chromosomes—are very common in plants. Such mutations are relatively rare in animals, possibly because they produce too much sexual and physiological unbalance and therefore are eliminated. At least three cases of triploidy (three sets of chromosomes) have been described in man.

One of the ways triploidy can arise is by failure of reduction of the chromosome number in the egg. For example, in a planarian flatworm, *Dugesia*, with a normal haploid number of 4, a strain was found that laid unreduced diploid eggs, and successive generations with 12, 16, and 20 chromosomes were produced by fertilizing them with normal sperm.

Induction of polyploidy has proved to be a useful tool in plant breeding. Not only can new polyploid varieties of a given species be produced, but altogether new species can be created. Mating between species almost always produces infertile offspring, because problems of pairing of chromosomes originating from the two different parents lead to failures to produce normal gametes. If, however the reduction division is inhibited, viable gametes can result in the production of an *amphidiploid*, containing a full set of chromosomes from each parent. The new form will have no chromosome pairing difficulties. Economically valuable food and ornamental plants have been produced by such methods.

A classical example of the production of an amphidiploid is that reported by the Russian geneticist, G. D. Karpechenko, who found that by doubling the number of chromosomes in a sterile hybrid between a radish (genus *Raphanus*) and a cabbage (genus *Brassica*), a new form of *Raphanobrassica* was produced. Unfortunately, the hybrid proved to have no gastronomic merit, and cabbages and radishes still have to be served separately at meals.

14.2 RATES OF POINT MUTATION

The rates at which point mutations occur must have optimal values in different species in order to provide a certain amount of new genetic variation, and yet without too great a cost in deleterious phenotypic expressions. As with any other property—biochemical, physiological, or morphological—control of mutation rates must be vested in the genetic information carried by the cells. Furthermore, the genes that regulate the rate of spontaneous mutation must be subject to natural selection. Hence, it is likely that many of the observed rates may be considered optimal.

In laboratory organisms it is possible to estimate what the mutation rates are under various conditions of observation. Since mutation rates are generally relatively low, the accuracy of estimating them varies with the organism. Viruses and bacteria that can be grown in millions in a short time provide the best estimates; mammals, which cannot be raised in such numbers, the poorest. Nevertheless, in experiments with mice, as many as several million gametes have been tested. Since mutation rates in mice are of the low order of ten per locus per million gametes (see Box 14.A), even such extensive tests have a large scope for error.

The basic technique of measuring mutation rates in such animals as mice is to prepare stocks with markers—for instance, with genes controlling coat color. These stocks are then inbred by brother to sister matings, and the litters examined for any deviation at the loci in question. Dominant mutations are readily detected in the generation of their occurrence. Recessive ones will segregate out in the first or following generations, depending on litter size.

BOX 14.A ESTIMATES OF THE RATES OF SPONTANEOUS MUTATIONS IN DIFFERENT ORGANISMS

Organism	Mutations per locus per million cells or gametes per generation
Viruses	0.001–100
Bacteria (*E. coli*)	0.001–10
Corn	1–100
Drosophila	0.1–10
Mouse[1]	8–11
Man[2]	1–100

[1] Estimates are available from a few loci only; mutation rate has been estimated at about 9 per million for forward and 3 per million for reverse mutations.
[2] Further estimates are given in Box 14.B; these shown here include estimates from cells grown in tissue culture, in which such traits as resistance to various chemicals may be studied.

Such techniques cannot be applied to man, but reasonably good estimates for dominant mutations can be made. For example, a Danish investigator who studied chondrodystrophic dwarfs—midgets whose growth was impaired, presumably by a deficiency in a pituitary hormone—found that among 94,075 babies born in a certain Copenhagen maternity hospital, there were 10 such dwarfs but only two of them had a midget parent. The other eight may be

BOX 14.B ESTIMATES OF HUMAN MUTATION RATES

The mutation rates given here for dominant and for sex-linked genes are, as is explained in the text, much more accurate than those for recessives. Many human geneticists view estimates for recessives with great skepticism, because of the uncertainties inherent in current methods of determination. They are given here merely to indicate the magnitude of the estimates made.

Trait	Mutations per million gametes per generation	Estimated fitness
Retinoblastoma		
Dominant; an eye tumor	15–23	0
Juvenile amaurotic idiocy		
Recessive; blindness, paralysis, mental deficiency, death, onset at about 6 years of age; common in Scandinavia	38	0
Infantile amaurotic idiocy (Tay-Sachs disease)		
Recessive; symptoms as above, but onset around 2 years of age; found in Jews.	11	0
Microcephaly		
Recessive; abnormally small skull	49	$\sim$0
Achondroplastic dwarfism		
Dominant	10–70	0.1
Hemophilia		
Sex-linked; see Box 14.C	25–32	0.25–0.33
Muscular dystrophy		
Sex-linked	43–100	0.30
Albinism		
Recessive	28	$<$1.0
Aniridia		
Dominant; absence of iris	5	?
Deaf-mutism		
Several loci	450	–
Low-grade mental defect		
Many loci	1500	–
All loci causing death before early adulthood	40,000	–

considered to have been caused by newly arisen mutations, giving a ratio of 8 out of about 188,000 genes or 43 per million. Estimates from other data, as shown in Box 14.B were found to vary around this figure.

Rates for recessive mutations present more of a problem. Only if the family history is known for many generations can the first manifestation of the trait be ascribed to mutation. Because human families are relatively small it is

---

BOX 14.C HEMOPHILIA

Blood-clotting is a rather complex process. It requires 13 different identified substances, starting with fibrinogen, a soluble protein in the blood plasma (plasma is blood from which blood cells have been removed; serum is plasma without fibrinogen) that is converted into fibrin, the substance that forms the clot. Deficiency of any one of the 13 substances will result in failure of clotting and consequently in continuous bleeding. All of them are probably under genetic control. Nine genes have been definitely identified as controlling one or another of these substances, and at least six more are suspected to have such a function. The best known of these genes is a sex-linked recessive responsible for the deficiency of factor VIII, the antihemophilic globulin that causes the disease spoken of as classical hemophilia.

The disease has been known since ancient times and, even though its genetic basis could not be properly explained until the discovery of sex linkage, some knowledge of the pattern of transmission from mother to son was appreciated in the early years of our era. Thus, in Talmudic law, boys whose two older brothers bled to death from circumcision were excused from the rite, on the basis of what is essentially a sib test. The exemption also extended to sororal nephews of mothers of such children, i.e., to sons of her sister—but not to the fathers' sons by other women. To the contemporaries of those who made them, these provisions were no doubt thought of only as typical examples of the intricacy of Talmudic law; but the provisions indicate some degree of understanding of the basis of inheritance of hemophilia.

The best known pedigree in which the disease appears is that of the descendants of Queen Victoria of Great Britain (1819–1901), an ancestor of

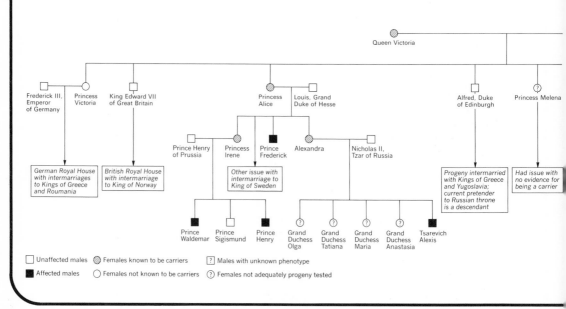

Unaffected males □   Females known to be carriers ◍   Males with unknown phenotype ?

Affected males ■   Females not known to be carriers ○   Females not adequately progeny tested ?

difficult to ascertain if a certain trait has been carried in a heterozygous state or is the result of a newly arisen mutation. Nevertheless, it is sometimes possible to trace a mutation to the individual in which it occurred. The mutation for the blood disease **hemophilia** appeared in one of the parents of Queen Victoria of Great Britain (or else early in her own prenatal life) and may have had some important historical repercussions (as related in Box 14.C). Identification

many members of European royalty and nobility.

As the pedigree shows, the British royal descendants escaped the disease, because King Edward VII, and consequently all his progeny, did not inherit the defective gene. Similarly, no evidence of the disease is found in other royal families descended from Victoria, except for two. In Russia, the only son of the last Tsar was a hemophiliac. Lacking an understanding of the nature of the disease, his mystically inclined mother, the Tsarina Alexandra, became increasingly reliant on a series of faith healers to control her son's affliction. The most notorious of them was the illiterate and dissolute Gregory Rasputin, whose baleful influence at court, financial manipulations, and personal debauchery contributed a great deal to the events leading to the Tsar's abdication and to the subsequent murder of his whole immediate family. Rasputin himself was

assassinated on the eve of the Russian revolution by a group of conspirators that included a Grand Duke, another relative of the Tsar by marriage, and a member of the Russian parliament.

Two sons of the last King of Spain, Alfonso XIII, were also hemophiliacs. Although there is no dramatic connection between the disease and the Spanish revolution that sent Alfonso into exile, the gene inherited from Queen Victoria certainly added little joy to the family life of the Bourbons.

The estimated mutation rate for hemophilia is given in Box 14.B. Some females are known to suffer from the disease, but they are extremely few, since they could only be produced as a result of an unlikely marriage between a hemophiliac and a woman heterozygous for the trait, or a mutation in similarly infrequent unions.

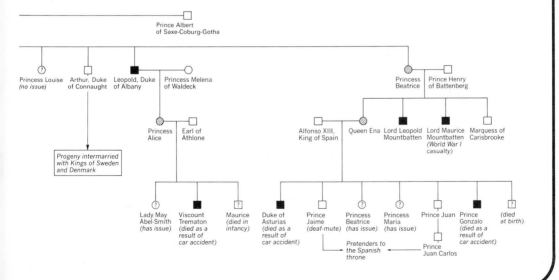

of the mutational event was possible because the diseases of members of royal families are on record, and because the trait is sex-linked and therefore behaves as a dominant in males.

Attempts have been made to estimate rates for recessive mutations by indirect methods. One method, based on the assumption that the population is in equilibrium, and applies the principle expounded in Box 12.A to the computation of m. But the estimates are not reliable, because (1) the postulate of equilibrium is almost always a tenuous one, except for fully penetrant lethal genes without heterozygous effects, (2) the value of s is not precisely known, (3) the degree of effect in the heterozygote may vary, and (4) the breeding structure of the population or the extent of departure from random mating is usually not precisely measurable. The figures given in Box 14.B should therefore not be taken as exact.

14.3 SOMATIC MUTATION

The time at which a somatic mutation occurs in the individual's life is of importance. If a metabolic block appears very soon after fertilization, the phenotypic effects may be similar to those produced by a germinal mutation, even though they are different in not being transmissable. But a somatic mutation involving, let us say, inability to produce liver enzymes in cells already differentiated into muscle tissue might have no consequences whatever.

Recent techniques for growing human cells in tissue culture, and treating them experimentally like microorganisms, permit a more precise study of human somatic mutation rates. Their magnitudes actually differ little from the m values cited in Box 14.B, but extrapolation from somatic to germinal mutation still involves an element of speculation. Nevertheless, the study of somatic mutants is of significance. It has the potential for solving a number of important problems including the nature of gene action and the nature of cancer. At the present time at least 14 different mutants are available for study in tissue culture. The use of the mutant causing a deficiency of the G6PD enzyme in verifying the validity of the Mary Lyon hypothesis has already been referred to in Section 8.3.

References have already been made, also, to the origin and growth of cancerous tissue. Single cancerous cells have been grown in tissue culture and all their descendants were found to have cancerous properties. Thus it is clear that cancer is the result of some impairment in the informational machinery of the cell—a mutation, in the broad sense of the word. Whether cancer is a result of somatic point mutation or differentiation into disorganized tissue is a much debated point. But since it is known that many viruses can induce tumors, the hypothesis that these tumors may be the result of somatic transduction is not an unreasonable one.

Another recent cause for excitement in the field of somatic cell genetics is the development of techniques for hybridizing cells of different species in tissue culture. One such method depends on the fact that cells of different species, when infected with viruses inactivated by light or by chemicals, tend to clump together; their cell membranes dissolve, and their contents fuse. Such hybrid cells can give rise to cell lines containing genetic material from both parents. Cell hybrids between rats and mice, hamsters and mice, and other combinations have been produced.

Recently, cell hybrids between mice and men have been obtained by means of a different technique. All of the chromosomes of the mouse continue to be present in the hybrid culture, but some of the human chromosomes are lost. The cells do, however, continue to exhibit some genetic traits of man, with human antigens found on their surfaces. Perhaps the culinary delights of tomorrow will include hybrids between the muscle cells of lobster and pheasant.

14.4 CAUSES OF MUTATION

Most causes of spontaneous mutation have yet to be accounted for. Some of them are known to be under genetic control, since there are so-called *mutator genes* that increase mutation rates in their carriers. Some of them affect only particular bases. In general, it is possible that part of the genetic information in cells contains instructions for the production of a certain proportion of errors in self-reproduction. These instructions may be the material on which natural selection for mutation rates referred to in the previous section operates, although it is difficult to visualize the mechanisms that might be involved. It is also known that there are many external mutagenic agents, some occurring naturally and others produced artificially.

The search for artificial mutagens was not successful until 1927, when **H. J. Muller** (1890–1967; Figure 14.4), by devising appropriate techniques, was able to demonstrate that X-rays were mutagenic. He later received a Nobel prize for this discovery. At about the same time, another American geneticist, **L. J. Stadler** (1896–1954), showed the mutagenic properties of X-rays on corn. Since then many other mutagens have been discovered, including a broad spectrum of chemicals.

Figure 14.4.

H. J. Muller. (Courtesy of
Mrs. H. J. Muller.)

In some instances, it is hard to distinguish between spontaneous and man-made sources of mutation. The effect of temperature is a case in point.

It is known that mutation rates, like the rates of other chemical processes, are affected by temperature. Most mammals have a temperature-regulating device that keeps the body warmer than the scrotum. Swedish investigators found that wearing tight trousers can raise scrotal temperatures from 30.7° to 34°C. This, on the basis of crude estimates of known mutation rates and the temperature effect, could increase the incidence of mutation by 85 percent, that is, nearly double it. It is an amusing possibility that perhaps half of what is considered to be spontaneous mutation originating in males is in reality contributed by current sexual taboos, and that the Scottish kilt may have more merits than its wearers suspect.

There are three important sources of mutation that might be considered as physical (in addition to visible light, which appears to have a mutagenic effect in some bacteria). They all form part of the **background radiation**—the natural radiation from (1) **cosmic rays**, (2) radioactive elements in the earth's crust, and (3) the radioactive elements ingested by man in his food. The effect of the first, the existence of which was discovered in 1912, varies with altitude. Between sea level and 15,000 feet there may be more than a five-fold difference in exposure to cosmic rays. No direct evidence, however, is available about the actual differences in mutation rates at various altitudes. It is true that the number of neonatal deaths increases with altitude (in the U.S., for instance, the death rate per 1,000 births varies from about 18 in the coastal plain at 300 feet to more than 21 in the Rocky Mountains at 5,000–6,000 feet) but full examination of the data suggests that the reduced oxygen tension, rather than the direct or indirect mutagenic effects of radiation, is responsible for the rise in death rate.

The amount of radiation from the earth's crust differs with location. If we take the average amount of radiation from the earth in France, the United States, and Japan to be 1, there are areas in the world where it exceeds 15 (Espirito Santo in Brazil) and even 85 (in a strip of land in Kerala province of India).

Geographic and geologic peculiarities in a locality in Kerala province have caused an accumulation of sands containing the heavy radioactive element thorium. This fact was discovered by German coconut buyers, who found the natives attempting to cheat them by filling sacks with sand instead of the nuts. The comical side of the story is that thorium is much more valuable than copra or coconut oil. In the pre-atomic age, it was used in the manufacture of gas mantles. The Germans attempted to capitalize on the situation by building a thorium-extracting plant. But the plant was completed just before World War I and was promptly confiscated by the British. A study was recently made of the wild rat population on that radioactive strip of land. Over a period of 300 generations of isolation these rats would have received about eight times as much radiation as rats in neighboring areas. No differences in phenotypic variability were found between the two groups. This does not exclude the possibility that some genetic effects may be present, but if there are they were not detectable by the survey method of study employed.

Human exposure to natural radiation by ingestion of food is a natural consequence of the incorporation by plants of radioactive elements from both the soil and the air; slowly decaying isotopes are eventually ingested by man either directly or indirectly, having passed through other links in the food chain.

Artificial chemical point mutagenesis was discovered in Scotland and the USSR about the time of World War II. Chemically induced polyploidy had been discovered earlier. The list of substances capable of inducing mutations is growing steadily. It includes both naturally occurring and manufactured chemicals, such as mustard gas, hydrogen peroxide, formaldehyde, carbolic acid, calcium chloride, various alkaloids, caffeine, and a great many others. Their effects have been tested on bacteria, fungi, various plants, Drosophila and mice. They may produce mutations, deletions, chromosome breakages, nondisjunctions, and other chromosomal abnormalities. It is difficult to tell what effect chemical mutagens have on human mutation rates. While there is not doubt that we are constantly exposed to substances that have mutagenic activity and ingest a great amount of them (for instance, in the form of coffee), it is not certain how many of them reach the gonads, or, for that matter, somatic cells, without having been broken down. The inclusion of huge amounts of coffee in mouse diets did not reveal a rise in point mutations, but raising Drosophila on caffeine-rich medium did increase the incidence of chromosome breakage and nondisjunction.

Before proceeding with the discussion of artificial mutagenesis, we may conclude this chapter by noting that in addition to mutagens, there is also a class of substances that exhibit *antimutagenic* activity. These substances tend to depress spontaneous mutation rates, although without having any effect on the rate of mutation induced by radiation.

15

ARTIFICIAL MUTAGENESIS

15.1 RADIATION

This chapter is concerned primarily with the problems arising from the great increases in recent years in the amount of man-made radiation, including the consequences of radioactive fallout. Although the effects of radiation on somatic cells are mentioned, our emphasis is on germinal cells. A brief review of the elementary physics of radiation phenomena appears in Box 15.A. In addition, several terms employed in measuring radiation intensity must be introduced. Their precise technical meanings need not be remembered, but since they are used in the discussion, the terms are introduced here. The *roentgen* (r), named after the discoverer of X-rays, is a unit of exposure used for X-rays and gamma rays. One r is equivalent to the amount of radiation that produces 2×10^9 ion pairs per cubic centimeter of air. The *rad*, a unit of absorption, equals 100 ergs of energy per gram of irradiated matter. The *rem*, or roentgen-equivalent-for-man, expresses the biological effect of 1 rad on man. It is computed by multiplying rads by the empirically determined relative biological effectiveness of the particular kind of radiation measured. Because the effects of radiation differ with the way in which the dose is administered, the rem may not be a very useful measure, but dosages are still expressed in this

BOX 15.A RADIATION

Radiation is a process by which energy travels through space. *Electromagnetic* radiation is basically a self-propagating electric and magnetic disturbance that affects the internal structure of matter. *Corpuscular* radiation consists of streams of atomic and subatomic particles that have the capacity to transfer their kinetic energy to whatever they strike.

It will be recalled that atoms consist of a nucleus containing various numbers of electrically uncharged *neutrons* and positively charged *protons*, around which negatively charged *electrons* orbit because of the attraction between the oppositely charged particles. If atom A comes close to atom B, its nuclear attraction may pull one or more of B's electrons into its own orbit. A will then become negatively charged because it has more electrons than protons, and B, having more protons than electrons, becomes positive. These atoms are then electrified *ions*, and, because of opposite charges, form ion pairs. Radiation that produces ion pairs is called **ionizing radiation**. Although some nonionizing radiation (such as ultraviolet or visible light) is mutagenic, it is ionizing radiation that concerns us most.

As the illustration of the electromagnetic spectrum shows, ionizing radiation is produced by the extremely short waves of X-rays and gamma rays.

The properties of the different kinds of radiation are shown in the following table:

Radiation	Source	Penetrance
Electromagnetic		
X-rays	X-ray tube	} Relatively penetrating
γ-rays	}	
Corpuscular	} Radioactive	
β-rays[1]	substances	Easily absorbed
α-rays[2]		Very easily absorbed
protons[3]	} Nuclear	Not penetrating
neutrons[4]	} fission	
Mixed		
cosmic rays	Of extra-terrestrial origin	} Highly penetrating

[1] High speed negatively charged electrons.
[2] Positively charged bare helium nuclei.
[3] Positively charged hydrogen nuclei.
[4] Electrically neutral particles.

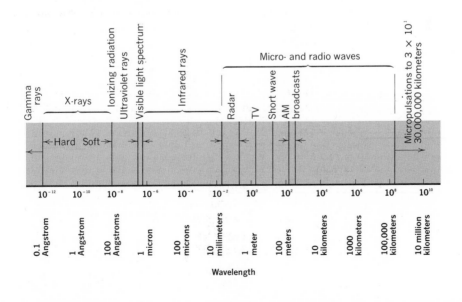

Wavelength

form in much of the literature. Although the roentgen, the rad, and the rem are not quantitatively identical, we shall use all three as being equivalent. Comparisons, however, are made within the framework of one unit of measurement at a time.

Most of the figures cited for man are expressed in terms of exposure per generation—that is, about 30 years, or the average period of exposure of the gonads before the gametes that form a zygote are produced.

In Section 14.4 we discussed the sources of natural radiation and the variation in exposure with altitude and geographic location. We can now restate the situation in quantitative terms. Estimates of the radiation exposure per generation from the earth's crust range from 0.7 rads in France, through an

---

BOX 15.B RADIATION EXPERIMENTS ON MICE

To compare mutation rates under different techniques of radiation, W. L. Russell and his associates at Oak Ridge prepared a strain of mice homozygous for seven recessive markers. Irradiated dominant homozygotes were then mated to this strain. The occurrence of a mutation at any one of the seven loci was signalled by the appearance of a recessive homozygote in the offspring.

Justice cannot be done here to the variety and scope of the series of experiments undertaken. In some of them more than a half million young mice were checked for various effects of irradiation. Only three of the experiments are summarized here to illustrate different aspects of the problems studied, and no attempt is made to generalize.

One experiment was designed to investigate the effect of the interval between the time at which females were irradiated with fission neutrons and the time of conception. In the 90,000 offspring born within the first seven weeks after irradiation, 59 mutations were observed. In the 120,000 offspring born after seven weeks, none were found. Similar results were obtained with X-rays and gamma rays. Whether the difference between the two periods is to be ascribed to differential sensitivity of the gametes at different stages of formation, to repair mechanisms, or to some other cause cannot be told as yet.

In another experiment designed to study the effect of fractionating a given dose of irradiation, male mice were irradiated at the rate of 90 r per minute until each had received a total dose of 1,000 r:

Dose administered in a fraction	Interval between irradiations	Mutations observed per locus per 10^5 gametes
1,000 r	0	6.7–10.3
500 r	2 hours	11.5
200 r	1 week	19.5
200 r	1 day	26.6
500 r	1 day	49.9

Again, definite interpretation is not yet possible. One hypothesis might be that the heavy single dose either kills the cells or damages them to the extent that they never form sperm.

The third experiment, also on males, dealt with differences in intensity of radiation, and as the table shows, demonstrated that acute doses in the range investigated are more harmful than chronic ones.

Source of radiation	Rate in r per minute	Dose	Mutations observed per locus per 10^5 gametes
γ rays from cesium 137	0.001	300	4.3
	0.001	600	5.9
X-rays	9	600	8.1
	90	300	8.7
	90	600	13.3

The important point about these experiments is that they show that many factors affect the degree of mutagenic activity of ionizing radiation, making exact quantitative statements about hazards to man impossible.

average of 0.9 in the U.S., to 15 in Espirito Santo and up to 84 in Kerala. At sea level a man may receive 1.1 rems from cosmic rays and 3 or 4 rems from the earth's radiation. At 15,000 feet the comparable figures may be 6, and again, 3 or 4. The totals are increased somewhat because of ingestion of radioactive substances. Hence, the full dosage received per generation is ordinarily about 4 to 10 rems.

These figures give only an approximation of the dosage and should not be taken too seriously. Clearly, the dosage differs markedly from one location to another, but the figures also reflect differences between various methods of estimating exposure.

The sources of man-made radiation include radioactive materials from nuclear reactors and other apparatus; X-ray tubes for medical, dental and industrial purposes, luminous compounds such as those used in watches, and artificially produced elements, manufactured in the laboratory or the result of atomic and thermonuclear explosions in the air. We shall discuss the effects of fallout in the next section. As we shall see, its genetic effects on the *world-wide* scale have *so far* been negligible compared to some other sources of man-made radiation.

To quantify the various aspects of artificial mutagenesis in man necessarily requires a great deal of guesswork. In the early years of the atomic age much extrapolation from Drosophila data was used, but more recent and extensive experiments with mice, particularly in the Oak Ridge laboratory, throw considerable doubt on the validity of drawing definitive conclusions at this time. It is not so much that the genetic material of Drosophila differs from that of mouse or man, but rather that many different factors contribute to the degree of mutagenic effect observed under different conditions. For example, many Drosophila experiments were based on irradiating mature sperm, which now turns out to differ in its response to radiation from sperm in earlier stages of gametogenesis. Male responses differ from female responses and further differences in response are also caused by temperature and level of oxygen tension. New evidence supports the existence of mechanisms that repair damage caused by radiation and indicates that different chemicals vary in their effect on the rate of mutation under radiation. In short, while we have found out a great deal about rates of artificially induced mutation under specific conditions and in specific organisms, we are a long way from generalizing what has been happening in man and is happening today. Box 15.B gives a sampling of some of the mouse experiments, the results of which rest on somewhat more secure grounds. It would be dangerous, however, to generalize about human genetics on the basis of what is known of seven selected loci of mice.

15.2 HAZARDS TO MAN

It cannot be overemphasized that the figures to be given in this section and in the next are, at best, educated guesses. They come from a variety of sources, and, as will be apparent, are not always consistent with each other. Nevertheless, they do give some indication of the relative magnitudes of effects from various sources of radiation.

It has been estimated that the average dosages per generation from occupational exposure now run about 0.005 rem. In one radiation research laboratory the ten highest individual levels of exposure ran 5 r per year. Therapy from X-rays and other sources of radiation contributes about 0.5 rem, and diagnostic radiation may add another 1.5–2.5 rem. Thus the radiation to which people are exposed today is perhaps 50–100 percent greater than that of those who lived before Roentgen's discovery. In terms of point mutation rates this may correspond to an increase of 6–15 percent, depending (as Box 15.B makes clear) on the time and manner of exposure. Later we shall translate these percentages into absolute numbers of humans affected.

We should also consider **fallout** from the testing of nuclear weapons. The explosion of atomic bombs produces a variety of unstable radioactive isotopes of many elements, and these decay at different rates by emission of beta particles. Strontium 90 has a half-life of 28 years (that is, every 28 years its radioactivity diminishes by a half), and cesium 137 a half-life of 30 years. It is these slowly decaying isotopes that present a long-term danger. They remain radioactive for a long time after they fall from the atmosphere onto the soil, and can be taken up by plants and pass through them into animal products, such as milk.

The **local fallout** (that in the immediate vicinity of the explosion) consists of the heavier elements. The **tropospheric fallout** (that in the lower part of the atmosphere) can be carried for many miles beyond the vicinity of the explosion. The **stratospheric fallout** (that in the upper part of the atmosphere) is produced by bombs larger than one megaton. It is made up of the relatively light particles, including strontium 90, and it eventually circulates throughout the world.

The extent of genetic damage from fallout has been the subject of heated debates. While there is no doubt that continued "unclean" testing or actual nuclear warfare can have nothing but dire genetic results, the accumulated fallout effects have so far been rather small compared to those from the use of X-rays. It has been estimated that the average increase in exposure from fallout before the 1963 test ban treaty amounted to no more than 0.05 r at sea level and a little more than 0.10 r at the altitude of Denver. This represents not much more than one percent of the background radiation, or what each one of us would receive in the course of three and a half months from natural sources. In effect, the increase is equivalent to that which would obtain should the average marriage age, or interval between generations, be increased by 3 or 4 months.

Although these figures have little to do with whether nuclear weapon testing and production should be continued or stopped, it is true that even this miniscule increase may result in the production of 2,000–12,000 genetically defective babies, or cause 25,000–100,000 cases of leukemia and bone tumors. Both possibilities are of course highly deplorable. The basic issue, however, is not one of genetics: it is political, and above all, ethical. Whether the development of nuclear weapons—or deterrents if you prefer euphemisms—at such costs in human life and suffering will prevent greater disasters than not developing them is not a question that geneticists are considered competent to answer. Yet any citizen—geneticist, bartender, or college freshman—can harbor a suspicion that the statesmen of Washington, Moscow, Peking, London, and

Paris are no more competent to answer it than he, even though their deliberations are based on many factors that may well be more important than the genetic hazards of fallout. (For the record, I should make explicit my personal bias. Although I am not a militant pacifist who opposes war under any and all conditions, I am an antimilitarist and consider wars and armament races to be immoral.)

Having considered the various amounts of exposure to radiation, let us examine next what their actual effects on individuals and populations may be. In general, the danger from excessive radiation lies in the development of cancers, tumors, and leukemia. It has been estimated that every additional 30 r of exposure will double the number of cases of leukemia in a population. There is some tolerance to exposure of limited areas of the body, which can even take doses of up to 1,000 r. In cancer therapy, where the attempt is made to kill the diseased cells without affecting the surrounding normal ones, fractionated doses of 1,500 r are administered from such sources as cobalt 60.

But the tolerance to total body radiation and to radiation of the gonads is much less. A dose of 50 r can cause temporary sterility and even 10 r may effect pathological changes in white blood cells. The agreed-upon maximum permissible dose for an individual over a span of 30 years is 450 r, but most safety standards run much below this figure. Accidents at nuclear reactors, of which at least five have been reported in the U.S., and one each in Yugoslavia and the Soviet Union, may, of course, result in much higher exposures: a technician in New York died after receiving 3,000 r total body radiation.

All of this, of course, calls for enforcing various precautionary measures, such as shielding all but the organs being investigated or treated by irradiation. The average X-ray machine in a U.S. private doctor's office delivers about 0.2 rems per exposure, but some machines deliver doses as high as 1.0 rem. Fluoroscopes similarly vary in dosage from 0.005 to 0.4 rems. Doctors are gradually beginning to realize the somatic dangers of indiscriminate use of X-rays. Many states have outlawed the use of X-ray machines for fitting shoes. In California the practice of scanning visitors to penal institutions with X-rays has been abolished under pressure from biophysicists and geneticists.

Estimates of genetic damage are highly speculative, but for whatever they are worth, some figures may be given. The following figures were derived by James F. Crow, who stresses their indicative nature rather than their precision. They express the possible effects of exposing a human population of 200 million to 10 r:

Form of damage	Number of cases in the first generation	In subsequent generations
Chondrodystrophic dwarfism	1,000	200
Gross mental or physical defects	80,000	720,000
Infant and childhood deaths	160,000	3,840,000
Embryonic and neonatal deaths	400,000	7,600,000

These figures apply to exposure in a single generation. If the same population were exposed to an additional dose, new and higher levels of equilibria for the mutant alleles would be established. Figure 15.1 diagrams the two situations for detrimental recessives under the most simplifying assumptions.

One method of measuring the damaging effects of exposure to radiation is

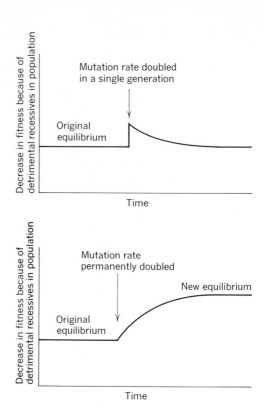

Figure 15.1.

The upper graph shows the effects of doubling
the mutation rate of detrimental recessives in a
single generation. The lower graph shows
the effects if the doubling is permanent.

to study the sex ratios among children of exposed and unexposed parents
Theoretically, this method would permit the estimation of the rate of induction
of sex-linked lethal mutations, as shown in Box 15.C, but the actual data available have not proved to be very informative. It is true that shifts of the sex
ratio in the expected direction have been reported following therapeutic irradiation among children of French and Dutch parents, as well as among those
of Japanese X-ray technicians. But children of American radiologists do not
show the effect, nor do the children of survivors of the atomic bombings of
Hiroshima and Nagasaki. Comparisons of some 70,000 babies of exposed
parents with a similar number of babies of parents who have not been exposed
show no difference in sex ratio, although an earlier and more limited study
gave a slight indication of a possible effect. This finding is, perhaps, a mixed
blessing. It may suggest to some that the atomic bombing of Japan did not
produce the dire genetic damage they feared; or it may suggest to others that
nuclear weapons can be used in warfare without threat to the children of
survivors.

Unequivocally less happy are the reports of the Atomic Bomb Casualty
Commission on the somatic consequences of exposure to the bomb explosion
and to fallout. Among many other findings on the victims of Hiroshima and
Nagasaki, the following may be listed. Of 183 children exposed before birth,
33 had microcephaly (head size considerably below the mean for their particular age group), and 15 of them were mentally retarded. Of their 15 mothers, 14
were less than 1.3 miles from the center of the explosion when the bomb fell.
Among 100,000 survivors who were closest to the center there is an annual

BOX 15.C RADIATION AND THE SEX RATIO

There are four possible ways of producing genetic damage in the sex chromosomes: recessive or dominant lethals may be induced, or the whole of a chromosome lost or inactivated. The diagram, in which the encircled letters indicate loss or death, shows the theoretical changes to be expected in the sex ratio of first generation offspring of exposed parents.

If the male parent has been exposed, an increase in the sex ratio may be expected on the assumption that dominant lethals are more frequent than losses of the Y chromosome. If the female parent has been exposed, the sex ratio is expected to drop independently of the relative frequency of occurrence of the three possible results diagrammed.

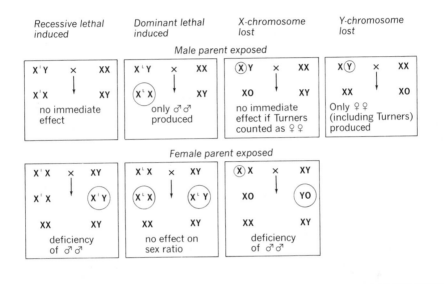

excess of 11 or 12 deaths per year over unexposed control groups, and half of the deaths are from leukemia. Chromosomal abnormalities, such as those illustrated in Figure 15.2, were found in about one-third of the subjects with heavy exposure. In one study 40 out of 94 survivors who had been exposed to doses of more than 200 rads showed chromosomal abnormalities in the form of rings, fragments, translocations, or two centromeres on the same chromosomes, while none were observed in the controls.

Similarly, in a group of 43 Marshall Islanders accidentally exposed to fallout when the winds shifted after detonation of a nuclear device in Bikini, 23 were revealed to have chromosomal aberrations when their white blood cells were examined in culture ten years later. The one redeeming fact is that so far no connection has been established between these abnormalities and the state of health of their carriers.

It should be pointed out that the increases in double breaks, such as shown in Figure 15.2, can mount astronomically under high exposure. If we assume that one single break will normally occur in 100,000 gametes, then the prob-

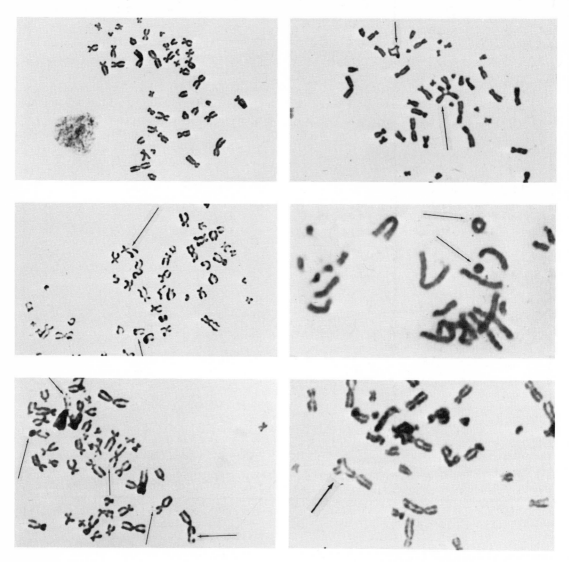

Figure 15.2.
The left column of photomicrographs shows examples of abnormalities arising from irradiation of human chromosomes in tissue culture. The top photomicrograph shows a control. Note the breaks and fragments in the middle and bottom pictures. The right column of photomicrographs show the consequences of breaks in several chromosomes with subsequent abnormal reunions of broken ends. (Photomicrographs courtesy of Theodore T. Puck.)

ability of a double break is $(1/100,000)^2$ or one in 10 billion. Taking the world's population at 3 billion people (coming from 6 billion gametes), we can see that a double break will occur on the average once in one or two generations. If radiation increases the probability of a single break by a factor of 10, or of 100, or of 1,000, the probability of double breaks will increase 10^2, 100^2, or $1,000^2$, respectively, and instead of a double-break chromosomal aberration appearing once in every other generation, there will be for the three cases cited 30, 3,000, and 300,000 occurrences in *each* generation.

To conclude this section let us examine the results of an interesting experiment done at Chalk River, Ontario—the Canadian equivalent of Oak Ridge. Rats were exposed to cumulative doses of 2,400–7,200 r over a period of 2–12 generations. They were subsequently tested for maze-running ability and on the average exhibited a decline, roughly equivalent to a drop of 5.35 points on the human I.Q. scale. Mentally retarded rats in this experiment may not have reduced fitness, as the Japanese microcephalic children probably do. Furthermore, reasoning by analogy and extrapolation from rat I.Q.'s to human I.Q.'s hardly permits one to draw any valid conclusions. Yet it is still worth noting the possibility that behavioral traits may be also subject to genetic deterioration due to increases in mutation rate.

15.3 PRACTICAL USES OF RADIATION

The nuclear age, with all its risks and perils is bringing man to a degree of control over nature undreamed of earlier. Most of the ways we use atomic energy (power, various engineering feats, medicine, and public health) fall completely beyond the scope of this book. However, a number of applications of radiation techniques in the pharmaceutical industry, in agriculture, and in pest control, are of practical genetic significance.

As shown in Figure 13.4, selection has been highly successful in increasing the yield of antibiotics. Most of the genetic variation utilized to obtain selection progress was induced by ultraviolet and X-ray irradiation. In horticulture and plant breeding, X-rays and gamma rays have been similarly employed to produce useful single gene mutations and to increase the genetic variation of polygenically determined traits, which permitted previously established plateaus of performance to be surpassed. Among the ornamental plants, new varieties of chrysanthemums, tulips, carnations, and snapdragons have been produced and marketed. It might be noted that U.S. law affords patent protection to such novelties, which is, of course, a great encouragement for breeders to employ artificial mutagenesis in the development of new varieties.

Examples of agriculturally important radiation-induced mutant forms abound. In Sweden new forms of barley have been developed that are better adapted to the conditions where this cereal crop is grown, and peas have been developed that give a higher yield. In both Sweden and Germany, as well as elsewhere, mildew-resistant barley has been produced. In the United States, peanut yields have been increased and rust-resistant oats have been obtained from irradiated and selected seed. In the USSR polyploid beets produced by chemical mutagenesis have been reported to yield 15 percent more sugar than the foundation stocks. In Japan new variation in many quantitative traits of rice was induced by irradiation, while in Australia the same was done with subterranean clover.

So far, it is not possible to predict the direction that the phenotypic expression of a mutation produced by one or another agent will take in higher organisms. Whether mutants with desirable characteristics will appear is a matter of chance or volume of the material exposed. But the ultimate aim of research workers in this field is to find means for directed mutagenesis. This may not be too remote a possibility; in microorganisms mutagens have been found that affect only specific bases.

In animals, with the exception of silkworms, artificial mutagenesis has so far received no application. Although the results of some pilot experiments on Drosophila indicated that radiation-induced variability can lead to gains in the characters which are selected for, the only experiment carried out with a domestic animal gave negative results. The experiment was an attempt to produce polygenic variation in a flock of chickens selected for egg production. One or more translocations were obtained, and variation in some quantitative traits was increased, but selection did not result in added gains in economically desirable traits. That no such gains were produced can be attributed to the scale of the attempt, which was quite small compared to the scale possible in plant and Drosophila experiments.

At least two applications of radiation to genetics have been devised to manipulate the sex of the silkworm. A biologist in the Soviet Union and another in Japan independently found that all male offspring can be obtained by destroying the nucleus of the egg and permitting it to be fertilized by two Z-carrying sperm (it may be recalled that male silkworms are homogametic). This procedure is economically useful, because male cocoons yield more silk than females. The other application, devised for the same purpose, is apparently now in commercial use in Japan. Irradiation was used to translocate a small piece of an autosome to the Z-chromosome. The section of the autosome carried with it a recessive allele w, the effect of which is to keep the white outer membrane of the silkworm egg from darkening, which it would normally do after several days of development. Matings between $Z^w Z^w$ males and $Z^W W$ females yield $Z^w Z^w$ male offspring whose eggs turn dark, and $Z^w W$ daughters whose eggs remain white. An electric-eye sexing machine can then pick out the white eggs and electrocute them, thus ensuring that only male cocoons are produced.

Sexual manipulation is also involved in the use of irradiation in pest control, which was originally developed by E. F. Knipling, a scientist in the U.S. Department of Agriculture. The screwworm fly is a livestock pest that causes millions of dollars in damage. The female lays a mass of 200–300 eggs in open wounds or abrasions of livestock, including the navels of newborn animals. When the larvae hatch they feed on the host, often to the point of killing it, especially because their presence attracts more egg-laying flies. The controlling technique Knipling worked out consisted in massively irradiating male flies in preadult stages to induce many dominant lethal mutations and render them sterile. The males were then released in great numbers in the affected areas, where they entered into sexual competition with normal fertile males. A large proportion of females that copulated with irradiated males then produced eggs that did not hatch. Repetition of the procedure for several generations eliminated the screwworm fly population completely in previously badly infested areas of Texas, New Mexico, Arizona, and California.

Another technique, the release of huge numbers of sterile insects, thus overloading demand for the available resources, is being experimentally tried with the fruit fly in Australia. Work with many other insects is also under way.

It would be a reasonably simple matter to assess the damage to mankind caused by increased mutation rates if a Platonic viewpoint could be adopted. That is to say, if there were an *ideal* genotype, homozygous at every locus, any deviation from it could be considered detrimental, and the harm done to our species by mutagenic agents would be directly proportional to the number of mutations they induced. But we know how far from reality oversimplification of this sort is.

It is possible to speak of a norm with reference to phenylketonuria, amaurotic idiocy, deafmutism and many other such defects; taken all together the incidence of these is about one percent of live-born infants. It is also possible to speak of norms for such gross chromosomal aberrations as trisomy 21 or the *cri du chat* syndrome found in another one percent of children born alive. But the genetic bases of many other developmental malformations and disorders that lead to mental diseases (which afflict perhaps 2 to 3 percent of living human beings) are so little understood that value judgments and definitions of norms are impossible. Even more significant in this connection is the existence of vast arrays of polymorphs, which express themselves not only biochemically but in every single kind of human attribute, including native abilities, temperament, and social behavior.

We have seen how abnormal hemoglobins can be of advantage to individual carriers and to human society depends on particular environmental situations. High reproductive fitness, the essential criterion of natural selection, might by definition always be thought to have a positive value. But even from the purely biological point of view, as Haldane has pointed out, this is true only for rare and scattered species competing with other species. As soon as the population becomes dense, intraspecific competition becomes inevitable and resources become overtaxed. Indeed, many species have become extinct because of selection in a direction advantageous to the individual but disastrous for the species. One possible example is the extinct Irish elk which developed the largest known antlers, and, perhaps, as Haldane says "literally sank under the weight of its own armaments." When we consider not only biology, but also social values, judgment as to what is optimal or ideal with reference to fitness or some other attribute becomes highly beclouded.

This is even truer in a world changing as rapidly as ours is, where the properties we admire today may become completely irrelevant to the world of tomorrow. Within a single lifetime, people have been known to change their idols from Lenin, Marx, and Sun-Yat-Sen to Lincoln, Schweitzer, and Einstein, and others have, no doubt, changed in the opposite direction. Even well-meaning and vigorous opponents of the typological approach sometimes fall into a trap in discussing this problem. A single quotation from a great biologist, humanist, and a champion of human diversity will suffice: "It is too easy to let our imagination strive for something with a body as beautiful as a Greek god, healthy and resistant to cold and heat, to alcohol and to infections, with the brain of an Einstein and the ethical sensitivity of a Schweitzer."

It may be questioned whether Bantu tribesmen or Chinese intellectuals share the standard of classical Greek beauty. And to some people the ethics of

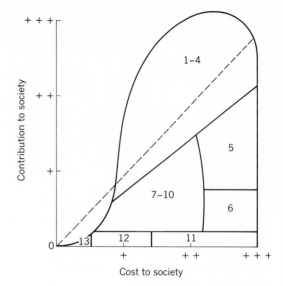

Figure 15.3.

Contributions and costs to
society of different phenotypic
classes. (After S. Wright.)

Schweitzer in his attitude to native Africans are a little difficult to distinguish from those of segregationists in the U.S. or Africa towards Negroes.

In any case, to return to the more direct issue under consideration, because we live in a world of heterozygotes and of unique genotypes, any attempt to assess which of the numerous multiple alleles at our numerous loci (alleles that produce practically an infinity of combinations) are superior, would be a puerile undertaking. A general nonspecific evaluation of the effects of increasing the clearly undesirable mutational reserves of the human gene pool is, nonetheless, worthwhile, if only to clarify our thinking on this matter. Such an appraisal has been undertaken by S. Wright, and the rest of this chapter is largely based on his discussion.

Figure 15.3 schematizes the relationship between the contributions and costs to society of different classes of phenotypes as visualized by Wright. Group 1 includes the bulk of the population, whose costs and contributions balance at a modest level. Group 2, whose costs and contributions balance at a relatively high level, includes professionals of average competence with a higher than average education and standard of living. Group 3 is a small one composed of individuals making extraordinary contributions at modest cost. Group 4 comprises men whose cost to society in terms of education is high, but whose contribution is even higher. Because these four groups include a great variety of types, who as a whole return to society at least as much as they cost, they are combined in Figure 15.3. Although the mutations that place individuals in these classes may be personally injurious, they do not damage society. Increases in defects that are due to new mutations but are subject to correction are costly, but because of advances in medicine and technology, only moderately so.

Group 5 includes individuals who have the capacity to contribute to society but do not do so because of such reasons as inherited wealth. The genetic component of the phenotypic variation of this class is probably exceedingly low, and hence will not be affected by increased mutation rates.

Group 6 is the category which is exceedingly costly to society because of its antisocial activities. To use Wright's labels for its members, this group comprises charlatans, political demagogues, criminals, and others who prey upon society. Whether increasing mutation rates would place more individuals into this group is difficult to assess. Such behavioral traits as egotism, aggressiveness, and impulsiveness are as likely to have a genetic component as those considered in Section 11.4, but practically nothing is known about their mode of inheritance, so that little can be said about them here.

The remaining groups consist of individuals whose costs outweigh their contributions. Group 7 includes individuals subnormal in health and physical constitution. Group 8 is composed of those who have low mentalities but are able to take care of themselves. Group 9 comprises individuals who suffer relatively early physical breakdown from accidents or infections and degenerative diseases. Group 10 includes the cases of mental breakdown from one of the major psychoses after maturity.

Groups 7–10 are combined in Figure 15.3 because the appraisal of mutation effects that can be made is about the same for all. The critical issue is the type of genetic basis underlying their characteristics. Oversimplifying matters considerably, we can divide all mutations into four classes:

    A. Polymorphic due to
       1. heterozygous advantage,
       2. frequency dependency.

    B. Mutation-selection balanced and
       1. completely recessive,
       2. with adverse effects in the heterozygote.

A fundamental difference exists between mutants of types A and B in the effects produced by changing their mutation rates. As has already been noted (Figure 15.1), increasing the mutation rate of type B increases the incidence of the defects. In contrast, increasing the mutation rate of type A would have only a small effect on incidence. Thus, increasing the mutation rate of the Hb^S gene would not increase sickle-cell anemia proportionately.

The answer to the question of how much damage artificial mutagenesis will have on groups 7–10 depends then on which kind of mutation is the more important in determining the genetic components of phenotypic variation. We know that both types A and B exist, but their relative importance still engenders somewhat heated debate among geneticists. Of particular importance in this connection are the investigations of the American geneticist B. Wallace, who found type A-1 mutations arising in Drosophila after irradiation. Although the interpretation of his data has been questioned, subsequent work on Drosophila and on flour beetles has lent it considerable support. Data on man are even more confusing. For instance, from the stabilizing selection model for intelligence, it follows that some of the low mentality in Group 8 is the cost to society for the high mentality of Group 4 (type A_1). On the other hand, Huntington's chorea, a progressive degeneration of the nervous system that begins in middle age and is due to a fully penetrant dominant gene (see Section 17.3) is definitely of type B.

Some evidence suggests that schizophrenia, the chief contributor to Group 10, and one of the socially most costly diseases, may also be of the type A. Perhaps, as Wright says, "the burden of overt schizophrenia is the price society pays for benefits conferred by persons of slightly schizoid type among the heterozygotes or the 90 percent homozygotes that do not break down."

Group 11 includes individuals who suffer complete physical or mental incapacity throughout a normal life-span and hence are extremely costly to society; Group 12 is less costly because its members die early. There is a considerable genetic component in these two groups as exemplified by PKU. Most geneticists hold that the majority of genes responsible for the conditions placing individuals in these two groups are of type B. If this view is correct, then social and personal costs would be adversely affected by increases in mutation rate, but it is difficult to determine whether a heterogyzous advantage in terms of some desirable human abilities (not in fitness) exists in some of the defects placing their carriers in these groups.

Group 13 comprises foetal and embryonic deaths, which are due not only to such nongenetic factors as maternal viral infections but also to various chromosomal abnormalities. Although an increase in these would, of course, add to personal grief, the cost to society is negligible. It may thus be seen that the question raised regarding the social effects of increasing mutation rates has no easy solution.

16

HUMAN DIVERSITY

16.1 RACE

The emotion-laden debate on human equality and human diversity that has gone on for centuries is still continuing with great intensity despite the clarification of issues that has resulted from nontypological evolutionary thinking and genetics. The description of the problem by Dobzhansky can hardly be improved upon:

"All men have been created equal; most certainly they are not all alike. The idea of equality derives from ethics; similarity and dissimilarity are observable facts. Human equality is not predicated on biological identity, not even on identity of ability. People need not be identical twins to be equal before the law, or to be entitled to an equality of opportunity.

"And yet, equality is often confused with identity, and diversity with inequality. They are confused so chronically, persistently, and obstinately that one cannot help suspecting that people have deep-seated wishes to confuse them. The source of these wishes is not hard to find. The glaring inequalities of the rich and the poor, the powerful and the weak, the masters and the slaves, are difficult to reconcile with the idea of universal brotherhood of men to which many people pay lip service. The escape from this paradox is made

BOX 16.A SOME HISTORICAL NOTES ON RACE

The history of the various concepts about race is exceedingly old and rich with ugly detail. No attempt to give a systematic outline is made here, and only a selection of illustrative points is presented. Much of the material in this box comes from the historian of the subject, T. Gossett.

Xenophobia and race prejudice can be traced in India perhaps to five millenia before our day; in China, to the pre-Christian era; and in the Western world, to the Biblical tradition of the Hebrews as the Chosen People. According to Talmudic legend, the three sons of Noah—Shem, Ham, and Japhet—gave rise respectively to the Semitic people, the dark-skinned races, and the other gentiles. The Hamites were considered inferior because of the curse laid on their founder for being disrespectful to his drunken father, according to the book of Genesis, and for a variety of other crimes related in supplementary legends.

In Greek mythology, the origin of differences between black and white populations is laid to Phaëthon, the son of Helios. Unable to control the sun chariot, which his father permitted him to drive once, he drove too close to some parts of the earth, burning the people there black, and too far away from other parts, causing the people of those regions to pale from the cold. Most of the Greek philosophers attributed the differences between populations to climate.

On the whole, racism seems to have been quite rare until modern times. Enslavement and oppression surely existed, but justification of these on the basis of racial superiority is recent.

It was in 1684 that the French physician François Bernier proposed in an article in a Paris journal that mankind is divided by appearance into four groups: Europeans, Far Easterners, "The Black," and Lapps. The great German philosopher and mathematican Leibniz in 1737 objected to the notion, likening the differences between the races to those between plants or between animals, and attributed them to the effects of climate, as the Greeks did. Nevertheless, Bernier's proposal was soon established in the mainstream of science and philosophy. Although Linnaeus, whose classification was consistent with his notions of special creation, thought that mankind was a single species, he recognized four subspecies, *H. s. europaeus*, *H. s. asiaticus*, *H. s. afer*, and *H. s. americanus*. The debate on causes of differences and the scale of superiority of one race over another had some religious overtones in the eighteenth and nineteenth centuries; but it was particularly the rise of colonialism and of Social Darwinism that caused the spread of racism in Europe, and in America it was the need for justifying Negro enslavement that led to the doctrine of white supremacy.

In Europe the cult of Aryanism, arising from Sanskrit legends about blond conquerors of darker-skinned inhabitants of India and Persia, spread and established itself, eventually culminating in the atrocities of Hitler. Even Galton, who, of course, must not be associated in any way with the brutal features of fascism, believed in Nordic superiority (just as, in America, Jefferson and, for most of his life, Lincoln, held the assumption of Negro inferiority).

The brutalities of Anglo-Saxon imperialism, and those of Southern racism during the postreconstruction period are too well known to be described here, but the following table is instructive in terms of statistics (available only since the 1880's):

Years	Lynchings in the U.S.	
	White	Negro
1882–1888	595	440
1889	76	94
1892	69	162
1906–1915	61	620
1918–1927	39	416

It is Gossett's thesis that the support of the intellectuals made racism in America possible. He credits the great American anthropologist of German-Jewish origin, **Franz Boas** (1858–1942), with first turning the tide against racial prejudice in this country. Although up until only a few years ago quotas for Jews were maintained at such institutions of learning as Columbia University, Princeton University, and New York University, the battle among intellectuals has now been won. There are still pockets of resistance as demonstrated by acrid exchanges that appear in the pages of such journals as *Science*. But the general changes in attitudes expressed by both biologists and intellectuals in other fields within a relatively short period of time are indeed remarkable. Whether the nonintellectual population of both the South and the North is prepared to follow enlightened leadership in these matters is, unfortunately, a moot point.

by blaming Nature, or the Creator, for having some of us able and others inept, some clever and others stupid, some hard-working and others lazy."

The debate has been especially virulent when dealing with differences among groups described as races (see Box 16.A). The dictionary definitions of the term "race" are vague, and have a remarkable tendency to produce misunderstanding and confusion. For this reason, the word has been largely avoided in previous chapters of this book, it is appropriate at this point to give it a genetic definition. According to Dobzhansky: **Races** *are populations which differ in the incidences of some genes* (see Box 16.C). This is not the common definition that anthropologists have used in the past. But gradually, as the influence of population genetics has extended to anthropology, the meanings assigned to "race" by geneticists and anthropologists have been converging. For example, a recent anthropological proposal has been to define races as groups between which gene flow has been restricted (W. S. Laughlin). Both of these definitions are, first of all, nontypological: no phenotypic prototype based on skin pigmentation, skull shape, hair form, or shape and size of body is assigned

---

BOX 16.B A GENETIC CLASSIFICATION OF HUMAN RACES

Anthropological classification of mankind into races on the bases of morphology and pigmentation is being replaced by a classification based on immunological and biochemical genetic differences (see Section 16.2 for some aspects of the new anthropology). A number of schemes, varying largely in the degree of subdivision proposed, have been devised. An example of one such scheme, the proposal of the Boston biochemist and immunologist W. C. Boyd is given here, but without the details of the manner in which the blood-group gene frequencies used as the basis of classification differ among the different races. It should be clearly apparent that Boyd is a lumper: he proposes subdivision of mankind into 13 races, whereas the anthropologist S. M. Garn, while recognizing nine major geographical races, lists 32 local races within them.

A. European Groups.

1. *Early Europeans.* This is a hypothetical group, now largely extinct, represented by the Basques (see Figure 16.1) and possibly by the Berbers of North Africa.

2. *The Lapps.* A small population but one sufficiently distinct from others to merit a separate position.

3. *Northwest Europeans.* The ABO frequencies of this group are also shown in Figure 16.1.

4. *Eastern and Central Europeans.*

5. *Mediterraneans.* This race includes southern Europeans, the inhabitants of the Middle East, and many of the people of North Africa.

B. African Groups.

6. *Africans.* This group includes the populations of Black Africa, although there are many local subgroups that differ from each other.

7. *Asians.* In Asia, too, there are many local geographical subraces.

8. *Indo-Dravidians.* The various sub- or *microgeographical* races dwelling on the Indian subcontinent are included in this group.

C. American Group.

9. *American Indians.* A very heterogeneous race of many isolates, including the Eskimos.

D. Pacific Groups.

10. *Indonesians.*

11. *Melanesians.*

12. *Polynesians.*

13. *Australian aborigines.*

All of these geographically distinguishable races have also distinct blood-group gene profiles.

BOX 16.C DIFFERENCES IN GENE FREQUENCIES BETWEEN POPULATIONS

We shall give below some examples of differences in gene frequencies, gathered from several sources, but primarily from the compilation by W. C. Boyd. The first important point to realize is that similarities between populations with respect to a single locus can be very misleading and that many loci are needed to diagnose relationship. For instance, if we look at the MN blood groups in Navajos and Eskimos, we find:

	Proportion among	
	Navajos	*Eskimos*
M	0.917	0.913
N	0.083	0.087

But, if we look at the ABO locus, the resemblance in frequencies in the two populations is no longer present:

A	0.013	0.333
B	0	0.027
O	0.987	0.642

The same comparisons between the English and the Australian aborigines show:

	Proportion among	
	English	*Aborigines*
A	0.250	0.216
B	0.050	0.023
O	0.692	0.766
M	0.524	0.176
N	0.476	0.824

Clearly, despite the similarity of frequencies at one locus, in both examples, the populations do not belong to the same gene pool.

Second, the figures should be understood to represent particular samples of data; in some of these samples, the number of people tested was small and the data are subject to sampling error. In other words, different samples taken from the same population can vary.

Five different traits have been selected to show differences in representative samples of different populations.

1. Diego blood group. This is a blood-group type controlled by a locus independent of that of the other blood groups (Chapter 18 discusses these), inherited as a simple dominant, *Di+*. It provides a good example of the immunoanthropological approach (see Section 16.2). The Diego blood-group type occurs at a low frequency in the peoples of eastern Asia; the Eskimos do not have it; it is rare in North American Indians but common in some Southern American tribes. Since American Indians are generally believed to have come to this continent across Kamchatka and Alaska, this pattern of distribution suggests the operation of the founder effect, with the Diego positives arriving in America in a migration preceding that of the Eskimos.

2. High excretors of a naturally occurring amino acid, β-aminoisobutyric acid or **BAIB**.

to a race. Second, both definitions imply the possibility of temporal changes in races. For example, the American Negro race is less than 350 years old: the first Negro slaves arrived in North America in 1619. It arose from a mixture of genes from the African Forest Negro and Bantu, with contributions from the Northwestern European, the Alpine, the Mediterranean, and other gene pools.

These definitions are, of course, not sufficiently precise to permit universal agreement in delimiting one race from another. There are lumpers and splitters among those who use the term, just as there are among those who use the word "species" (Box 16.B). But philosophically speaking, this is the way it must be if the classification is not to be static, but rather as dynamic as the gene pools themselves.

There are constant differences between individuals in the amount of this substance excreted in the urine, and a high rate appears to depend on a single recessive gene.

3. Haptoglobin types. It will be recalled that haptoglobin is the hemoglobin-binding protein of plasma. Four phenotypes for the kind of haptoglobin present in humans have been identified. They apparently represent four different genotypes.

4. Ability to taste *phenylthiocarbamide, PTC*. This is a substance that to some people tastes exceedingly bitter (although other reactions have also been reported), while to others it has no taste at all. Nontasters are recessive homozygotes.

The polymorphism at this locus seems to have some adaptive significance. PTC is related chemically to goitrogenic substances, and among patients with nodular goiter (a disease of the thyroid) the frequency of nontasters is higher than expected by chance. The possible significance of the gene frequency difference between Ohio and Alabama samples of Negroes will become apparent in Section 16.4.

5. Fingerprint patterns. This is a highly heritable trait (see Box 11.B), although its mode of inheritance is not very well understood. It would be a misnomer to refer to the figures given in the last two columns of the table as gene frequencies.

| Population | Proportion of | | Proportion of high BAIB secretors | Haptoglobin types | | | | Proportion of PTC tasters | Fingerprint patterns | |
	Diego+	Diego−		0	11	21	22		Percent arches	Percent whorls
Australian aborigines	0	1.00		0	0.12	0.68	0.20	0.27		
Chinese	0.05	0.95						0.93	0.03	0.50
English	0	1.00	0.09	0.03	0.10	0.55	0.32	0.69	0.07	0.25
Eskimos	0	1.00	0.23					0.59		
North American Indians	0.02	0.98	0.59					0.97	0.05	0.50
South American Indians	0.86	0.14								
Japanese	0.07	0.93						0.91		
American Negroes										
Ohio								0.91		
Alabama								0.77		
New York			0.29							
Seattle				0.04	0.26	0.48	0.21			

In any event, the genetic definition does not permit the confounding of criteria of race that has become so common in the layman's world. Most importantly, it puts to an end the ridiculous notion of racial purity, or the existence of "pure races," that has dominated the mentality of racists for so long. Another confusion that the definition circumvents is the supposed relationship between biological race and language, which provided one of the bases for Hitler's notions of Aryanism. One of the chief proponents of the theory of Aryanism (see Box 16.A), the nineteenth-century philologist Friedrich Max Müller, who originally believed that race and language were related, spent the last years of his life deploring the belief: "I have declared again and again that if I say Aryans, I mean neither blood nor bones nor hair nor skull, I mean those who speak an Aryan language." Of the many examples that dispute the

BOX 16.D UNESCO STATEMENT ON RACE

In July 1952, UNESCO issued a statement prepared by an international group of geneticists and anthropologists on the nature of race and race differences. In minor ways, it is now somewhat out of date, partly because of the great deal of new information on individual gene differences between populations obtained since then, and partly because of newly acquired understanding of the feedback between biological and cultural evolution. But the principles embodied in the statement are still valid. Listed below are verbatim extracts from the eight major points that were made.

1. Scientists are generally agreed that all men living today belong to a single species, *Homo sapiens*, and are derived from a common stock, even though there is some dispute as to when and how human groups diverged from this common stock.

2. Some of the physical differences between human groups are due to differences in hereditary constitution and some to differences in the environments in which they have been brought up.

3. National, religious, geographical, linguistic, and cultural groups do not necessarily coincide with racial groups.

4. Broadly speaking, individuals belonging to major groups of mankind are distinguishable by virtue of their physical characters, but individual members, or small groups, belonging to different races within the same major group are usually not so distinguishable.

5. Studies within a single race have shown that both innate capacity and environmental opportunity determine the results of tests of intelligence and temperament, though their relative importance is disputed.

6. The scientific material available to us at present does not justify the conclusion that inherited genetic differences are a major factor in producing the differences between the cultures and cultural achievement of different peoples or groups.

7. There is no evidence for the existence of the so-called "pure" races. In regard to race mixture, the evidence points to the fact that human hybridization has been going on for an indefinite but considerable time.

8. We wish to emphasize that equality of opportunity and equality in law in no way depend, as ethical principles, upon the assertion that human beings are in fact equal in endowment.

With the exception of point 6, one cannot take issue with the assertions made in the extracts above. But the example of the interaction between culture and the gene-pool content given in Section 7.4 does throw some question on the validity of the sixth point. A better formulation would emphasize the fact that genetically determined cultural differences do not warrant popularly held notions of racial superiority or inferiority; this point is in fact made in the complete statement, but in another context.

A similar report more specifically addressing itself to the status of the American Negro was issued in 1963 by a committee of the American Association for the Advancement of Science.

relationship, we need cite but one—that of Iceland. Although the language of Icelanders is Scandinavian, the blood-group and gene-frequency profiles make them biologically akin to Celts, whose language is quite different.

Parenthetically, it may be noted that there are claims for some relationships between gene frequencies and linguistic preferences. Thus, in Europe, it has been alleged (although most linguists are not convinced) that the English *th* sound is found in the languages of populations in which the frequency of the *O* gene exceeds 65: this sound is found in the languages of Iceland, Britain, and Spain (but not Portugal); and in those of Greece and Italy, where it was present in the language of its ancient inhabitants, the Etruscans. In the languages of populations having an *O* gene frequency between 60 and 65, as in those of the Scandinavian peninsula and Germany, the sound used to exist but no longer does, and in the languages of populations having a frequency under 60, the phoneme *th* is absent.

Confusion also exists in regard to race and religion. Jews are often spoken of as a single race. In fact, however, their populations are derived from several gene pools. We have seen in Section 12.1 how varied the frequencies of the G6PD gene are among Israelis of different geographical origin. In general, gene frequencies in Jewish populations tend to be similar to those among gentiles immediately surrounding them. Thus, Yemenite Jews are low in *A* and *B* and high in *O*, as are Yemenite Arabs; and Cochin Jews are reasonably high in *A* and *B*, as are Cochin Hindus.

One notable exception to this generalization is the Roman ghetto. Between 1554 and 1870 it was virtually sealed off from the rest of Italy and probably no gene flow into or out of it occurred. As a result of this isolation, the blood-group frequencies of present-day Roman Jews differ from those of the other populations of Italy. For instance, the frequency of the *B* allele among them is 27 percent but in no other populations on the Italian mainland does it rise above 11 percent.

Race and morphology have also been confounded. By many criteria of classical anthropology, even full sibs could be, because of differences in appearance, classified as belonging to different races. This could not occur under the genetic definition because that definition is statistical and not typological.

Enough has probably been said by now to clarify what the geneticists mean by "race." As a summary, excerpts from a statement prepared under the auspices of the United Nations Educational, Scientific, and Cultural Organization are given in Box 16.D.

16.2 BIOCHEMICAL ANTHROPOLOGY AND IMMUNOANTHROPOLOGY

There is no need here to discuss in detail the origin of human races. Essentially the same evolutionary forces—mutation, selection, and drift—that produce speciation (described in Section 4.3) act in race formation, with one major difference in their operation. In speciation, the process goes to completion and groups that do not interbreed become established as species (see the evolutionary tree in Figure 5.1); but in the establishment of gene pools in human populations, the relative shortness of the period of partial isolation and the continued gene interchange by means of hybridization have made it impossible for barriers to interbreeding to arise. All races are capable of crossing to produce fertile offspring. Because of this major difference, the process of race formation is more clearly diagrammed by a reticulum, or network, than by a tree, such as that used to represent speciation. Some races are dissolved in the course of history by interbreeding and disappear or lose their identity, as did many during the successive waves of migrations to Europe from the East at the beginning of Western civilization. Other races are of recent origin, as are

Figure 16.1.

Maps showing isogen lines in Western Europe
(*isogens* are lines placed on a map to delimit
areas of the same gene frequency, as an isobar
does for temperature). On the left, *A* has a
frequency of <25 percent in the dark shaded areas
and >25 percent in the light ones. In the middle
O has a frequency of >70 percent in the dark and
<70 percent in the light areas. On the right, the
frequency of *B* is <5 percent in the dark areas
and >5 percent in the light areas. (Adapted
from G. de Beer.)

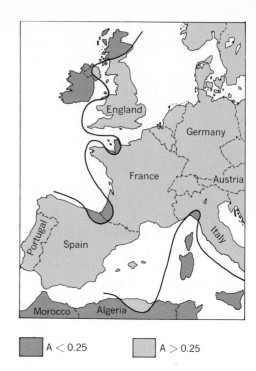

A < 0.25   A > 0.25

the American Negro race, the South African "colored" population (which has
genes from Bushman Hottentot, Bantu, European, Malaysian, and Indian
pools), and the Neo-Hawaiian complex of European, Polynesian, Chinese,
Japanese, and Filipino genes.

The historical reconstruction of race formation and dissolution is being
greatly aided by the discoveries of increasing numbers of gene markers, such
as serum proteins and blood-group alleles. Instead of relying on various anthropometric measurements of traits, whose polygenic inheritance caused dissimilar genotypes to have similar phenotypes and thus obscured the biological
relationships between populations, anthropologists now can use traits for
which the gene frequencies can be computed from phenotypic frequencies.
For instance, the study of the distribution of the ABO blood groups in Western
Europe depicted in Figure 16.1 has contributed to the solutions of some
archaeological, and linguistic puzzles. Thus, for a long time there has been
unexplained evidence of a link between western Britain and the Mediterranean
that dates back to the Neolithic Age. The similarity in frequencies of A and
O between the two (compare the top left-hand and bottom right-hand corners
of Figure 16.1) definitely suggests that populations of Mediterranean origin
did inhabit Ireland and Scotland at one time, leaving their imprint on the
present gene pool.

Similarly, that the Hungarian gypsies originated in India—as they themselves have claimed and as the linguistic connection between their language

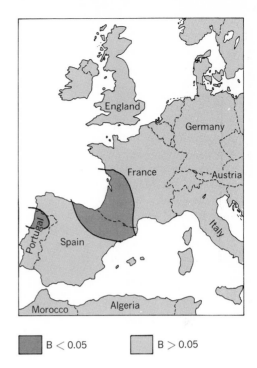

| | O > 0.70 | | | O < 0.70 | | | B < 0.05 | | | B > 0.05 |

and Sanskrit has indicated—has been confirmed (although too much reliance should not be placed on a single locus) by blood group studies summarized in the following table:

Population	Percentage			
	O	A	B	AB
Hungarians	31	38	19	12
Hungarian gypsies	34	21	39	6
Indians	31	19	41	9

The question about the origin of the Lapps was equally controversial: however, examination of their blood-group frequencies has ascertained that the Lapps are of European, rather than Asiatic, descent. Lapps were found to have a high frequency of one of the multiple alleles at the ABO locus (A_2; see Chapter 18), which is absent in mongoloid populations. Frequencies at other loci support this interpretation.

Even more exciting possibilities for historical research lie in the development of techniques of blood-typing material from the dead. Some blood-group substances, which are present in the blood cells, are found and are identifiable in hair and various other tissues and organs. This makes it possible to investigate the gene frequencies, not only of contemporary populations, but also of their ancestors and of extinct populations. Thus, when the techniques

BOX 16.E HUMAN PHYLOGENIES

The Italian geneticist L. L. Cavalli-Sforza, in collaboration with the English statistician A. W. F. Edwards, employed elaborate computer-based methods in an attempt to reconstruct human phylogenies. They used, on the one hand, data on gene frequencies at five blood-group loci, and, on the other, a set of 26 various anthropometric measurements, such as stature, weight, skeletal dimensions, skin color, and hair thickness. In both investigations combined information allowed them to make the most likely statistical estimate of the degree of resemblance between the different populations studied, and of the lengths of time that had elapsed since they diverged from each other, indicated by the lengths of the lines in the diagram.

As the graphs show, there are many similarities in the results obtained. There are also some startling differences. Note in particular the groups designated A and B: in the graph based on blood groups, Eskimos are closely related to South American Indians and are not very distant from the New Zealand Maoris, but in that made from the anthropometric data, these three groups are widely separated.

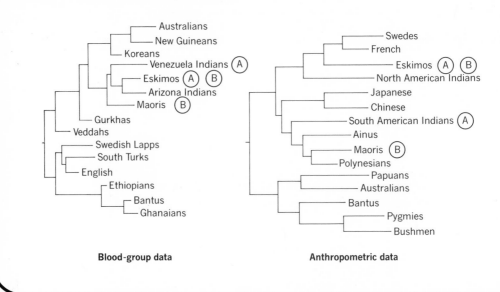

Blood-group data   **Anthropometric data**

of *paleoserology* have been perfected, it may be possible to solve the identity of the Etruscans, the pre-Roman inhabitants of Italy whose origin has baffled historians for so long.

The field of immunoanthropology is only beginning to develop and there is yet much to be learned about it. In Box 16.E., a computer-aided study of human phylogenies is described, and the results obtained from serological data are compared with those obtained from conventional anthropometric measurements. It is too soon to say how the differences between the results obtained are to be reconciled, but as more and more biochemical polymorphisms are discovered, and the nature of their selective advantages is more clearly understood, reconstructions of human phylogenies will certainly have increasing assurance of validity.

16.3 ADAPTATION

As races form, the differences that develop in their characteristics, other than those established by drift or recent hybridization, are due to natural selection. Some possible examples of adaptive values of blood-group, vision, and nasal structure genes have already been alluded to, but racial differences can be very great in many other traits. Our information on most of these traits is so incomplete that we can classify them into two categories; these categories differ only in the immediate potentialities of dispelling our ignorance of their genetic bases.

The first category includes characteristics that may indicate racial differences but that are not subject at present to objective evaluation. In this category are included mental and behavioral traits, whose genetics have been discussed in Chapter 11. In the absence of tests that take cultural differences into account, the comparison of specific mental abilities and biologically determined differences in temperament is not possible. Hence, we cannot draw conclusions beyond trivial generalizations such as this: that in hunting societies a temperament that makes a good hunter would be selected for, whereas in, let us say, rice-growing societies, behavior helping a person to grow more rice would be the target of selection. It has, however, also been argued that primary selection of mental characteristics in the course of human history has not been for special abilities, but rather for the general properties of educability, capacity to profit by experience, plasticity of behavior under a wide variety of conditions, and psychological homeostasis. This is an egalitarian argument, from which it would follow that, because selection is in the same direction in all races, no differences between the races in average mental and behavioral attributes are to be expected. There undoubtedly is great merit to this proposition, but it does not seem likely that it tells the whole story. Unfortunately, since the matter cannot be solved at this time by observation or experiment, it must remain one of opinion rather than fact.

The second category comprises traits that can be measured, but whose physiological bases of adaptation are so little understood that only speculation about them is possible.

Although we are not much more informed about them than we are about the first group, research can help us to study them. We know the various environmental conditions under which races of mankind developed and live, and physiological investigations about the nature of adaptation to these conditions is possible. Much is already known about adaptations of animals to climate. For instance, we are aware of the frequent occurrence of smaller body size and longer extremities in warmer regions; both characteristics are clearly related to conservation and dissipation of heat. Whether man, who has invented clothing and housing as artificial homeostatic devices, would be subject to selection for body size and proportions in the same way as other mammals is by no means clear. Yet ratios of stature to weight appear to increase in human populations as one proceeds from north to south. For example, the Tusi, the ruling class of cattle-grazers of the Runid people in East Africa, live next to the Pygmy rain-forest hunters who are shorter on the average by slightly more than a foot; but height-weight ratios in both groups are considerably higher than in any European group.

Many other morphological and physiological characteristics, such as the number of sweat glands, the amount of facial hair (relative beardlessness might be an advantage to the Eskimo because of icicles that would form on the beard), the shape of the nose, and the amount of body hair have been speculated about, but few firm conclusions have been drawn. Perhaps the characteristic that has received most attention is skin pigmentation.

There are four pigments in the human skin, including melanin, melanoid, hemoglobin, and carotenoid. The first of these is primarily responsible for skin color differences between races. Whereas dark-skinned people have large amounts of melanin distributed throughout the different layers of the skin, light-skinned people have a smaller amount confined to one epidermal layer. The pinkish complexions of the northern Europeans are caused by the blood pigments showing through. Their skin may reflect 20 to 40 percent of the light; the darkest human skin, only one percent.

Melanin formation depends on exposure to ultraviolet radiation, and all people except for albinos (carriers of a metabolic block in the tyrosine pathway; see Box 6.E. and Figure 6.6) have the capacity for suntanning. Quantitative studies on the degree of melanization made by measuring skin reflectance curves, must therefore be carried out under standard conditions of exposure to ultraviolet light.

Skin pigmentation appears to be under the control of several loci. The hypothesis that the range of color from the fair to the extremely dark, as observed in the total United States population, depends on segregation of about five pairs of additive alleles has been proposed. It seems to conform reasonably well with observations, as has been demonstrated by Stern.

Speculation about the biological significance of melanin has been widespread. In the opinion of some, whatever adaptive value a dark skin may have, it has nothing to do with exposure to the sun; rather, dark pigmentation could have served as protective coloration to tropical rain-forest dwellers. Most theories, however, attempt to link it with protection from excessive ultraviolet light. It has been shown that, although Negroes exhibit the same kinds of other cancers as whites, there is almost no incidence of skin carcinomas. Yet this would hardly be an important selective agent, since the average age of cancer manifestation is such a late one that skin cancer would have little effect on fitness. Protection from the immediate burning effects of solar radiation and better thermo-regulation have been invoked as possible selective agents. A hypothesis that draws considerable support is that the selection for this character is correlated with vitamin D production.

Vitamin D controls absorption of calcium from the intestine and its deposition in the bones. Although it is present in such materials as fish-liver oils, it is not found in required amounts in ordinary diets and normally is manufactured from precursors by mediation of ultraviolet rays from the sun. Deficiency in vitamin D leads to rickets, but excess is also harmful, producing hypervitaminosis D, which causes calcification of soft tissues.

The hypothesis of vitamin D production as the selective agent maintains that in the original dark-skinned hominids, selection pressure was in the direction of intense pigmentation, because in equatorial latitudes the danger was in too much, rather than too little, absorption of ultraviolet rays and therefore in too much vitamin D production. As the early hominids spread north, the direction of selection was changed. Because of the seasonal exposure to the sun in the summer and the lack of it in the winter, the capacity for reversible melanization by suntanning was advantageous and permitted white-skinned groups to occupy northern latitudes. In the mongoloid races, the biological problem of protection against ultraviolet rays was solved by natural selection in a different manner: these races developed a keratinized horny layer of the skin, keratin being a yellow-tinged substance like that found in nails, hoofs, and feathers. This theory regarding vitamin D production is an attractive one, but it needs further substantiation. It provides one more example of different biological solutions to the same question. Sex determination and resistance to malaria are other examples of other alternative solutions to attainment of increased fitness of populations discussed earlier.

16.4 THE AMERICAN NEGRO

Of all problems in the biology of race, none looms larger at present than that of the American Negro. Because the widespread social effects of this problem contribute so greatly to the socioeconomic and moral crisis in the United States today, it seems essential that both the Negro and the white segments of our population be well informed about prejudice and as disabused of it as possible. And yet, strange as it seems, of the three most recent textbooks on human genetics, all written by well-informed and clearly well-meaning biologists, not one has a single entry referring to the American Negro in its index.

Because the American Negro racial group is a recent one, it is not at all likely to be in equilibrium. The contributions of different gene pools to the current American Negro pool have been computed on the basis of the gene frequencies for blood groups and other markers that have been found in the African descendants of the Negro's ancestors, in Europeans, in American Indians, and in the Negroes themselves. Although these computations are subject to some error because of uncertainties about selection pressures and other factors, it seems highly probable that about 30 percent of autosomal genes in the current American Negro population is of European origin, and that the American Indian contribution is negligible. There are undoubted differences in this figure between subpopulations. Thus, the difference between Alabama and Ohio Negroes noted in Box 16.C might reflect the fact that the gene flow of the white pool to the Negro pool has been greater in the South than in the North (although that this is indeed the cause of this difference is outright speculation).

As we know, this gene flow occurred in the slave culture below the Mason-Dixon line, when many Negro women bore children of their white masters; it has not been due to the lust that racists claim Negro males bear for white women. If it is accepted that the gene for hairy ears is indeed Y-borne (Box 8.A), and if certain assumptions about its frequency in Africa are made, it can be computed that about 0.40 percent of Y-chromosomes in today's Negroes are of European origin. Although this figure is derived from insufficient evidence, it may nevertheless be the best evidence available for Y-chromosome inheritance of the trait. Similarly, only 15 to 20 percent of sex-linked genes in the Negro gene-pool would be derived from the white population.

On the bases of known gene frequencies, and the assumptions that (1) fitness is independent of color and (2) random mating will take place among Negroes without further gene flow from the European pool, it is predictable that in another generation hardly any Negro will not be the bearer of some white genes. If random mating were to be instituted for the whole of the population of the United States, one might expect, on the basis of Stern's hypothesis of inheritance of pigmentation, a uniform distribution of color variation. Such a distribution is shown in Figure 16.2, with the equilibrium average pigmentation score after a thousand years of random mating being just a shade darker than today's average white population.

In fact, however, random mating does not occur and is not immediately likely to occur across color barriers. Among the Negroes themselves, there is positive assortment that is partly related to considerations of social status (see Chapter 19 for a more general discussion of human mating systems). Despite recent publicity on individual racial intermarriages, the incidence of marriage between whites and Negores is still negligible. Thus, for the 33 states in the United States marriage registration area, the percentage of actual marriages between whites and nonwhites to that expected on the basis of random mating was 2.3 for 1960. Only four states report Negro-white marriages, and the latest figures available for this percentage are: California (1959), 2.9; Hawaii (1964), 45.8; Michigan (1963), 1.7; Nebraska (1964), 0.6. However, the percentage is rising in all four states: the increase has been slowest in California, but has approximately doubled in Hawaii and Michigan within ten years; the percentages available for Nebraska were 0, 0, 0.3 for the three years preceding 1964.

The pattern of future matings between Americans is, of course, not predictable. The effects of expanding social consciousness, and of educating the whites about the biological nature of races, about the absence of pure races, and about the lack of foundation for the belief that interracial crosses have harmful effects may lead toward randomness. But the rise of the Negro as a power group may have a restraining effect on the Negro attitude toward interracial mating. There exist other intangibles that are related to the Negro's fear of loss of identity among the lighter-skinned individuals, and to the offspring of interracial marriage. In any case, the biological issues (but, of course, not the social issues) are necessarily long-range because of the 25- to 30-year interval between generations. All of these considerations may become irrelevant if it is indeed eventually possible for genetical engineering to change the genetic instructions on skin color. What is urgent, however, is that the biological truths about races be introduced into the American mores so that they may influence our views and actions on racial equality and social justice.

That valid judgments about the biological significance of differences in tests of mental abilities are impossible has already been stressed in preceding sections. This is a point that cannot be overemphasized in view of the immediacy of the racial problems confronting the United States at this time. Various proposals have been advanced by probably well-intentioned people that suggest how meaningful investigation of genetic rather than phenotypic differences in intelligence and achievement might be carried out. Most of these individuals suffer from the obstinate inability to see the methodological difficulties and inherent biases of their schemes. Some anthropologists even opine that such studies are irrelevant or too vulnerable to misinterpretation and too fraught

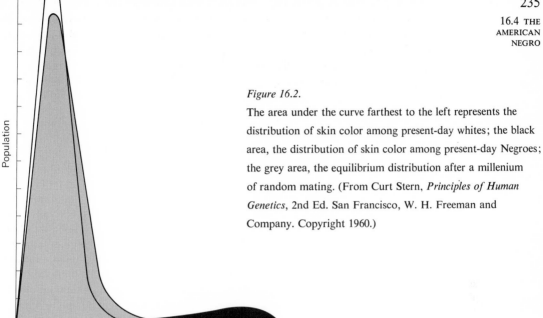

Figure 16.2.

The area under the curve farthest to the left represents the
distribution of skin color among present-day whites; the black
area, the distribution of skin color among present-day Negroes;
the grey area, the equilibrium distribution after a millenium
of random mating. (From Curt Stern, *Principles of Human
Genetics*, 2nd Ed. San Francisco, W. H. Freeman and
Company. Copyright 1960.)

with political danger to be undertaken. This may or may not be true, but it is a
fact that generations of discrimination have made direct comparisons of mental traits between Negroes and whites not biologically meaningful.

An example is provided by life expectancy figures. In the United States in
1900, for a white male the life expectancy at birth was 48 years; for a Negro
male it was 32 years. In 1940 and in 1958, the respective figures were 62 years
and 67 years for whites; and 52 years and 61 years for Negroes. To assume that
the differences in the environment that reduced life expectancy in the Negro
in 1900 by 50 percent had no effect on his intellectual performance in life or
on a psychological test, would seem to be an utter folly. Furthermore, the
dramatic changes in half a century must be attributed largely to environmental
causes, since not enough time has elapsed to permit operation of genetic causes
of the prolongation of the life-span.

This chapter opened with a quotation from the geneticist Dobzhansky, and
it may be appropriate to conclude it with one from the anthropologist S. L.
Washburn, who is also the source of the data given in the preceding paragraph.
In his presidential address to the American Anthropological Association, he
said, "I am sometimes surprised to hear it stated that if Negroes were given an
equal opportunity, their IQ would be the same as the whites'. If one looks at
the degree of social discrimination against Negroes and their lack of education,
and also takes into account the tremendous amount of overlapping between
the observed IQ's of both, one can make an equally good case that, given a

comparable chance to that of the whites, their IQ's would test out ahead. Of course, it would be absolutely unimportant in a democratic society if this were to be true, because the vast majority of individuals of both groups would be of comparable intelligence, whatever the mean of these intelligence tests would show."

Whether one agrees or disagrees with the first part of the statement, the last sentence summarizes the moral of the preceding discussion.

17

FORMAL GENETICS
OF MAN

17.1 HISTORICAL

Although genetics as a science is considered to have been born with the rediscovery of Mendel's laws in 1900, speculations about human inheritance trace
back to the very beginnings of our civilization. Plato's proposal for an eugenic
program and the apparent understanding of the mode of inheritance of hemophilia by the writers of the Talmud 1,500–1,600 years before the disease was
formally described as an inherited one have already been mentioned. In 1752,
the French astronomer Maupertuis, one of Mendel's great predecessors,
published a four-generation pedigree showing that a number of the members
of a certain family were born with extra digits (an autosomal dominant) and a
computation demonstrating that such a collection of developmental errors
among relatives was not likely to have been a chance event. Familial incidence
of color blindness was described in 1777. In 1814, Joseph Adams, a British
physician and apothecary, published a book in which he not only recognized
diseases with dominant and recessive bases of inheritance, but also acknowledged the existence of genotype-environment interaction. He also discussed
the increased incidence of defects in marriages between relatives, which today
is known to be due to the increased probability of the union of gametes carrying the same deleterious recessive allele.

Figure 17.1.

Sir Archibald Garrod.

(Courtesy of the Royal Society.)

Galton's pre-Mendelian contributions to the study of human inheritance have already been discussed (Box 10.B). In 1901, **Karl Landsteiner** (1868–1944) discovered the ABO blood groups, although it took another quarter century before the multiple-allelic basis of their inheritance was properly understood. Landsteiner, with collaborators, also discovered the MN blood-group locus in 1927, and the Rhesus factor (see Chapter 18) in 1940.

In 1901, the British physician **Archibald E. Garrod** (1858–1936; Figure 17.1), described eleven cases of alkaptonuria (Box 6.E), and noted that at least three of the patients were offspring of consanguineous matings. A year later, taking a clue from Bateson, he identified this **inborn error of metabolism** as being due to a single recessive gene. He extended the concept of hereditary enzymatic deficiency to other diseases in his book *"The Inborn Errors of Metabolism"* published in 1908. Garrod thus is the founder not only of modern human genetics, but also of biochemical genetics, which, however, did not attain its full development until after his death.

In the half-century following Garrod's initial discovery, many contributions to medical and formal human genetics were made that were largely based on pedigree analysis and population genetics. But only in the last decade did the great advances that we have been discussing come about. They are due to a number of technical breakthroughs in several disciplines and many of them were based on research seemingly not directly related to human welfare. Mission-oriented research, that is, research directed towards the solution of some specific applied problem (for example, prevention and cure of cancer), cannot be efficient or for the matter, successful, unless it feeds on basic research. The jibes that often appear in the press—usually supplied by economy-minded congressmen—about the worth of some of the basic research for which Federal support is sought, are based on misinformation and lack of understanding of the nature of scientific endeavor. To have ridiculed Mendel's studies on garden peas as being useless would have been all too easy, but without Mendelism there would be no medical genetics.

Among the recent breakthroughs of most significance to human genetics were those of molecular and biochemical genetics. The development of cyto-genetic techniques of handling human chromosomes is another: not until 1956 was the correct number of chromosomes in man established. Before then it was thought that man had 24 pairs of chromosomes ($2N = 48$). The designing of computer techniques and information retrieval machinery formed another frontier of advance in studies of demographic and population genetics. Immunogenetics and studies on graft and organ transplant tolerance are still other areas of current significance. And to repeat one mentioned earlier, the discovery of methods of maintaining human cells in culture is making a great impact on our understanding of biological processes.

17.2 EXEMPLARY

A recently published catalogue of human genes that are definitely known or reasonably postulated describes 1,837 dominant, 531 recessive, and 119 sex-linked phenotypes. If polygenically determined traits are added to these, the totality of characters in man investigated genetically becomes a formidable number. A comprehensive survey of human genetics is, of course, not within the province of this book, and only a sampling to illustrate specific points can be presented here. Molecular and biochemical examples of the operation and effects of human genes have already been given; inherited morphological, physiological, and behavioral traits have also been described. Chapter 18 contains more information about characters such as blood groups. The purpose of this section is merely to extend the variety of examples for a broader appreciation of the fact that genetic components are ubiquitous and cover the full range of human attributes.

First, with respect to metabolic variation, a list published in 1965 includes eleven different enzymes for which electrophoretic variants are known in man. Some of them are found in red blood cells, others in the serum, placenta, liver, and other tissues. Each of them is responsible for mediating some specific metabolic reaction, such as is exemplified by the several blocks in the meta-bolic pathway of phenylalanine (Box 6.E). Cognate variants of these eleven enzymes have been identified in many other species. For example, different esterases (enzymes that accelerate chemical reactions of the ester class of sub-stances) have been discovered in rabbits, mice, birds, newts, Drosophila, and corn.

At least 28 hereditary metabolic diseases associated with mental deficiency have now been described, and for nine of them, the specific enzyme that is deficient has been identified. In addition to those which have already been discussed, we may mention the maple syrup urine disease, which is controlled by an autosomal recessive gene and so named because the urine of affected individuals smells like maple syrup. Both physical and mental retardation accompany the disease. Apparently a block in the metabolism of some essen-tial amino acids causes excretion of the odiferous substance.

Less harmful are two other genes determining similar failures of breakdown of ingested substances. It has been postulated that a single dominant gene con-

240

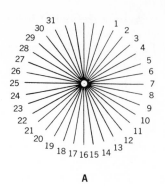

A

Figure 17.2.

Biochemical individuality as expressed by taste sensitivity to
31 different substances. The length of lines under **A** represents
average sensitivity of all persons tested. Deviations from the average
are indicated by the relative length of lines for four individuals,
of which **D** and **E** are identical twins. (From **R. J. Williams.**)

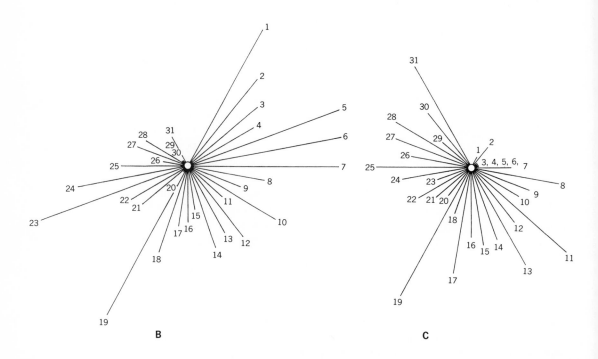

B

C

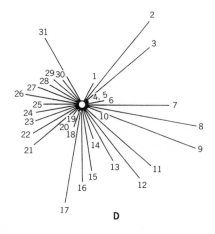

D

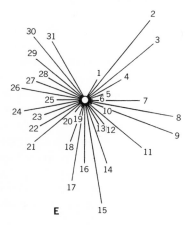

E

trols the excretion of methyl mercaptan after ingestion of asparagus. Its frequency in an English population is estimated at 0.23. The strong odor characteristic of the urine of carriers after they have eaten asparagus is detectable even if they eat as little as three or four stalks. Individuals who are homozygous for the recessive allele at this locus can eat as much as a pound of asparagus without displaying the trait. The other gene, which also appears to be harmless, controls the breakdown of the red pigment of beets. This seems to be a recessive with a frequency of 0.31 in an English sample tested and causes the urine of recessive homozygotes to be red after they eat moderate amounts of beets.

Differences in ability to taste, which are likely to have a hereditary basis, are found not only with respect to phenylthiocarbamide (PTC) referred to in Box 16.B, but also for a variety of other substances. In a Swedish experiment a number of subjects were asked to describe the taste of various chemical compounds. The following table shows a remarkable variation among people in the taste of the same substance, or at least in the way they describe it. The numbers indicate how many persons reported the taste sensations described by the column headings.

| | Predominant taste quality | | | | |
Compound	Salty	Sour	Bitter	Sweet	Other
Salt	249	2	11	18	29
Hydrochloric acid	7	243	10	8	24
Quinine	2	3	226	48	47
Strychnine	2	0	180	43	55
Sugar	0	3	21	251	19

Differences of this type make each of us biochemically unique, with different dietary preferences, different dietary needs, and different excretion of substances, even if we are not aware of them. Dogs, having a more sensitive perception of odors than humans, have been reported to be confused when trying to identify one or another of identical twins.

The American biochemist R. J. Williams has investigated taste sensitivity for a number of substances and found that each subject has a different "taste profile." As Figure 17.2 shows, however, identical twins were very much alike. Once more, these findings point to the absurdity of the typological approach with ideals or archetypes in categorizing human beings. If the average for some variable trait is taken as the norm, then every human being would be abnormal when only a few characters are considered together. Even if we allow the variability for each character to include 95 percent of the population (that is, only five percent would be considered abnormal), a combination of 15 traits would leave only 0.6 percent normal for all of them.

For the majority of inherited characters studied in man, the primary gene products affected are not known. It is often difficult even to imagine the kinds of differences in biochemical developmental pathways—starting with a mutational change in a polypeptide chain that produce phenotypic variation—in such characters as the ability to fold or roll one's tongue, the normal pattern of clasping one's own hand (right or left thumb uppermost), tone deafness, placement of voice with respect to normal speaking pitch, right- or left-handedness, and any number of other characteristics for which a hereditary basis has been postulated. As a matter of fact, none of the traits listed above has been

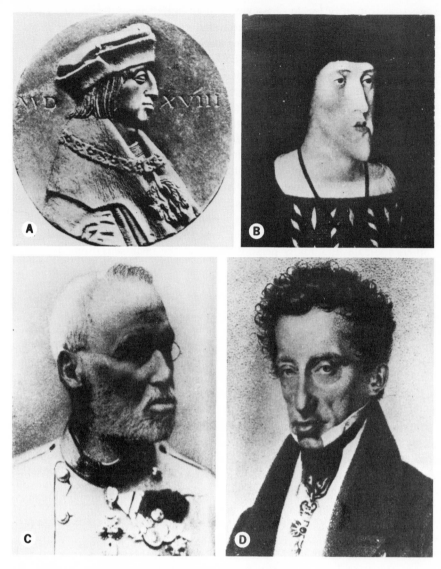

Figure 17.3.
The expression of the dominant prognathous jaw, the *Hapsburg lip*, over four
centuries. **A**: Emperor Maximilian I (1549–1519). **B**: Emperor Charles V (1500–1558),
grandson of **A**. **C**: Archduke Charles (1771–1847). **D**: Archduke Albrecht (1817–1895),
son of **C**. (From Strohmayer, *Nova Acta Leopoldina*, 5, 1937).

unequivocally proven to depend on simply expressed single gene differences.
Nevertheless, from all we know, they depend on differences in biochemical
pathways, and it is the task of developmental genetics to investigate them. In
organisms like Drosophila, the enzymatic basis of such developmental traits as
failure of head emergence is now being studied.

With respect to well-established human mutations that express themselves in
morphological or physiological changes, a great variety of abnormalities may

be mentioned in addition to those we have already considered. They include, among many others, short digits, absence of canine teeth or lateral incisors, cataracts, hypersensitivity to cold, progressive deafness, absence of finger-prints, malformation of nipples, a form of muscular distrophy, webbed fingers, white forelocks, and prognathous jaw (the Hapsburg lip, illustrated in Fig-ure 17.3), all inherited as dominants, although some also have recessive forms. Other recessive genes known to determine abnormalities include those for a type of anemia, hairlessness, congenital paralysis of cranial nerves, glau-coma, hydrocephaly, and hereditary goiter accompanied by deafness. Among sex-linked deleterious genes that have not been so far mentioned are those for congenital cataracts, absence of central incisors, progressive and congenital deafness, and scaly skin (for others, see Section 8.3).

17.3 FOUNDER EFFECTS

Founder effects (Section 4.3) may be expected to have occurred in primitive hunting populations, which probably consisted of less than 50 persons. But they can also be detected in larger populations. The royal families of Europe (and they did represent a deme) had, for a number of generations after Queen Victoria, a high frequency of the gene for hemophilia. Whether it is extinct by now depends on whether the current female descendants of Lady May Abel-Smith and the two Spanish princesses, Beatriz and Maria (Box 14.C), are carriers. However, with the passing of so many of the royal houses and the rapidly changing pattern of mating, with an increasing number of royalty-commoner marriages, this group is no longer even a partial isolate.

A similarly disappearing founder effect has been demonstrated with respect to the dominant gene causing night blindness. Over a period of 11 generations some 135 descendants (out of several hundred) of a Provencal butcher, who settled in a small village near Montpellier, were discovered to suffer from the defect. These findings were published in 1907, but when a follow-up study was attempted some forty years later, his descendants were found to have dispersed from the village, destroying the partial isolate of several centuries' duration. No doubt, the defective allele is scattered throughout various parts of France.

Another dominant gene that has been thoroughly investigated is that for *porphyria variegata*, the failure to metabolize porphyrin, a derivative of a res-piratory pigment connected with hemoglobin. This defect, diagnosed by the presence of porphyrin in the stool, causes formation of brown skin patches and sensitivity to barbiturates, produces abdominal pains, neurotic symptoms and can lead to paralysis and death. In South Africa, the ancestry of some 8,000 carriers of the gene can be traced to a couple married in 1688. In that year, eight girls from a Rotterdam orphanage were sent to South Africa to provide wives for Dutch farmers. One of them, Ariaantje Jacobs, married Gerrit Jansz, himself a recent emigrant from Holland, and four of their eight children figure in the pedigrees of the currently affected persons. Incidentally, a defective gene is not the only cause of porphyria. A disastrous outbreak of it among Turkish children, who suffered liver damage as a result, came from their eating seeds treated with a fungicide.

In the Atlantic Ocean midway between South Africa and South America, there lies a group of small islands called Tristan da Cunha. Although the British garrison stationed there in 1814 was withdrawn three years later, a community was established there when one of the British soldiers and his South African wife decided to stay. They were joined by others, including an English sailor and his Negro wife from St. Helena. One of the 15 persons in the founder group must have carried a recessive gene for *retinitis pigmentosa*, which in the homozygous state causes an optical disease starting with night blindness and culminating in total blindness at age 50 or 60. (The common form of night blindness caused by a gene at a different locus is not progressive.)

In 1961 a violent eruption took place on Tristan da Cunha and the whole population of 262 persons was evacuated to Great Britain. Two years later 240 of them returned to the islands. The evacuation to Britain was accompanied by a full battery of medical tests and physical examinations administered to the whole group. Four of them were found to be afflicted with retinitis pigmentosa. An interesting detail emerges if we start from the assumption that selection has not operated against this gene in the gene pool, so that each of the 15 founders contributed an equal number of alleles to the present gene pool. The number of defective alleles expected, using this assumption, among the 524 at the given locus is 17. One of the unaffected parents and every child of the affected individuals must be a carrier. There are nine such persons living. Adding nine alleles to the eight carried by the recessive homozygotes makes the total exactly 17.

Further examples of the spread of a gene from a single ancestor is provided by *Huntington's chorea*. This insidious disease produces a progressive degeneration of the nervous system and leads to a complete breakdown of physical and mental powers. It is inherited through a dominant gene, which may possibly have an overdominant effect on fitness, and has a variable age of onset. The average age is 40–45, which means that a person does not know if he is afflicted until after his reproductive period is largely over. Since there is no way of identifying carriers before the symptoms of involuntary jerking movements begin, children of diseased individuals are doomed to a life of anxiety in the knowledge that they have a 50 percent probability of being afflicted too.

In the Australian state of Tasmania, in a population of about 350,000, there are 120 cases of Huntington's chorea. Every one of them traces his ancestry to a Huguenot woman who left England in 1848 to settle in the Antipodes. In the United States there 7,000 known sufferers scattered from New England to Hawaii. Pedigree tracing is difficult in the United States but over one thousand cases derive from a woman who lived in Suffolk at the beginning of the seventeenth century and whose three sons (all by different fathers) immigrated to America. And it is likely that she had other descendants or affected relatives because the incidence of the disease in Suffolk today is twelve times that for England as a whole. Furthermore, another large New England kindred carrying the disease can be traced back to a shipyard and hotel owner from a town only ten miles away from the Suffolk woman's residence.

As a final example of founder effects in man, the religious community of the Old Order Amish in Lancaster County, Pennsylvania, may be given. A recessive type of dwarfism, with homozygotes having extra digits and other physical deformities, is a rare disease known to have affected some 100 persons in the whole world since 1860, when it was first described. Over 55 of these (24 are alive today) come from the Amish group. These can all be traced to a pair of ancestors who arrived in the U.S. in 1744. Of the 8,000 present-day Amish in this population, about 13 percent are heterozygous for this gene.

17.4 DIAGNOSIS AND COUNSELING

The significance of genetics in medicine and public health should by now be painfully clear. Yet it is only recently that medical schools have begun to recognize this fact and to incorporate genetics into their curricula and research programs. New diseases and syndromes are being added practically daily to the list of those known to be genetically determined. Yet the majority of the medical profession is as innocent of genetic knowledge as the uninformed laity, and very few hospitals that are not affiliated with universities have either a genetically trained physician or a consulting geneticist on their staffs.

A welcome development has been the establishment of genetic units for diagnostic purposes and of counseling centers for doctors, hospitals, adoption and welfare agencies, and individuals. A variety of newly acquired tools are being used for these purposes. One of these, a catalogue of human genes, presents a great advance for ease of reference to what is known about hereditary diseases. This should be followed by the development of computerized diagnosis in which symptoms could be given to a computer that would then retrieve from its memory bank the answer to whether the syndrome has a genetic basis, and, if it does, what the genetic basis is and what therapy may be possible. Obviously, in the general practice of medicine, other clinical, laboratory, and therapeutic information could also be computerized.

A new diagnostic tool in the form of dermatoglyphics, or study of fingerprint and palm and sole patterns, is being developed both for hereditary and other types of diseases. Diagnosis of various chromosomal abnormalities, which are also recognizable cytogenetically, is aided by the fact that they are accompanied by characteristic dermatoglyphic features. Over 40 types of chromosome aberrations have such perceivable attributes. Similarly, at least ten disorders arising on a single-gene basis, including PKU, Huntington's chorea, and the Amish type of dwarfism, are apparently associated with recognizable departures from normal dermatoglyphs, as are a dozen or more diseases of unknown genetic bases or due to toxic or traumatic factors.

The variety of services that counseling centers can render is large. In many instances, advisers do not need to have medical training to be of help. Perhaps the most common kind of advice sought is that by families which have produced abnormal children, asking about the probability that subsequent children would have the same abnormality. Recurrence risk figures are computed from knowledge of the genetic basis of a disease and its incidence in the population. Box 17.A gives such probabilities in a general form; for many disorders more specific values can be given. For example, although among the general white population of the United States the incidence of harelip is about 1 in 1,000, two normal parents who have one child so affected run a five percent risk that their next child will also have the defect. For a couple with two children born with harelip, the recurrence risk is ten percent.

BOX 17.A RECURRENCE RISKS

The figures are percentage probabilities that a succeeding child will be affected after one offspring has manifested the given trait. (Modified from A. G. Motulsky and F. Hecht.)

Magnitude of risk		Genetic basis
Total	100	Both parents are homozygous recessives. (No progeny test is needed.)
High	75	Both parents are heterozygous for an autosomal dominant with full penetrance.
	50	One parent is heterozygous for an autosomal dominant.
		For sons in case of a sex-linked gene carried by mother.
Moderate	25	Recessives with full penetrance. Incompletely penetrant autosomal dominants.
Low	5 or less	Congenital malformations with unknown causes.
		Trisomy 21.

Another type of counsel available is for barren couples who want to have a child, especially those with histories of unsuccessful pregnancies. Genetic reasons for such pregnancies can be diagnosed by blood typing if there are incompatibilities (see Chapter 18) or by cytological examination. A University of Michigan genetic counselor reports the case of a Roman Catholic mother, one of whose children had the phenotypic symptoms of trisomy 21. The woman wanted to encourage one of her other children to become a priest. She went to the counselor because she thought that if any of her sons were a carrier of the abnormality (in this instance, a translocation), he should be the one to enter this celibate profession and, thus, avoid passing on the defect to the next generation. Although disclaiming responsibility for the decision of which child would be urged to become a priest, the counselor was able to sort out the normal and the abnormal offspring by looking at their chromosomes.

A disease within the family affecting relatives other than sons or daughters may be the reason for other inquiries. Counseling for such inquiries includes premarital guidance, of particular importance when consanguineous marriages are contemplated. For reasons already noted, the incidence of recessive defects appearing among the offspring of genetically related couples is higher than in the general population. The frequency of first-cousin marriages in the general population is about one-half to one percent, but 33 percent of children suffering from alkaptonuria are progeny of such marriages. The comparable figure for albinism is 17 percent, and for total color blindness, 11 percent (see also Chapter 19).

Diagnosis of zygosity in twins is also part of genetic counseling. Finally, disputes about parentage can sometimes be settled by genetic investigations. Such medicolegal genetics forms part of the broader field of immunogenetics, which is the subject of the next chapter. Meanwhile, it is only to be hoped that the use of genetic counseling increases and becomes a commonplace social service. Freedom of action on the advice is a matter entirely apart, but people with genetic problems should seek advice, not only out of personal concern, but surely also as a social obligation.

18

IMMUNOGENETICS

18.1 HUMAN BLOOD GROUPS

In Section 16.2 some examples involving inherited differences in red blood cell antigens were given, and in Section 13.1 attention was drawn to the possible selective value of the ABO system. The many polymorphisms found in human blood types are of tremendous usefulness in human genetics and in anthropology. Although some of the systems contain complex multiple allelic relationships, basically the inheritance of blood type is straightforward. Since blood types are determined by fully penetrant codominant genes, they provide ready material of individuals and populations.

Box 18.A lists the essential information about currently known antigens under control of various loci. Since a new blood-group type was found as recently as 1965, it is by no means certain that all existing antigens have been discovered. The evolutionary antiquity of human blood types has been studied by testing human antigens and antibodies in apes and monkeys. Orangutans and gibbons were found to be polymorphic for the human ABO group, whereas all other simians tested have A or B or both. Chimpanzees are the most similar to man for this system, and gorillas the most different, resembling more the old-world monkeys. The one human antigen known to be sex-linked, X_g, appears to be sex-linked in the gibbons also. In addition to the antigens they share with man, apes also have specific simian blood-group systems.

In our discussion here we shall emphasize two of the systems, ABO in this section, and the Rhesus (Rh) in the next. The ABO system comprises six antigens; H, present in varying amounts in all humans (note, however, the rare "Bombay phenotype" in Box 18.A); four subvarieties of A, which we shall group together under A; and B. Antibodies to all are naturally occurring substances, that is they are not elicited by the presence of the antigen but are circulating in the serum of the appropriate genotypes. The following table, in which *A*, *B*, and *O* are used to designate the different alleles, summarizes the genetic basis of ABO inheritance.

Blood group	Genotype	Red blood cells have antigen	Serum has antibodies	Clumping will occur in introduced blood	Blood groups acceptable in transfusion
O	*OO*	none (universal donor)	anti-A and anti-B	A, B, AB	O
A	*AA, AO* (not distinguishable phenotypically)	A	anti-B	B, AB	A, O
B	*BB, BO* (not distinguishable phenotypically)	B	anti-A	A, AB	B, O
AB	*AB*	A, B	none	none	all (universal recipient)

Figure 18.1 shows diagrammatically the method of blood typing derived from the information in this table. In addition to problems raised in blood transfusion by the polymorphism at the ABO locus, there is a further medical aspect to this system. If a foetus whose mother is of *OO* genotype receives either the *A* or *B* alleles from the father, A or B antibodies from the mother's serum can diffuse through the placenta and cause severe damage to the foetus. The disease is a *hemolytic* (blood-destroying) one, called **erythroblastosis foetalis**, and may cause abortion. A Japanese study found that from such **incompatible** matings as between an A-type father and an O-type mother, there was a significant shortage of live A children and an excess of live O children. Presumably, the missing AO phenotypes represent unsuccessful pregnancies. Such losses have been estimated to account for 8–35 percent of the conceptions in incompatible matings. The incidence varies in different populations simply because of the differences in gene frequencies which make differences in the proportions of incompatible matings. Thus, for example, in the Sioux Indians of South Dakota, among whom the frequency of the O type is 91 percent, incompatibility presents very little of a problem, whereas in the Bangkok Siamese, 37 percent of whom are O, nearly a quarter of the marriages (0.37×0.63) would be theoretically incompatible. However, not all antibodies are

BOX 18.A BLOOD-GROUP SYSTEMS

There are about 80 known red blood cell antigens in man grouped into several systems. Each major system is controlled by alleles at a different locus. Some information about these major systems follows (from V. A. McKusick and R. C. Lewontin):

System	Year of discovery	Number of antigens known	Estimate of average heterozygosity in an English population[1]
ABO	1900	6	0.51
MNS	1927	18	0.70
P	1927	3	0.50
Rhesus[2]	1940	17	0.66
Lutheran	1945	2	0.08
Kell-Cellano	1946	5	0.12
Lewis	1946	2	0.30
Duffy	1950	2	0.52
Kidd	1951	2	0.50
Diego	1955	1	0
Auberger	1961	1	0.49
X_g[3]	1962	1	0.46
Dombruck	1965	1	0.46

[1] Based on the assumption of random mating.
[2] See Section 18.2.
[3] Sex-linked.

With the exception noted, all antigens are inherited as codominants. In addition to antigens of the major systems, there are also antigens that have either been found only in single families (private systems) or are common to most humans (public systems):

Private systems		Public systems
Levay	Romunde	I
Jobbins	Chr	Vel
Becker	Swann	Yt
Ven	Good	Gerbich
Cavaliere	Bi	Lan
Berrens	Tr	Sm
Wright	Webb	
Batty		

The genetic relationships of these systems to the major systems are not known. Other genes may also be considered as belonging to the category of blood-group determinants. One, for instance, is the rare recessive "Bombay phenotype" for the absence of the H antigen (of the ABO system), which ordinarily is present in all people.

White blood cells also have antigenic properties, but their genetics is only now beginning to be worked out. In the broadest sense of the word the polymorphic serum protein types (haptoglobins, transferrins, and gamma-globulins, see Box 3.D and Section 18.3) may also be described as blood-group systems.

diffusable, and their concentration in the foetus may reach only a low level with mild effects. A disease more serious for the afflicted individual, although less serious for the population, is erythroblastosis induced by Rh incompatibility, which is considered in the next section.

The MN system has a somewhat complex form of inheritance. Contrary to the mechanism for ABO, the antibodies are not naturally found in human serum, but can be induced to form in rabbits or other animals, as shown in Figure 18.2. This group does not appear to present medical problems but still presents some genetic mysteries: some human populations show an excess of heterozygotes at this locus compared with expectations based on gene frequency. Associated with the MN blood groups is antigen S, which causes the ABO antigens to become water soluble and, thus, detectable in the saliva. The MN system is sometimes designated as MNS.

Besides anthropological and medical significance, blood groups have also legal significance, particularly in cases of disputed parentage. Using as many systems as possible makes it feasible to rule on some claims of paternity and to identify the parentage of a child if there has been a mix-up of babies in a hospital.

Group	Antigens in red blood cells	Antibody present in serum	Reaction to serum (listed to left) of red blood cells from group			
			O	A	B	AB
O	O	Anti-A Anti-B				
A	A	Anti-B				
B	B	Anti-A				
AB	AB	—				

Figure 18.1.
The clumping reaction of red blood cells exposed to antibodies. (From Curt Stern, *Principles of Human Genetics*, 2nd Ed. San Francisco, W. H. Freeman and Company. Copyright 1960.)

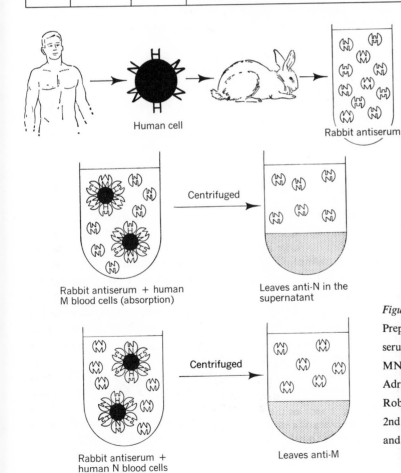

Human cell

Rabbit antiserum

Rabbit antiserum + human M blood cells (absorption)

Centrifuged

Leaves anti-N in the supernatant

Rabbit antiserum + human N blood cells

Centrifuged

Leaves anti-M

Figure 18.2.
Preparation of anti-N and anti-M serum by injecting blood from an MN individual into a rabbit. (From Adrian M. Srb, Ray D. Owen, and Robert S. Edgar, *General Genetics*, 2nd Ed. San Francisco, W. H. Freeman and Company. Copyright 1965.)

Clearly, in arguments over paternity, the real father cannot be positively identified. But if a putative father happens to possess a genotype not congruous with that of the child (for example, an AB man cannot be the father of an O child), the claim of paternity can be dismissed. The more systems that are used in the test, the greater is the possibility of exclusion. Thus, R. R. Race and R. Sanger present a table under the title "The chances of an Englishman being exonerated by the blood groups of a false charge of paternity brought by an Englishwoman," showing the cumulative effect of adding tests for the different systems as follows:

ABO alone	0.176
adding	
MNS	0.373
Rh	0.531
Kell-Cellano	0.549
Lutheran	0.564
Duffy	0.584
Kidd	0.596

For the U.S. white population the total probability of exclusion has been computed at 0.716. In many of the states, laws have been passed that permit the courts to order blood tests in cases for which they would be relevant or that make the results of voluntary tests admissable evidence. It may be noted in passing that where artificial insemination is used in cattle reproduction, blood typing is commonly done to verify paternity. There is one very useful blood-group system in cattle that has more than 250 identifiable antigenic combinations.

Blood-group typing has also been used to determine what percentage of children born to married women were conceived in extramarital intercourse. In one study in a Detroit hospital, in testing for eight systems, it was found that 1.4 percent of white children and 8.9 percent of Negro children were not sired by the legal husbands.

18.2 THE RHESUS SYSTEM

The significant antigen in the **Rhesus (Rh)** system was first discovered by using Rhesus monkeys. Blood from the monkeys was injected into rabbits and guinea pigs, the antibodies of which then agglutinated some kinds of human blood cells. There still is some question whether a multiple allelic series of a group of three tightly linked loci is involved in the inheritance of this system. For practical purposes, we shall be concerned only with three genotypes: Rhesus-positive homozygote (DD), Rhesus-negative homozygote (dd), and the heterozygote (Dd). There are considerable differences in the frequency of the D gene in different populations. In white Europeans, q_d is approximately 0.4, although in some subgroups, for example, the Basques, it may tend to be closer to 0.5. African populations have lower frequencies, centering on 0.25. Asian, American Indian, and native Australian populations are nearly 100 percent Rhesus positive.

As with ABO incompatibility, a marriage between a Rhesus-positive man and a Rhesus-negative woman is an incompatible one. The first heterozygous

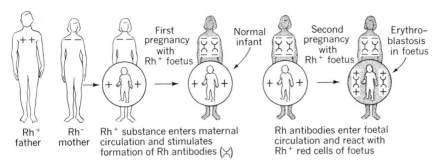

Rh⁺   Rh⁻   Rh⁺ substance enters maternal   Rh antibodies enter foetal
father   mother   circulation and stimulates   circulation and react with
                          formation of Rh antibodies (⋈)   Rh⁺ red cells of foetus

Figure 18.3.
The sequence of events in Rh incompatibility. (From Adrian M. Srb, Ray D. Owen,
and R. S. Edgar, *General Genetics*, 2nd Ed. San Francisco, W. H. Freeman
and Company. Copyright 1965.)

child does not suffer any ill effects. But his mother starts producing antibodies
against the D antigen during the pregnancy. Her subsequent heterozygous
children are exposed to the antigens, which diffuse through the placenta, and
they become liable to develop a form of erythroblastosis or *hemolytic jaundice*
that is lethal if treatment is not given. Figure 18.3 diagrams events in the origin
of erythroblastosis. The incidence of risk in a European white population can
be computed from the following table, which gives the frequencies of the different genotype combinations expected assuming random mating.

			Frequency of the paternal genotypes		
			DD	Dd	dd
			0.36	0.48	0.16
Frequency of the maternal genotypes	DD	0.36	12.96	17.28	5.76
	Dd	0.48	17.28	23.04	7.68
	dd	0.16	5.76	7.68	2.56

The combinations enclosed in boxes are the incompatible ones. Not all of
the roughly 14 percent of the matings that are incompatible will produce a
diseased child. If the mating is between a *dd* ♀ and a *Dd* ♂, the following
possibilities are open:

    first child, *dd*,   no effect;
    first child, *Dd*,   no effect;
    subsequent children, *dd*,   no effect;
    subsequent children, *Dd*,   jaundice.

Sometimes, if the building up of the antibody concentration in the mother
is slow because her placentas are less permeable than average, she may bear
more than one heterozygous child before the disease appears in subsequent
sibs.

The Rh situation provides an example of nongenetic *telegony*, a phenotypic
effect of a previous mating on the characteristics of offspring of subsequent
matings. The existence of such an effect was widely believed in pre-Mendelian
days but then was generally discredited, except for venereal infection, until the
discovery of Rh disease.

From the population standpoint, Rh inheritance provides an example of natural selection against heterozygotes. This is not an equilibrium situation, since every time a heterozygous individual dies, the rarer allele suffers proportionately greater loss than the more common allele. This would mean that the *d* allele should be gradually disappearing in European populations. Whether this is happening, and, for that matter, what the evolutionary history of the genes at the Rh locus was, is a completely speculative matter. Theoretically, however, Rh disease may provide an exception to the notion that interracial crosses can have no detrimental effects. Should a massive migration of Europeans to China take place, and should it be followed by interbreeding, the effect on the new Chinese gene pool would be dysgenic: previously unknown erythroblastosis would start manifesting itself. Should the reverse migration take place, the effect on the European population would be beneficial, for the frequency of the *D* allele would increase in its gene pool.

Another point of interest is the fact that Rh-negative mothers may be sensitized not only by the antigens of their heterozygous foetuses, but also by transfusion of mismatched blood. There is also an incompletely understood relationship between ABO and Rh incompatibilities. The former is known to exercise a sparing action on the latter: hemolytic jaundice rarely develops in children who—from their genotypes for Rh—might be expected to have it if they are also incompatible for ABO. It is not impossible that this situation arises because the ABO incompatibility somehow causes the destruction of the Rh-positive cells of the foetus circulating in the mother's bloodstream, before a high level of Rh antibodies is built up in the mother. On the population level, there also seems to be a coadaptive mechanism operating to adjust gene frequencies at loci for diseases caused by ABO, Rhesus, G6PD, and thalassemia genes.

There are presently three treatments for prevention of Rh-hemolytic disease. The oldest in use is an exchange transfusion at birth, by which the blood of the newborn infant is replaced with blood lacking the antibodies. Some 7,000 such transfusions are performed annually in the U.S. Second, techniques for intrauterine transfusion before birth have also been developed. More recently, the method of injecting specific anti-Rh gamma-globulins into the mother after the birth of a heterozygous child has been developed. These destroy the Rh-positive cells of the body circulating in the mother and prevent the build-up of antibodies that otherwise would affect subsequent children.

18.3 GRAFT TOLERANCE AND TRANSPLANTATION

Antibodies are produced in the ribosomes of specialized white blood cells, the *plasma cells*. Their proteins—the gamma-globulins or immunoglobins—have a molecule, which contains two light chains (about 200 amino acids each) and two heavy chains (450–700 amino acids) joined by sulphur bonds as shown in Figure 18.4. The specificity of each antibody with respect to the antigen it combines with resides in the amino acid sequences of both kinds of chains. One end of the chains is invariable. The region (the NH_2 end) where specificity is determined has a variable sequence of amino acids. At first, there was a

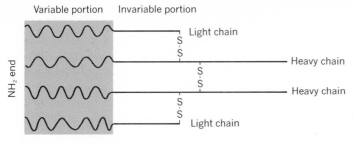

Variable portion   Invariable portion

NH₂ end

Light chain
Heavy chain
Heavy chain
Light chain

Figure 18.4.
The four linked chains of the gamma-globulin protein. The variable sequences of amino acids endow the molecule with specificity to react against a certain antigen.

problem as to the number of genes involved in gamma-globulin production, because there are thousands and thousands of kinds of potential antibodies to correspond to the number of antigens. But the discovery that both kinds of chains contribute to specificity alleviated the need to postulate a huge number of genes. In each case one gene can code for the light chain and another for the heavy chain. The number of antibodies coded for, then, is the product of the number of different light chains multiplied by the number of different heavy chains. Thus 100 pairs of genes can code for 10,000 different antibodies, and 1,000 pairs for a million. Several different hypotheses about the precise origin of differences in the variable parts of the chains have been suggested, but they need not concern us here.

The full story of what happens when a plasma cell is exposed to an antigen is still under investigation. Two varieties of theories are being discussed. They are represented in simple diagrammatic form in Figure 18.5.

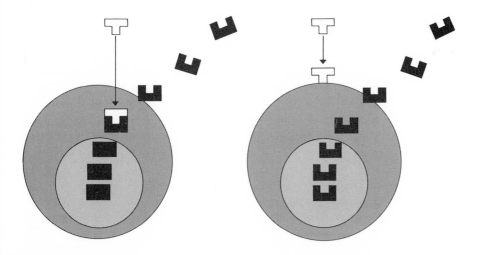

Figure 18.5.
Two theories of immunity. On the left is represented the instructional hypothesis under which an antigen enters a plasma cell and serves as a pattern for manufacture of complementary antibodies. On the right, the clonal selection theory, according to which the contact of a given antigen with a plasma cell signals for the manufacture of appropriate mRNA instructing the ribosomes to produce the specific kind of antibody. (From G. J. V. Nossal, "How Cells Make Antibodies." Copyright © 1964 by Scientific American, Inc. All rights reserved.)

Investigation of globulin synthesis and function is of uppermost significance to the problems of grafting and the transplantation of tissues and organs. Whether single cells, suspension of cells, or whole organs are transplanted, an immune response against the foreign antigens usually occurs. Some tissues, however, are transplantable. For instance, corneal grafts are accepted by hosts with genotypes different from the donors. The use of immunosuppressive drugs and X-rays before grafting may allow a transplant to be accepted temporarily. In cases of temporary kidney failure, for which a flushing-out of accumulated toxic products is essential, human lives have been saved by transplants of chimpanzee or baboon kidneys. Such transplants may function long enough to do the necessary job. Resort in such cases may also be made to artificial organs, but they are very costly, expensive to maintain, and in short supply.

A very significant area in this field of research deals with the development of immunological tolerance to foreign proteins. Nobel prizes for such investigations have been awarded to the British biologist **Sir Peter Medawar** and the Australian **Sir Macfarlane Burnet**, and we seem to be on the threshold of further important discoveries. It appears that an organism learns to recognize its own antigens by early exposure to them (see also references to auto-immune diseases in Section 3.5 and to cattle twins in Section 11.1). It is possible to induce acceptance of a graft from a donor whose proteins the host was exposed to as an embryo. Recently, it has also been found that tolerance in young mice and rats can be induced by exposure to small parts of a protein molecule. Thus, short polypeptides of about 300 amino acids from a given bacterium injected into a mouse will make it tolerant to the whole bacterium. The potential medical significance of these developments is obvious.

Mating systems, the final major topic in our overview of formal human genetics, are discussed in the next chapter.

19

MATING SYSTEMS IN MAN

19.1 KINSHIP AND MATING SYSTEMS

Among different societies there are many varieties of mating systems, which may include mating taboos based on kinship, birthplace or socioeconomic status. They may also be *prescriptive*, specifically designating who must marry whom. A man may be required to marry his father's mother's brother's son's daughter, or a woman from a particular village or tribe. Anthropologists, as a rule, have been interested in the cultural aspects and consequences of particular marriage systems. To geneticists, the primary interest lies in their biological and evolutionary consequences. Many of the systems are clearly based on property or other economic considerations that have trivial or un-determined genetic consequences.

For instance, the Hindu custom of *niyoga*, in which a sonless man may have a person appointed to beget a child by his wife, has definite economic effects in terms of succession to property. From the standpoint of population genetics,

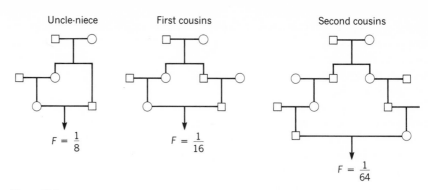

Figure 19.1.
Examples of consanguineous matings with coefficients of inbreeding of offspring.
(This measure of inbreeding is discussed in Section 19.3.)

unless selective considerations enter the picture, this custom is no different from the artificial insemination by a donor's sperm resorted to by childless couples in our own society. Similarly the systems of *levirate* among ancient Hebrews, in which a childless widow must be married to her late husband's brother, or of *sororate*, in which a man marries his wife's sisters, do not seem to have clear-cut, fully worked-out genetic effects. Also of no biological significance was the prohibition of marriage between a man and his deceased wife's sister in Britain, where it was repealed only in our century after an exceedingly prolonged parliamentary wrangle.

On the other hand, the Attic law specifying that the nearest male relative of an heiress of an intestate father was entitled to divorce his wife in order to marry the heiress, had both economic and biological effects, since the law permitted uncle-niece and even half-sib matings under these circumstances.

In general, prescriptive and prohibitive marriage systems will have genetic consequences when they affect population size or the degree of inbreeding. Perhaps the one marriage taboo that is an ethnological universal is the ban on unions between mother and son. Avoidance of mother-son sexual relations has also been observed in some species of monkeys. Most human cultures have other incest restrictions, but they vary greatly from group to group.

In Minnesota individuals more closely related than second cousins are not allowed to marry. (The bottom part of Figure 19.1 diagrams a pedigree for a second-cousin marriage.) In Wyoming first cousins are permitted to marry only if the woman is older than 50. In the Roman Catholic Church, special dispensation from the Vatican is required for a marriage between cousins. This makes Italy and other predominantly Catholic countries a fertile source of studies of consanguineous marriages, because of the availability of accurately documented evidence that spans several centuries.

The proportions of marriages that are consanguineous differ a good deal from one society to another. Among the Parsees of India some 13 percent of all marriages are between cousins; the corresponding statistic for Germany at the beginning of the century is less than half of one percent. In the province of

Andra Pradesh, on the east coast of India, as many as 25 percent of all marriages are between uncle and niece. The percentage varies with caste from high among shepherds and fishermen, to low among Brahmans as well as among Moslems. In Japanese feudal families as many as 20 percent of the marriages were consanguineous.

In some societies, special circumstances dictate departures from incest bans. Among the Thai tribe of Black-bellied Yaos, unlike-sexed twins are separated at birth and reared apart, but eventually must marry each other. In some African tribes royal marriages included a very high proportion of consanguineous mating (Box 19.A).

The XVIII dynasty of Egypt (1580–1350 B.C.) as well as the Ptolemaic dynasty (1323–30 B. C.), which ended with Cleopatra, is said to have required that reproduction be through sib mating. In fact, however, the pedigrees are not at all clear. The interpretation made by Egyptologists of the degree of relationship of successive royal marriages seems to have been rather arbitrary. Furthermore, outbreeding has been found to occur in different generations. Every time this happened, the cumulative increase in homozygosity expected under continued inbreeding would be interrupted and heterozygosity restored, at least in the immediate offspring. Whether the similar sib-mating rule of the later Inca Emperors of Peru was honored mostly in the breach is not known. The Kings of Hawaii had the best of both worlds through a requirement that they each contract two marriages, one with a sister and one with an unrelated woman. Many royal families of Europe also practiced inbreeding.

BOX 19.A CONSANGUINEOUS MARRIAGES IN BECHUANALAND

The British anthropologist I. Schapera made an exhaustive study of the mating system in Bechuanaland. He found that first-cousin and uncle-niece marriages were quite usual among commoners, and, that the proportion of such marriages was exceedingly high in the families of tribal chiefs. With the spread of Christianity and other western influences, the rate of consanguineous marriage is declining.

Examination of the genealogies of 485 persons who were chiefs, and sons and agnate (tracing through the male) grandsons of chiefs from 1841 to 1940, who between them contracted 777 marriages with one to eight wives each, revealed that over 70 percent married close relatives. The most common form of consanguineous mating was to the father's brother's daughters. Marriages between first cousins, uncles and nieces, nephews and aunts, and three between agnate half-sibs are also on record.

Schapera's interpretation of this unusually high proportion of consanguineous marriages is that such marriages serve in this society to reinforce social ties between different and potentially hostile branches of the royal line. He quotes a native proverb that says, "Child of my father's younger brother, marry me, so that the cattle may return to our kraal."

Other societies have different reasons for consanguineous marriages. A study of such reasons in Japan by the American geneticist W. J. Schull indicates that 40 percent of such marriages are explained by saying that the couple was acquainted when they were very young. The next most common explanation cites economic reasons.

Carlos II (1661–1700), the last Hapsburg king of Spain, was the issue of an uncle-niece marriage. His grandmother, who appears on both the paternal and maternal sides of the pedigree, was also a product of an uncle-niece union.

In general, the origin of incest taboos is clouded in mystery. A number of different theories have been proposed, some of them rather unlikely. The religious view takes it that there is a divine law against incest. This, at best, is a description and not an explanation. Freud and his followers attributed incest taboos to totemistic considerations for which the Oedipus myth provided the basis: murder and incest were the two fundamental crimes in the primitive society, corresponding to the two components in the Oedipus complex. After observing various primitive cultures, many anthropologists have questioned the general validity of this notion.

It has also been suggested that the taboos came into being after observation of biological ill effects. This seems highly unlikely since a much greater level of sophistication than is found in many primitive societies that have such taboos is required to detect the biological consequences of inbreeding. Some Australian tribes that have inbreeding apparently do not even understand the cause and effect relation of copulation and procreation, although there are semantic problems that might obscure the precise meaning of the explanations given by the aborigines to anthropologists on this subject.

Natural selection between populations, some of which have adopted restrictions fortuitously, has also been suggested as a source of taboos. That is to say, small primitive populations in which *endogamy* (inbreeding or marriage within a tribe) was practiced were at a disadvantage in competing with *exogamous* (marrying outside the tribe) populations, because of the burden of recessive homozygous defectives they had to carry. Whether this hypothesis is true for a given group of populations depends to a great degree on the size of the various isolates or partial isolates concerned, and on other factors not fully known.

Economic natural selection has been suggested, too, as a cause of mating restrictions. Exogamous tribes have marriage connections with others, which may naturally lead to alliances, to agreements about hunting territories and war, and to increased social resources, in general. Whether the initial regulations were fortuitously arrived at or deliberately established remains a question to those who support this hypothesis. There are also numerous other theories. According to a socialization theory, a child's erotic impulses must be directed outside of his family if he is to be motivated to accept his role in society. A demographic theory postulates that the number of persons surviving to breeding age in primitive families was so small that outbreeding had to be resorted to. More complex hypotheses that include economic and demographic considerations peculiar to the development of family organization in early hunting societies have also been proposed. Finally, it may be noted that mating systems are not permanent in all populations. The fact that they have evolved culturally and hence are modifiable is obvious. But changes of mating systems can also happen in a species for purely biological reasons. For instance, the South American ancestor of the domestic tomato was always cross-fertilized or outbred. When it was domesticated in the absence of the insect normally responsible for pollination, the tomato adapted itself to reproduce under the highest degree of inbreeding possible, self-fertilization.

The genetic effects of the departure from random mating in the direction of positive assortment have already been noted in discussing the possible future of the American Negro (Section 16.4). Box 19.B gives some figures on the extent of this phenomenon in Swedish, British, and American populations. The general effect of high positive assortment for monogenically determined traits is to increase the proportions of homozygotes at the expense of heterozygotes, with an eventual subdivision of the population into isolates theoretically possible. But unless assortment is complete, such subdivision is not only an exceedingly slow process, but also one that never reaches the state of complete isolation between groups. For polygenically determined traits, assortative mating acts somewhat like selection, extending the range of character expression. It has been argued, for instance, that the establishment of the Oak Ridge scientific community should lead to increased assortment for a high I.Q. If in a general population only one person out of 300 has an I.Q. of 140, then an intermarrying group with an average I.Q. of 140 should produce offspring among which one out of 300 would have an I.Q. of 180, and one out of 2,000 an I.Q. of 190.

BOX 19.B ASSORTATIVE MATING IN MAN

The degree of assortment can be measured in metric characters by the correlation between mates, and in all-or-none traits by comparing the proportion of marriages observed in which the partners share the given trait with that expected on the basis of chance. The following comparison, from a Swedish population, shows a significant degree of assortment.

| | | Husbands | |
		Dark eyes	Blue eyes
Wives	Dark eyes	observed	92	117
		expected	73	136
	Blue eyes	observed	77	197
		expected	96	178

A similar study among Swedish Lapps showed no assortment with respect to eye color, but for hair color it did.

Studies in Britain and the U.S. by various investigators indicate a high degree of assortment for many environmentally or partially genetically determined traits. Among the statistically significant correlations between mates were the following.

Trait	Correlation
age	0.76
memory	0.57
intelligence	0.47
neurotic tendency	0.30
stature	0.28
eye color	0.26
weight	0.21

No correlation was found in skull proportions, fingerprint ridge counts, or head length, indicating the unlikelihood of prospective mates going around measuring each other's heads. However, certain facial features and conformation characters showed significant correlation.

Trait	Correlation
ear-lobe length	0.40
ear length	0.40
waist circumference	0.38
hip circumference	0.22
neck circumference	0.20

The effect of computer dating on the future of assortative mating has not yet been ascertained.

The causes of assortative preferences in mating of humans generally are not known, although in special cases (for example, assortative mating among the deaf) they may be guessed at. If the statement that there is positive assortment in man is paraphrased to say that men tend to marry women resembling their mothers, and women tend to marry men who are like their fathers, Freudian overtones are introduced into the search for an explanation of the phenomenon. In animals, the tendency towards assortative mating is in part explained by the occurrence of **imprinting**. This is a phenomenon that imposes a certain behavior pattern on individuals by very early exposure to a given stimulus. Thus, newly hatched ducks or geese tend to follow the moving object that stimulated them visually during hatching, whether it be a bird or a human being. In Saint Thomas More's *Utopia*, he refers to artificially incubated baby chicks following those who feed them just as the naturally incubated ones follow the hen. Auditory forms of imprinting have also been found: chicks exposed before hatching to a given pattern of noise recognize it after hatching and respond to it but not to others.

Imprinting has been observed in insects, in fishes, in birds, and in such mammals as are capable of locomotion almost immediately after birth: sheep, goats, deer, and buffalo. In cattle, identical twins become each other's objects of imprinting; even if they are separated when very young, they will recognize one another when they are brought together again and will renew their association.

Imprinting develops mating preferences in the subject for the kind of individual resembling the object; yet in some observations on birds, sibs from the same hatch are negatively imprinted: they will not mate together despite early exposure to each other. The sexual preferences are exercised when the individual is offered a choice of mates. It has been suggested that failure of some species of animals to reproduce in zoos is connected with their imprinting on keepers or various objects around them. Several instances of positive assortment in certain birds, for example, the pigeon, the Arctic skua, and the blue-lesser snow goose, have been described. In the blue-lesser snow goose there is polymorphism for color, blue (dominant) and white (recessive), and it appears that males tend to select mates with the plumage color like their own and that of their mothers. Theoretically, such assortment can have evolutionary consequences leading to the formation of noninterbreeding populations. Although processes much like imprinting have been observed in infant monkeys, it is not known what role imprinting plays in human biology.

19.3 INBREEDING

The main feature of inbreeding is its power to fix alleles. Under persistent consanguineous mating, heterozygosity declines within a population; if several groups each undergo consanguineous mating, the differences between isolates increase. Plant and animal breeders produce inbred lines through self-fertilization of plants, and full- or half-sib matings of animals, and use them for crossing to obtain hybrid vigor.

The rate of inbreeding or the degree to which an individual is inbred is measurable by the **coefficient of inbreeding** F, devised by Sewall Wright. Its

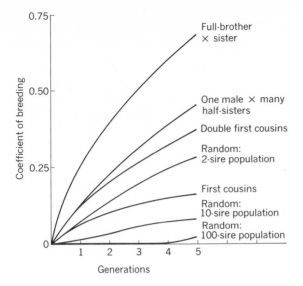

Figure 19.2.

Increase in homozygosity

under inbreeding.

exact formula need not concern us here, but essentially, F may be considered to express the probability that the two alleles at a locus are derived from a common ancestral allele. Alternatively, F may be viewed as measuring the proportionate decline of the average number of heterozygous loci in the population. The value of F may range from zero in a large random breeding population to unity when complete homozygosity at all loci is attained.

The increase in F under different systems of inbreeding possible in animal populations is shown in Figure 19.2, which is derived from Wright. A single generation of inbreeding between parent and offspring or between full sibs produces an F of $\frac{1}{4}$; between uncle and niece, $\frac{1}{2}$; first cousins, $\frac{1}{16}$; second cousins, $\frac{1}{64}$; and third cousins, $\frac{1}{256}$. Risks of expression of deleterious recessives in matings between relatives can be computed from F values. These risks increase with rising inbreeding coefficients, and account for the observed **inbreeding degeneration** in many traits of experimental plants and animals, and especially in those connected with fitness. Figure 19.3 shows how inbreeding, equivalent to one generation of full-sib mating, decreased the effective reproductive capacity, that is, the number of offspring surviving to breeding age, in chickens. The causes of inbreeding degeneration lie partially in the increased possibility of uncovering deleterious recessive alleles and partially in rendering certain genes homozygous, which are advantageous in the heterozygous state.

Consider the example of a first-cousin mating in man, such as represented in Figure 19.1. Let us make the assumption, which is probably an underestimate, that every human being carries on the average eight detrimental recessive alleles in a heterozygous state. Suppose the great-grandfather in the pedigree was a carrier of such alleles, which we may number from 1 through 8, and his wife a carrier of such alleles, numbered from 9 through 16. The probability that two great-grandchildren who are first cousins would both be carriers of any of these 16 alleles is $F = \frac{1}{16}$. This means that the probability of their not having it in common is $\frac{15}{16}$. For 16 loci this becomes $(\frac{15}{16})^{16}$, or 0.356, meaning that the chance of any one of the 16 being present in both cousins is $1 - 0.356$

264

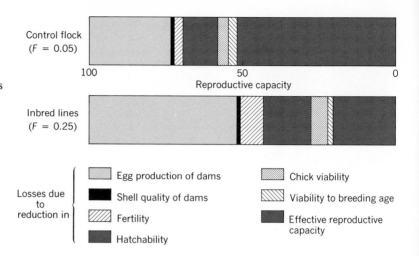

Figure 19.3.

Reduction in various components of fitness in inbred lines of chickens. The first six blocks represent the proportionate reduction from the possible maximum; the last block, the average proportion per dam of potential offspring alive at 9 months of age. (From an analysis by O. Düzgüneş.)

BOX 19.C INBREEDING EFFECTS IN MAN

Genetic literature abounds in statistics of the effects of consanguineous marriage on the offspring. No doubt the risks that deleterious recessive genes will be expressed are increased in matings between relatives. From the standpoint of the population as a whole, inbreeding provides an opportunity for natural selection to remove detrimental alleles. At the same time, their manifestation is a social and personal burden. A sampling of reports from a variety of sources follows. The figures must not be considered as reflecting genetic effects only. There are differences in rates of marriages between relatives in different countries and socioeconomic classes. Note the great variability between the various reports.

Hiroshima Study (from J. V. Neel)

Trait		Noninbred control	Offspring of first-cousin mating	Percent change
One or more major defects, percent	♂	7.4	9.0	21.6
	♀	9.0	10.3	14.5
Height at 10 years, in cm	♂	130	129	0.4
	♀	130	129	0.4
Verbal ability test score	♂	59	55	4.7
	♀	57	53	4.8
Average grade in mathematics	♂	3.2	3.0	4.0
	♀	3.2	3.0	4.1

Japan (from W. J. Schull)

Abnormality	Frequency per 10,000 births		
	First-cousin mating	Second-cousin mating	Unrelated
Club foot	10.5	8.6	9.2
Harelip	17.6	17.2	18.8
All anomalies	84.3	77.5	46.7

$= 0.644$. The risk of expression is, of course, $\frac{1}{4}$, so that the prospects for a defect to be manifested is about 16 percent. Box 19.C gives examples of observations on consanguineous matings.

We have already discussed a number of examples of the degree to which consanguineous mating is practiced in different human populations, and some further examples follow. Even within a single mating system, however, there may be considerable variation in the proportion of consanguineous mating because of social, economic, and other factors. Thus, within the diocese of Parma in Italy, the proportion of marriages between 1640 and 1965 that required papal dispensation because of consanguinity, varied geographically: in cities it was 0.68 percent, in the countryside plains 0.63 percent, in foothill villages 1.64 percent, and in high mountain villages 7.13 percent. Part of the reason for this variation lies in the differences in population sizes, and hence, in the numbers of eligible mates. Inbreeding in endogamous groups derived

Minnesota Study on Mental Retardation (from E. W. and S. C. Reed)

	Degree of inbreeding (F)			
	$\frac{1}{4}$	$\frac{1}{8}$	$\frac{1}{16}$ or less	Total
Percent mentally retarded surviving children	60.0	33.3	8.6	10.2

J. V. Neel Compilation

	Death to various pre-reproductive ages	
	Offspring of first-cousin marriages	Offspring of un-related controls
Negroes		
Brazil	46.0	31.2
Tanganyika	32.1	34.3
Asians		
Japan	13.0	9.1
Europeans		
U.S.A.	16.8	11.6
France	12.2	5.4
Sweden	25.6	31.4
Brazil	31.1	31.1
Germany	32.2	29.5

Italy (from F. Conterio)

	Inbreeding coefficient				
	$\frac{1}{8}$	$\frac{1}{16}$	$\frac{1}{32}$	$\frac{1}{64}$	0
Number of families	6	127	80	279	420
Percent childless	16.7	12.6	8.8	10.0	10.5
Percent abortions	8.3	13.9	13.6	8.9	10.0
Percent stillbirths	8.3	15.8	17.2	11.0	11.6
Percent postnatal mortality	8.3	10.3	7.1	8.7	8.7

from small founder populations may arise merely from the fact that the whole population tends to become highly interrelated.

Several examples of inbred populations in the United States are provided by religious communities established by immigrants from Europe. The founder effects in the Old Order Amish were noted in Section 17.3. This sect originated in Switzerland in 1693 and was established in eastern Pennsylvania, as founder members immigrated between 1720 and 1770. The Amish, numbering today about 45,000 in Pennsylvania, Ohio, and Indiana are descended from no more than 200 original settlers. The extent of inbreeding that they have undergone can be gathered from the fact that only eight different surnames account for 81 percent of the group in Lancaster County, Pennsylvania, which settled before the American Revolution. Eight other names account for 77 percent of the Amish in Holmes County, Ohio. The history of the Amish is clearly that of sub-isolate formation.

Another similar group is the Hutterites of German origin now living in the Dakotas, Montana, and on the Canadian prairies. The nearly 10,000 Hutterites now alive descended from 101 settling couples. Although inbreeding cannot be assigned the full responsibility (since the Hutterites are a cultural as well as a biological isolate), the Hutterites rank second in the proportion of psychotics among eight populations compared, exceeded only by a group in northern Sweden.

Still another religious community of interest to geneticists is the German Baptist Brethren, or Dunkers. Founded by an original group of fifty families between 1719 and 1729, they numbered 58,000 by 1882. Apparently the exact degree of inbreeding in their population has not been studied; nevertheless, they provide an example of the operation of drift. Not only was their A blood-group frequency (60 percent) different from that of populations either in West Germany (45 percent) or in the U.S. (40 percent), but so were the M and N frequencies. In both West Germany and the U.S., the frequencies are 30 percent for M, 20 percent for N, and 50 percent for the heterozygous type MN; the corresponding figures for the Dunkers are 44.5, 13.5, and 42.0. And not only has there been a startling shift in frequencies of the M and N phenotypes, but the proportion of heterozygotes has declined, as would be expected in a largely endogamous group. These figures show a combination of drift and inbreeding effects. Other traits for which drift can be suspected that have been studied in the Dunkers include hitchhiker's thumb (the ability to bend the thumb backwards at an angle of 50 degrees or less), and presence of hair on the middle segment of the fingers, which is controlled by a single dominant gene.

19.4 BREAKDOWN OF ISOLATES

One of the important phenomena that we are witnessing at present is the gradual breakdown of isolates due to increased human mobility, both geographical and social. Individuals are beginning to have an increasingly wider choice of mates, and the incidence of consanguineous marriages is dropping as a result. This is evident not only in the melting-pot gene pool of the U.S.A., but in many European local populations. Box 19.D shows three examples of this phenomenon. Another reason for decrease in consanguineous marriages lies in birth control and limitation of family size, which reduces the proportion of eligible relatives among prospective mates. Incidentally, the effect of reducing family size is accompanied by the lowering of the average age of mothers at the time of pregnancy, and this in turn leads to a reduction in birth abnormalities correlated with maternal age.

BOX 19.D TRENDS IN INCIDENCE OF CONSANGUINEOUS MARRIAGES IN EUROPEAN COUNTRIES

The illustration at right (after Dahlberg) shows the dropping rate of consanguineous marriages in Prussia.

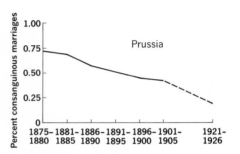

The next diagram (after Sutter and Tabah) shows an even more dramatic decrease in the initially high frequency of consanguineous marriages in two departments in France. The results shown in this diagram included marriages up to those between second cousins.

The last figure below is taken from the monumental study of Professor Antonio Moroni of Parma who has analyzed the Vatican records of the province of Reggio Emilia for the last four centuries. The rise in incidence of consanguineous marriages after the Industrial Revolution and its fall after World War I is clearly in evidence.

The upper line includes marriages resulting in F values from $\frac{1}{256}$ to $\frac{1}{8}$. Only data up to 1917 have been analyzed. The lower line is confined to F values from $\frac{1}{64}$ to $\frac{1}{8}$.

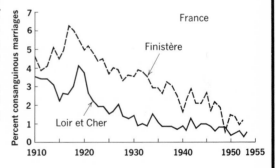

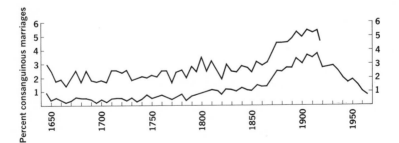

Thus, the introduction of legal abortion in Japan after 1947 has produced the following statistics:

Variable	1947	1953	1960
Number of births	2,600,000	1,800,000	1,600,000
Percentage of births that were no later than the third in the family	64	75	90
Deaths from congenital malformation per 1,000	23.7	21.1	19.0

In addition, there was a 40 percent reduction in trisomy 21 and a 50 percent reduction in the incidence of erythroblastosis.

The breakdown of isolates has an effect opposite to that of inbreeding. Among the Hutterites, stature has been shown to decline under inbreeding, but wherever isolates are breaking down, stature is on the increase, as shown in Sweden, Italy, and the mountain villages of Switzerland. This effect may, in part, be due to improved nutrition, but to some degree it must also be attributed to increased exogamy. Similarly, we might expect a considerable decline in the frequency of expressed genetic abnormalities that are inherited as recessives to accompany the breakdown of isolates. In fact, the halving of the incidence of juvenile amaurotic idiocy observed in the last 30 years in Sweden has been attributed to the breakdown of geographical and social isolation.

The one possible advantage of endogamous marriages may lie in a lower incidence of blood-group incompatibilities. For all other factors, we should benefit by decreasing genetic burdens from generation to generation because of the trend towards a single world gene pool replacing numerous small isolates. It is true that from the standpoint of evolutionary strategy, subdivision into partially isolated demes is a more efficient process. But it is difficult to see why such consideration should apply to human beings. First, convincing arguments that we should accelerate our evolution are lacking. Second, not only the biological, but also the social, and the moral, costs must be considered when dealing with the management of human genetic resources.

Having completed the survey of what is known of organic evolution and the genetics of man, we turn in the remaining chapters to a number of issues concerning the present and future of mankind that this knowledge places before us.

20

MANAGEMENT OF THE HUMAN GENE POOL

20.1 EUGENIC PROPOSALS

The social climate at the time Mendel's laws were rediscovered was such that eugenic movements could prosper. This was true in England where eugenics was initiated by Galton. It was true in Germany where the discipline took the name of "race hygiene" and eventually culminated in sterilization laws and genocide. (Some geneticists and anthropologists who are still active acclaimed Hitler for making a public policy of racist nonsense in the guise of science.) It was true in the United States, where intoxication with the elegance of Mendel's laws led some human geneticists to allege they had discovered such improbable examples of single-gene-determined behavior as tendency to nomadism or wild temperament. By the 1920's American eugenics degenerated into a mixture of pseudo-science, Bible belt religion, extreme reactionary politics, and racism, so that the very term became repulsive to geneticists. The same movement still continues to flourish in a mad sort of way among uninformed bigots on the fringes of society who are supported by a few conservative rich. Its principal tenets revolve around restriction of immigration to the U.S. and compulsory prevention of reproduction of phenotypes that are described as undesirable.

The example of PKU in Section 12.3 has already shown how ineffective a *negative* eugenics program would be. Meanwhile, *positive* eugenic proposals have been put forward on allegedly sounder biological grounds. A revival of interest and a considerable amount of public exposure has been given the new eugenics—which by no means should be confused with the movement of the twenties—by such eminent figures as H. J. Muller and the British biologist Sir Julian Huxley.

One eugenic measure, sometimes called *eutelegenesis* to repudiate any connection with the discredited ideas, was first suggested in the Soviet Union by A. S. Serebrovsky, and later independently in America. It proposes that sperm of men adjudged to be superior be used for artificial insemination, thereby increasing the frequency of desirable genes in the human gene pool. Many ramifications have been put forth for programs based on this idea. Sperm may now be preserved by freezing (a common practice in cattle breeding), making possible the establishment of human sperm banks. Indeed, at least one such bank is in operation; according to report, it is in southern California. Eventually, egg banks might also be established. In one formal scheme for eutelegenesis a birth certificate of the future has been devised that would list five parents for each child: the legal father and mother, the two genetic parents, and the incubator proxy mother, into whose uterus the artificially fertilized egg would be implanted. Sperm of all men could be deposited in banks, and kept there to be used only after an individual's superiority had been established by his achievements or, even better, by progeny tests. Perhaps sperm drives will be held in the future just as blood bank drives are held today.

A further, and as yet somewhat visionary, proposal is to clone superior individuals by growing cells from them in tissue cultures (see Section 11.1). This procedure would make possible production of any number of replicates of the future's counterparts of Shakespeare and Leonardo, should they constitute the popular ideals (in a democriatic society) or the personal ideals of state managers (in a dictatorship). Such suggestions should be understood to come, not from cranks, but from some exceedingly brilliant, informed, and well-meaning scientists, imbued with ideas of social justice. In their zeal for the preservation and improvement of mankind, however, they do not agree with the views of other equally well-meaning biologists that there is more than one difficulty and danger in putting their proposals into operation. For example, should the tastes run to the likes of Hitler or Al Capone, they too could be cloned.

First of all, then, there is the problem of values. Perhaps today everybody can agree in some general terms on some standards of value (see Section 15.4). Intelligence, adaptability, mental stability, courage, energy, and perseverance are generally admired, even though we have no way of testing individuals for the genetic components of these virtues. We have no clue as to how relevant these properties will be to the human situation a thousand years hence, which would be short-range planning in a human eugenic program. Indeed, we are actually very much confused about some values rather important to us even today. The Nobel laureate physiologist A. Szent-Györgyi has said that we might reflect on a list of the most common crimes in decreasing order of gravity: murder, robbery, rape, destruction, lying. They are commonly held crimes when committed by individuals within groups. But, ironically, it seems that they become virtues when one's own group commits them against others. Statesmen and diplomats are rewarded for the most outrageous lies; pilots and generals are decorated for wholesale destruction and murder; annexation of territories after wars adds to national glory; and the rape of the Sabine women is still held to be a heroic chapter of Roman history.

Second, there is the problem of correlated traits. There are no perfect genotypes: each gamete of a great man, who is held great by whatever standard is chosen, carries in it numerous genes for traits undesirable by any standard. With respect to genes controlling physical defects, this is unquestionable. With respect to less tangible traits, there is no warrant to believe that such generally admired traits as musical ability, goodness of character, mental stability, scientific aptitude, and moral probity are genetically positively correlated.

Third, the acceptability of eutelegenesis in our present state of social development may be questioned. Proponents of positive eugenics often point to the success of animal breeders in improving their stocks, but this is a poor analogy, because animal breeders became successful only when they had a Platonic ideal, such as a fat steer, a lilliputian dog, or a fine-wooled sheep, in mind. They selected for uniformity; whereas mankind, perhaps, wants diversity. They used inbreeding, to a degree not generally accepted for mankind. They selected by ruthless culling and complete prevention of reproduction of the majority of of animals under control. They used progeny testing, which in human terms would mean wholesale reproduction for testing purposes with full knowledge that the great majority of persons so produced would be barred from contributing to the next generation's gene pool.

Fourth, the efficacy of the degree of eutelegenesis that might be acceptable has been brought in question. Thus the British geneticist J. Maynard Smith made some computations on the basis of several reasonable assumptions, taking intelligence as the desideratum. Let us say that one percent of women will agree to have half of their children by AID (artificial insemination by donor). Let us further assume that the real husbands of these women are a random sample of the population. Under assortative mating, it likely would be the more intelligent couples who would appreciate the alleged benefits of eutelegenesis to the world and themselves. Let us further assume that the donors have an average I.Q. 15 points higher than the mean, which would provide a reasonably strong selection pressure. Finally, we can postulate a 50 percent heritability for the I.Q. It works out that the expected change in the mean I.Q. of the population under these circumstances would be 0.04 points a year. It would take a century to raise the average by 4 points. As the previously cited evidence for Philadelphia Negroes (Section 11.2) indicates, nine years of schooling would be twice as effective as one hundred years of selection (although it must be emphasized that the methods are not mutually exclusive).

And, indeed, as Joshua Lederberg points out, there is a negative correlation between the level of acceptability and the efficiency of selection progress of programs of positive eugenics. It may then be asked if eugenics should be abandoned completely. The answer is no. There are many different measures that can have positive effects. We must grant that these effects may not be very great on a world-wide scale but nevertheless they are of value because they could eliminate much personal grief and lighten some social burdens.

Among such measures is genetic counseling, already considered in Section 17.4. Widespread use of this service implies a need for dissemination of information on genetics among the medical profession and the public at large. Adoption of children in marriages between first cousins or between known heterozygotes for the same serious defects would reduce the proportion of expressed defects. Restriction of family size has been demonstrated (Section 19.4) to lower the frequency of congenital malformation and the incidence of trisomy 21 and of erythroblastosis. Since the use of AID is spreading among childless or incompatible couples, an intelligent choice of donors could be of help. Most donor sperm comes from medical students and interns, and yet, to quote H. J. Muller, this source is used "without regard for the fact that U.S. Army I.Q. tests have indicated this group to have the lowest mental ratings of all professions tested."

It has been asserted that man has now the ability to control his own evolution. This, as the previous discussion shows, is actually true only in a very limited sense. Without infringement of personal liberty, all that can be done is to reduce somewhat the expressed gross defects in each crop of babies. We still do not know how to stop recurrence of undesirable mutations. Even if the values of the future could be somehow foreseen, we still know little about measuring genetic worth. Above all, the social organization of a democratic society may be incompatible with exercising whatever powers of controlling our gene pool we may have. Nowhere is this dilemma more evident than in connection with the population explosion (Section 5.3). The right of individuals to have children is held by most segments of our population to be an inalienable one. Yet we are headed for disaster if it is exercised indiscriminatively. Proposals have been made to limit population growth by providing a financial incentive—in other words, by placing a tax on children instead of granting exemptions for them—but should this measure, distasteful in principle to the majority, be adopted, the social and psychological consequences for those children whose parents are so irresponsible as to continue having babies without worrying about supporting them, may be a stiff price to pay. All in all, humanity has a serious problem on its hands, and no easy solution is in sight, despite all the advances in biological knowledge.

20.2 EUPHENICS AND GENETICAL ENGINEERING

Euphenics deals with the improvement of the phenotype by biological means. The term was first proposed in the twenties by the Russian biologist N. K. Koltsov, and formulated independently in the sixties by Joshua Lederberg. Essentially, euphenics involves the incorporation into preventive and therapeutic medical practice, the broad advances that are being made in molecular biology, immunology, neurophysiology, and other rapidly growing biological fields. Lederberg, in particular, has been a strong advocate of euphenics as a corrective measure for our genetic ills.

He emphasizes the ineffectiveness, unacceptability, and exceeding slowness of action of eugenic measures, whereas investment in euphenics can lead to many immediate benefits. Specific examples would include a crash program for development of artificial organs, and of industrial methodology for the synthesis of hormones, enzymes, antigens, and other proteins. These could be used to supply individuals suffering from genetic or acquired metabolic blocks, to solve problems of transplantation of organs man to man, or animal to man, and to induce immunological tolerance during foetal life. An eugenic program for primates is also suggested as a means of providing material for compatible grafts.

Possibilities of radical changes in man's brain structure and function by euphenic means are also open. As noted in Box 5.A, the correlation between brain size and intelligence is a tenuous one. Yet in rats, environmentally controlled differences in learning experiences were found to lead to increases in brain size as long as the animals were learning. Furthermore, a significant correlation between body size and intelligence of children was found in some English studies. And the psychologist Lewis M. Terman found that although less than 2 percent of all babies born in California weigh over 10 pounds, 17 percent of California children having genius I.Q.'s did weigh 10 or more pounds at birth. The brain of modern man has not changed substantially since Cro-Magnon days. Lederberg suggests that stabilizing selection for brain size (see Section 11.2), based on obstetric considerations of incompatibility between large crania at birth and female pelvic dimensions, may be at work. Adoption of a universal practice of birth by Caesarian operation would remove this limitation. Although it is not known whether the approximately 10 billion nerve cells of the human brain need to be increased in number for added intelligence, it is likely that development of more complex interconnections, which brain enlargement may lead to, would have an effect of increasing intelligence. Euphenic changes in kinds of brain function can also be visualized. Thus, H. J. Muller suggests that rapid transmission of abstract thought or telepathic communication between men may be achieved by providing brains with machinery for direct transmission and reception of light waves. Pharmacological manipulation of the developing brain will certainly be possible before too long, bringing with it the obvious dangers of thought control (see Section 20.3). Aside from that, the genotype that would be desired when specific brain hormones are isolated might be one not for their fastest rate or greatest amount of production, but for the greatest capacity to respond to them, a further instance of the unpredictability of genetic value judgments in advance.

Another example of the interaction and feedback between euphenics and eugenics is provided by the possibilities of early culture of human fertilized eggs. As noted in Section 8.5, the sex of the zygotes could be identified and an eugenic control of sex-linked disorders, such as hemophilia, instituted by having known carriers produce only female children.

Somewhat more distant are the prospects for genetical engineering, the direct manipulation of the genetic message by changing, subtracting, or adding to the instructions received by the cell (a possible fortuitous instance has been described in Section 6.5). This potentiality is open at two levels. Transduction, transformation, or directed mutation of the message received by somatic cells could affect the gene pool content adversely. For example, after application of engineering correctives, a PKU child's liver would be able to synthesize the missing enzyme, but the genes such an individual would transmit to the next generation would still be defective. If, however, the correction could be applied to germinal cells, positive eugenic effects would ensue: the genes passed on to the next generation would be normal. Of some appeal is the tongue-in-cheek suggestion of the Rockefeller University biochemist R. D. Hotchkiss that problems of human food supply could be solved by incorporating a gene for the ability to digest cellulose into the human genotype. He himself is particularly attracted to the idea, he claims, because he would then be able, truthfully, to tell a correspondent how much he enjoyed his letter.

A further opportunity for genetical engineers lies in the manipulation of regulator genes (Box 6.C), which could be made to turn on and turn off synthesis of proteins by supplying a cell with the appropriate regulatory substances.

One suggestion made is that even teleduplication, creating replicas of a human being across vast distances, by feeding a computer his DNA specifications, and having a receiver on another planet reconstruct him instantly, will be possible in the twenty-second century. Problems of personal identity of the subjects of such experiments and operations and in cases where a man emerges from successive transplants with a set of completely new organs including the brain, would become a worry not only to theologians. Mankind will have its hands full long before then in having to sort out and put in their rightful places the range of beings that the prophets of genetical engineering confidently promise will be manufactured by introducing various human chromosomes into primate genotypes. Such an accomplishment could, of course, throw much light on the problem of what happens in trisomy 21 and similar diseases (for instance, would an extra human X-chromosome added to the genotype of a male ape produce the Klinefelter syndrome?).

All of this is, of course, heady stuff. But whereas only a few years ago these possibilities were out of the scope even of science fiction writers, today they are being advanced and seriously discussed by leading biologists and biochemists as definite prospects for our future. How soon the various possibilities will materialize, no one can say.

Clearly, whatever biological problems the wonders of euphenics and genetical engineering may solve, they will create many unprecedented social and ethical problems, for the solution of which much collective wisdom will be needed. The requisite wisdom is unlikely to come from the genetical engineers alone, because it involves moral issues on which they are not experts. The traditional ethical guidelines have come from religion, but the new religion of science and technology that is arising, with its hierarchy of scientists instead of priests, with its sacred language of mathematics instead of Latin, with its sacrifices of traffic casualties instead of heretics, and with space-exploration for its Crusades, is as yet not capable of providing any (see Section 22.3). And therein lies still one more reason why the gulf between C. P. Snow's two cultures, or more likely a much greater number of subcultures, must be bridged, if mankind is to extricate itself from the pitfalls that inevitably accompany the blessings that modern biology has brought and will continue to create.

Improvement in the environment, **euthenics**, and educational and psychological engineering, mentioned in Section 11.2, which by analogy we may call **eupsychics**, provide further ways of managing human biological resources. And, similarly, social engineering involves methods of restructuring our society and institutions to meet the problems of the age of atomic physics and molecular biology. We shall discuss these only very briefly, since the details are clearly beyond the scope of the book and the competence of the writer.

Producers of food and fiber practice both eugenics and euthenics on their plants and animals. It is possible, for example, to select lines of animals for heat resistance. At the same time, one can provide cooling devices in the environment of nonresistant genotypes. This is clearly applicable to the human situation. Both unplanned and planned environmental effects have relevance here. With respect to the first, as Lederberg points out, human mobility permitted by the jet airplane has already had incalculably greater consequences to the genetic structure of human populations than any conceivably feasible program of eugenics would.

The planned measures could be exercised effectively in education and in the control of human behavior. Psychologists and psychiatrists have never been known to hide their lights under a bushel so far as their alleged powers to manage human beings are concerned. Freud was not the only one to set an example. The modest pronouncement that the father of behavioral psychology John B. Watson made over 40 years ago may be recalled: "Give me a dozen healthy infants, well-formed, and my own specified world to bring them up and I'll guarantee to take any one at random and train him to become any type of specialist I might select—doctor, lawyer, artist, merchant-chief and, yes, even beggarman and thief, regardless of his talents, penchants, tendencies, abilities, vocations, and race of his ancestors."

Watson himself admitted that he was stretching the point. Yet it seems that if differences between genotypes are recognized and educational techniques, probably of the computerized type, appropriate to each genotype are devised, it is not impossible that the neo-Watsons of the twenty-first century may be able, if allowed, to do just what Watson claimed.

According to the standards of a good part of mankind, not necessarily including believers in the supremacy of white Nordics or orthodox Jews inalterably wedded to the Chosen People concept, human diversity is one of our basic resources or treasures. One of the reasons that man continues and is likely to continue to be the dominant species on earth lies in the enormous variation in his gene pool, in the large number of polymorphisms it maintains, and in his control of environmental factors that permit him both to exploit the near-infinity of natural riches available and to create any number of artificial ones.

The dangers from restricting human phenotypic variation by eugenic means are trivial, but those from euthenic methods and particularly from educational engineering are real.

There is little doubt that educational engineering could be used to make similar genotypes into widely different phenotypes by custom-tailoring the educational process. But the concern that is felt is for the use of these methods to nullify differences between genotypes by similar tailoring in the opposite direction to produce uniformity. To quote the American psychologist R. S. Crutchfield:

> . . . the most striking new factor in the increasing threat to independent thought in a conformist world is the development of far-reaching new psychological methods for behavior control—direct electrical stimulation of the brain, high-speed computer control of man-machine systems . . . so-called teaching machines. . . . Just as there is a race between peaceful and destructive uses of nuclear energy and a race between medical advances which reduce death rate and those which control birth rate, so there is a race between the destructive and constructive use of these radically new techniques of behavior control.

Behavior control is not a new phenomenon: there is (or at least there used to be) control by the parents, by laws, by customs, by one's own subconscious drives. Presumably in the totality of things these controls are benevolent. Even if subconscious drives on occasion produce murdering rampages, on the whole they must have a positive adaptive value, since otherwise they would have faced negative natural selection. The peril lies in the possibility that educational and psychopharmacological or electrical means of control can fall into the hands of antisocial types that Wright places in group 6 (Figure 15.3). An example of genocide through manipulation of behavior by drugs is to be found in the deliberate use of alcohol by the white settlers to destroy resistance of Indian tribes. And the technology of anxiety-inducing, hallucinogenic, and other drugs that affect information storage and retrieval in the brain is only beginning to develop.

There are other problems of eupsychics which are connected with changes that may be expected from social engineering. As has been pointed out by many, the views of Western man on private property, murder, rape, and adultery have been very nearly static for three millenia. Sexual behavior patterns may undergo a complete revolution with the introduction of cheap and effective contraceptive devices. In such a revolution, the institution of the family would certainly undergo a change and might even disappear. The psychological effects on the individual and the genetic effects on the gene pool of this change in society are unpredictable, but they will have to be faced if such a revolution takes place. The decline of the family might modify social structure in either one or both of two directions: (1) a centrifugal broadening of the individual's loyalties from parish to nation, and from nation to the whole world, and (2) an increased tendency for personal differentiation and loss of group identity or status.

We have stressed the biochemical uniqueness of the individual. Socially, members of the plumber's union are now practically completely interchangeable, as are members of the fisherman caste in India. In the world of tomorrow this may not be so. Indeed, when enough human loci are known to discriminate between each and every human being, our social identities will be determined by the catalogues of our genes. This may be a distasteful prospect, but might have a somewhat greater significance than discrimination between men by zip codes and social security, telephone, and charge account numbers.

21
GENETICS AND POLITICS

21.1 THE RISE AND FALL OF LYSENKO

We have already noted the subversion of genetics in Germany for political uses and the racist aspects of the negative eugenics movement. Perhaps the most bizarre chapter in the political history of genetics was written in the USSR during the last thirty-odd years. Its climax came in 1948 when a fanatical charlatan, **Trofim D. Lysenko**, was established as a dictator of genetics. On August 26, 1948 a decree of the Praesidium of the Soviet Academy of Sciences appeared in *Pravda*, basically directing what biological doctrines were to be taught and what kind of research was to be permitted. This decree signalled the end of genetics in the Soviet Union for years to come. Lysenko bore a great deal of responsibility for the dismissal, exile, and execution of a number of Russian geneticists, a fact previously inferred in the West but now being fully documented in the Soviet press. Only after Khrushchev's resignation did Lysenko lose his power; subsequently he was publicly disgraced and exposed as head of a school of wholesale faking of data. This episode in the history of genetics in the USSR has such an important bearing on the relationship between science and politics and on the vitally important problem of governmental control of science, that it is worth examining at some length.

Science in Russia has always followed the generally authoritarian European tradition. Even in prerevolutionary days, dissent within a research institute or a university department was not tolerated. This condition, combined with political dictatorship, set the stage for what was to follow. We can take the year 1925 as a starting point of this chapter of Soviet genetics. In that year, Lysenko, a young agronomist of peasant origin lacking rigorous biological education, started his career as a junior plant breeding specialist in an Azerbaijan agricultural experiment station. At that time genetic research in Russia was just beginning to develop into the enormous enterprise it became within a few years. A little earlier, its direction, and particularly its harnessing to the needs of Soviet agriculture, had been, by Lenin's personal instructions, entrusted to **N. I. Vavilov** (1887–1943). A botanist and plant geographer who had studied abroad, and traveled around the world, Vavilov was a scientist who achieved an international reputation. He was one of the few non-Communists to become a member of the USSR Central Executive Committee, and from all evidence, he was an organizer and administrator of exceptional brilliance.

Under Vavilov's leadership, a network of research institutes and experiment stations, employing eventually more than 20,000 people, was built up. In addition to the botanical work under his immediate direction, genetic research developed rapidly along many other fronts. It would be an exaggeration to say that the Russians were responsible for the majority of genetic advances in the 1930's, but no history of genetics for that period would be complete without footnotes referring to many Russian contributions.

Lysenko had no claims to being a geneticist in 1925. In an autobiographical note he described his primary interest at that time as being in the pshyiological problem of the length of the vegetative period in plants. By 1928 he was able to formulate a theory of plant development having a bearing on the nature of the process of maturation. His investigations were reported at a Congress of Genetics, Selection, Plant and Animal Breeding, which was held in Leningrad in January, 1929. Lysenko's report apparently excited no comment. This was understandable, since the audience of 1,400 also listened to 268 other contributions, examined 943 exhibits, and in general was subjected to a menu of genetic fare of a breadth and range probably unsurpassed until that time at a specialized scientific meeting. The general theme of the Congress was the conversion of theory into practice; its slogan, voiced by Vavilov, to "raise the level of our agriculture"; its cardinal problem to ensure that scientific results and information "reach and spread among the many millioned peasantry" of the Soviet Union.

Somewhat before this meeting, Lysenko had moved to the Odessa Institute of Selection and Genetics (later renamed after him) where he continued his investigations, and what is more significant historically, took his notions of agronomic practice into the field. Among these notions, a number that were innovations as far as Russia was concerned, although they appear to have been practiced elsewhere, were put into operation on collective farms. Some were partially successful, such as the summer planting of potatoes; others failed, such as certain methods of pretreatment of seed. In general, improvement in agricultural practice ensued, which ensured personal support for Lysenko on the part of thousands of collective farm workers.

Such support from provincial sources peripheral to science enabled Lysenko eventually to raise the flag of insurrection against Vavilov. In January, 1932, the first issue of a Lysenko-edited journal appeared in Odessa. Roughly one-half of its 80 pages came from the pen of Lysenko himself, while another 10 pages were devoted to a series of resolutions of various local bodies, the main gist of which was that "in spite of the great importance of the original scientific work of comrade Lysenko an unobjective and inimical attitude toward his researchers was noted among certain representatives of agricultural science."

In Odessa, Lysenko formed a partnership with a philosopher of the dialectical-materialism persuasion named I. I. Prezent. In 1931 Prezent published one of his first contributions having bearing on biology, a hostile philosophical analysis of the excursion of Filipchenko, a Russian geneticist by then deceased, into the realm of eugenics. It so happens that Filipchenko's stand on matters of human genetics was related to the eugenics movement of the day. Prezent's attack, which incidentally revealed his magnificent gifts for vituperation and argumentation *ad hominem* was less on Filipchenko's biology than on his class motivation.

Disentangling the mutual influences of Lysenko and Prezent is difficult, but it is with the formation of this partnership that Lysenko first emerged as a contender for genetic honors. By Lysenko's own admission it was Prezent who first "cranked-up" the attack on genetics and Mendelism. The collaboration bore its first fruit in the production of a book in which the putative genetic implications of Lysenko's theory of plant development were elaborated.

In the meantime all was not quiet on the genetic front even outside the Lysenko orbit. The Russian tradition of introspection, and the general European heritage of viewing scientific endeavor as part of a general system of natural philosophy, did not die with the political revolution. Neither did many of the specifically biological philosophies that were at variance with views held by the current officials. Such was the case with Lamarckism (Box 3.A) that had been up to then interpreted by most biologists in Russia as an idealistic rather than a materialistic concept. Yet among some scientists, and among more nonscientists, the idea of inheritance of acquired characters was held in favor. It had mass appeal, was easy to understand, and, if true, would give man a much easier way of changing nature than was otherwise available.

There were various other philosophical bones of contention among geneticists. Some were accused of deviation from the party line in the form of "menshevizing idealism"; others were subjected to criticism for advocating the extension of genetic principles to human society. The whole field of human genetics was subjected to attack on the twin grounds that its study led to racism, and that extension of laboratory results with animals to humans degraded man to the level of beasts. By the end of 1936 all studies on human genetics were suspended in Russia, and concurrently, an event of even greater importance took place.

This was a session of the Lenin All-Union Academy of Agricultural Sciences, a body of which Vavilov was at that time a vice-president, held in Moscow in December, 1936. There the first full-dress attack on Vavilov, on genetic theories, and on genetic practice was launched by Lysenko, Prezent, and their supporters. At that time, Lysenko denied that he was a Lamarckian. He said "it is difficult to find a greater enemy of Lamarckism than I. I. Prezent." He stated that "starting from Lamarckian positions, the work of remaking the nature of plants by 'education' cannot lead to positive results. If, however, we are successful in remaking, by means of appropriate education of plants, the nature of their heredity in the desired direction, this already speaks for the fact that we are not Lamarckians and do not set out from the Lamarckian position." But Lysenko insisted on the indivisibility of an organism, denying that it is possible by any means to separate hereditary from environmental influences. His theory assigned what essentially amounts to free will to individual plants, who not only can select their nutrients, but enter "love marriages," wherein a female gamete selects in fertilization a particular pollen grain, or "lad," as Prezent quaintly described it. Heredity was most often defined by Lysenko in a somewhat meaningless way as "the property of the living body to demand definite conditions for its life, its development, and to react definitely to these or other conditions." "The conservatism of the nature of organisms" —in other words, their genetic endowment—can in Lysenko's view be liquidated. Genes, or units of heredity, do not exist. Mendelian segregation and recombination are statistical phenomena without biological significance. The whole structure of genetics is void of any but metaphysical meaning. Above all, Lysenko raised the question whether genetics contributed anything to the development of agriculture.

The 1936 conference was officially declared a draw, but it nevertheless presented a clear-cut victory of the Lysenko forces. The duties of Vavilov were sharply circumscribed, and Lysenko moved to Moscow to take over direction of a considerable amount of agricultural research in the whole Soviet Union. There was apparently no suppression of genetics in fields outside of agriculture and medicine, and a great deal of useful and important work in many phases of genetics was carried out for another ten years.

Even in agriculture, Lysenko's control was as yet incomplete. Although rumors and denials flew thickly in the West about the safety of Vavilov's person and that of others, little authentic information was at hand. An International Congress of Genetics originally scheduled to be held in Moscow in 1937 was postponed by the Russians and later cancelled. When the Congress was eventually held in Edinburgh, just at the time that Germany marched into Poland, no Russians attended, even though Vavilov had been elected President of the Congress. Shortly thereafter (October, 1939), the second formal round of the battle took place, when the party journal *Under the Banner of Marxism* arranged another conference. This time the meeting was a melancholy and tragic affair resembling a trial more than a scientific conclave. Vavilov and others offered an honest defense of their scientific views, but in their philosophical argumentation were forced to proceed according to Zeno's unfortunate theory that knavery is the best defense against knaves. There is little point in relating the details of this encounter. Tempers were short, any pretense of impersonal discussion was abandoned, and both the attackers and defenders relinquished dignity and logic to establish their respective points. Mendelian laws of segregation were attacked most severely, together with other valid genetic ideas, and many more ideas that no geneticists shared.

Meanwhile, the Stalinist purges of 1938 took their toll of many scientists. Vavilov was arrested as a British spy in 1940, sentenced to death, and died in prison three years later. The demands of war halted the onslaught on genetics, but after the war was over, the battle was joined again. In 1948 came the climactic conference, a surrealistic inquisition of the surviving Mendelians. On its last day, Lysenko produced a bombshell. To quote from *Pravda*, he said:

" 'Before starting my concluding speech I must answer a note sent to the Praesidium. I am asked: what is the attitude of the Central Committee of the Party towards the report I gave at this session. I reply: the Central Committee [of the Party] has examined my report *The situation in biological science* [an outline of his theories] and approved it. . . .' The communication of the president elicited universal animation among the participants of the session. In a united burst of enthusiasm all those present rose from their seats and a tempestuous, lengthy ovation ensued in honor of the Central Committee of the Party of Lenin-Stalin, in honor of the wise leader and teacher of the Soviet people, the greatest scientist of our era, comrade Stalin."

This statement initiated Lysenko's full control over agriculture and most of biology, and the extermination of genetics as a discipline. By now, Lysenko's Lamarckism was no longer concealed. Said he: ". . . the well-known Lamarckian propositions, which recognize the active role of the conditions of external environment in the formation of the living body and the inheritance of acquired characters, in contrast to the metaphysics of Neo-Darwinism . . . are indeed not faulty, but on the contrary perfectly correct and entirely scientific."

While textbooks were being rewritten, and names and pictures were ordered blacked out in the books still in use, Vavilov disappeared from history precisely as if put down the memory hole in Orwell's *1984*: all mention of his existence was erased. The less brave of the remaining geneticists indulged in public recantation, admission of error, and pledging of support to Lysenko. The more courageous ones refused to knuckle under, were sent to work camps, became ornithologists, entered cancer or antibiotic research, or were forced to be laboratory technicians, librarians, or farmers on the Afghanistan border. How many perished is not yet ascertained; the names are just beginning to be published piecemeal.

Lysenko was elevated to semidivine status and at least one monument to him was erected. His pronouncements and claims, no matter how unbelievable, were unchallengeable. He was decorated as much as any war hero, with three Stalin prizes, six orders of Lenin, and the order of the Red Banner. He was proclaimed a Hero of Socialist Labor, became a deputy and vice-president of the Supreme Soviet and of the Central Committee of the Party.

In the USSR and the satellite countries, Lysenko's rule was supreme. Indeed, China still seems to be oriented towards Lysenkoism, which is not unexpected in the present circumstances. As Lysenko took over the genetic reins, Soviet investigators were completely sealed off from the Western world of genetics. The whole corpus of genetical knowledge—painstakingly accumulated in thousands of experiments throughout the world in the course of half a century—was discarded by simply stating that it came from the capitalist world. Of all the living and dead western biologists, only Darwin appears to have been granted honorary Soviet citizenship, largely because he was vouched for by Marx and Engels. The nationalistic criterion of scientific validity reached absurd heights in the statement of one of Lysenko's supporters whose work had been criticized abroad: "This attitude of foreign scientists not only does not worry us but, on the contrary, fills us with joy. Apparently, we are on the right track, if we are abused by the other side."

After the post-Stalin thaw, Lysenko supporters began appearing at international meetings, invariably bringing back home reports of the interest in their work and enthusiasm with which it has been received. In fact, however, outside of a handful of iconoclastic geneticists, the interest largely lay in seeing what breed of men these self-styled scientists were. When an invitation was issued for Lysenkoites to demonstrate their experiments in the United States (ironically enough, their expenses were to be borne by the Rockefeller Foundation, which is satirized in the Soviet cartoons that are reproduced as Figure 21.1), it was rejected. Similarly, a suggestion to Lysenko by the Soviet physical chemist N. Semenov (later a Nobel laureate) to permit western geneticists to observe the experiments in Lysenko's laboratory was turned down out of hand. Nevertheless, attempts to establish Lysenkoism as a respectable doctrine abroad continued for a number of years without success. Only after Lysenko's dismissal did Soviet geneticists really rejoin the international family of geneticists.

Lysenko's reign lasted until well after Stalin's death in 1953. The dramatic disclosures by Khruschev of Stalin's misdeeds permitted some relaxation. A few geneticists returned to their former pursuits, but in the guise of doing medical, radiation, or biochemical research. Khruschev, a personal friend of Lysenko, continued his support of the genetic dictator. Several attempts at scientific insurrection were not too successful. In 1964 more voices began to be heard; the failures of Soviet agriculture were becoming too serious a matter to be ignored. Reliance on Lysenko in these matters was at least one of the reasons claimed for the downfall of Khruschev. In any case, soon after this event Lysenko was dismissed from his administrative positions. Investigating committees established wholesale fraud not only in reports claiming increased agricultural yields but also in the presumably scientifically conducted experiments providing evidence of the validity of Lysenko's theories.

Posthumous rehabilitations followed. Vavilov's reputation was rescued and stamps bearing his portrait appeared. A revision of school curricula to include the teaching of Mendelism followed, and translations of western textbooks on genetics were ordered. Teaching of biology in high schools was suspended for a year while textbooks were being revised. Mendel, no longer officially portrayed as a sinister tool of the Catholic Church, became a hero. A spate of articles vilifying Lysenko began appearing in scientific and popular journals of all kinds, whether they dealt with sport, education, science, or literature. Wholesale conversion to Mendelism by philosophers, teachers, writers, and agronomists ensued. New institutes, research programs, and journals on genetics are now being established. At the moment, it seems as if only Prezent has stuck with Lysenko.

The picture for the nonce is an optimistic one. But there are still many unredeemed ex-Lysenkoites in high places and the effect of the lack of trained geneticists in the country will be felt for a long time to come. There is a missing generation of trained geneticists. At an international celebration of Mendel's centennial, held in Czechoslovakia after Lysenko's fall, the USSR was represented by a handful of men in their late fifties or sixties, survivors of the Lysenko debacle, and by fifty or so in their twenties and early thirties—but none of the intermediate ages. What the future holds is impossible to tell. The atmosphere of Soviet science still limits the freedom of research endeavor. The authoritarian tradition still dominates, and a struggle for peck order among the senior geneticists is clearly evident. One can only hope for the best.

A coherent account of Lysenkoism is difficult because of its very irrationality. Its essence included the rejection of the role of the chromosomes and of DNA in heredity, belief in inheritance of acquired characters, and in the possibility of spontaneous origin of one species from acellular material of another. Some of the experimental claims made by Lysenkoites are remarkable for their effrontery. They include miraculous transformations of wheat into rye, barley, oats, and even cornflowers; beets into cabbage, pine into fir, a tree of the hornbeam group into a forest walnut (using doctored photographs as evidence), and even the hatching of cuckoos from eggs laid by warblers, as well as the origin of mammalian cells from cereals.

Numerous experiments purporting to show the successful and permanent transformation of small white fowl into large black ones by blood transfusions were reported. When a French publication claimed that injection of DNA from one breed of ducks into another produced heritable changes in the descendants of recipients, there was both jubilation and consternation in the Lysenko camp. The first came from the alleged confirmation of the possibility of modifying heredity by such means; the second from the fact that DNA was the transforming agent. Since chicken blood cells have nuclei and hence DNA, the previous Lysenko experiments would implicate nucleic acids in the hereditary machinery. Immediatly results of new experiments were reported, in which it was supposedly found that serum lacking blood cells (and hence DNA) was even more efficient in producing transformations.

As it happened, the French experiment was found not to be repeatable. Its results may well have originated in the hybrid origin of the recipients. Many other large-scale attempts outside of the Soviet orbit to repeat the reported results were negative, with two exceptions, neither of which appears to have adequate controls. Since Lysenko's fall, Soviet geneticists themselves failed to confirm his findings. This is not to say that means of transforming genetic messages into higher organisms do not exist, but injection of blood or of pure DNA into the body does not seem to be one of them. There are, however, some experiments on record with such plants as flax and eggplant that appear to show environmentally induced transformation, but these have not yet been fully explained.

Another of Lysenko's tenets concerns the impropriety of mathematical analysis to biology. Thus, one of his assistants published a great number of F_2 Mendelian ratios from individual crosses, pointing out that the proportion in them was hardly ever exactly 3:1. When Kolmogorov, one of Russia's most brilliant statisticians, showed that on statistical grounds the data not only did not disprove the existence of the ratio, but provided one of the best confirmations of it, he was answered with a chain of intricate syllogisms. Kolmogorov's notions of probability were founded on those of the German (later American) von Mises; he in turn was a follower of the Austrian philosopher Mach, whose concepts in their turn were allegedly demolished by Lenin because they derived from the idealistic views of Bishop Berkeley. Therefore, it was said, Mendelian ratios do not exist. One experiment pointing out that sex ratios do not approximate 100 but can be as low as 40 was later found to be based on a single litter of rabbits consisting of two males and five females.

Experiments of the Lysenko school usually lacked controls. Their outcome was predetermined by the experimenter's *a priori* notions of the results desired. A direct quote from Lysenko says: "to obtain a certain result, one must wish to obtain such a particular result: if you want a particular result you will obtain it." And talking of selecting his staff, he said: "I need only people who will obtain what I require."

Alogical discourse, that is, discourse which is outside of any logical system, and circular reasoning are other attributes of Lysenko's methodology. Usually it was explained that certain results could be obtained only "under particular conditions," and the conditions were then defined as those under which the particular results were obtained. Simplification of reasoning was involved in most of Lysenko's philosophy. His attitude was: If the Hardy-Weinberg equilibrium is too difficult to understand, let us handle the matter by denying its existence. Examples of similar fuzzy thinking can be found closer to home, as in the attempt by a Kansas legislator to fix the value of π in his state by making it a rational number.

Especially in the dialectic of debate did Lysenko's school indulge in spectacular methods. Windmills were readily attacked. Some assertions of western geneticists were put to question in 1948 by citing articles from the 1917 edition of the *Encyclopedia Britannica*, as if Einstein could be proven wrong by attacking the cosmology of Ptolemy. In the Soviet intellectual climate, associative arguments have a powerful weight. Given the infallibility and canonical status of Engels, Marx, Lenin, Stalin, and eventually of Lysenko himself, any reference to their views was tantamount to proof.

Ridicule, caricature, and the equation of Mendelism with Fascism (Figure 21.1) was freely resorted to. The *argumentum ad hominem* was constantly employed: Mendel was a priest, hence his laws were invalid, to which charge even Vavilov was impelled to reply that Bateson was an agnostic. At the first of the international meetings where Lysenkoites appeared, a startled American geneticist asked what the effect of the discovery of transforming properties of blood would have for human blood transfusions. The reply was immediate and unblushing. The speaker had no information on the subject since in the civilized Soviet Union, experiment with humans is prohibited. And then he expressed surprise that the question was raised by an American: were there not separate blood banks for Negroes and whites during the war? Now, the American's question was not whether bigotry, ignorance, and prejudice exist in the United States. This is a matter of record: the Georgia legislature passed a law as recently as 1960 by a vote of 107 to 2 prohibiting blood transfusion between different races (whatever they meant by the term "race"). The original question, however, had been addressed to biological issues.

The Lysenko propaganda machine also worked at full speed in agricultural practice. The post-Lysenko era description of its operation by Semenov may be cited: "If now we turn to T. D. Lysenko's own recommendations, their usual history was as follows. First a certain promise was made which was widely advertised. Assurances were given that grandiose successes would be attained in an exceedingly short time and at very meager cost. After a while, a report would appear that the promise had been basically fulfilled, and that the methods worked out must be incorporated into practice on the widest scale. As a rule, all this was accompanied by noise about still newer achieve-

Figure 21.1.
Four views of western genetics from the pen of the famed Soviet caricaturist
Boris Efimov, which appeared in the 1949 *Ogonyok*, a popular journal, to illustrate
an article entitled "Flylovers—Manhaters." The inscription on the flag reads
"The banner of pure science."

ments. Gradually, however, the method was being less and less practiced or
mentioned in the press: its economic unprofitableness had been established.
But the flop was masked by a boom around the new promise, the history of
which differs from the one described only in details."

The question arises why a society, presumably dedicated to the betterment
of mankind's condition, which has done so much to ameliorate the lot of the
peasant and the worker, which brought in education, and which has the capa-
bility of advanced space exploration, would wilfully proceed in this way to its
own detriment both in theory and in practice.

We must seek explanation not in philosophy or genetics as such, but probably in the political outlook and the internal struggles for power. Up to now
the USSR has been a monocultural society, one organized as a unity according
to explicitly formulated principles involving abolition of capitalism. Bona-
partism and personality cults can flourish in such an atmosphere. Lysenkoism was successful in precisely the way Stalinism was. The slogan of the revolution, "who is not with us, is against us," played as much of a role in one as

in the other. There are some exact parallels in the rise of Lysenko and Stalin: oversimplification of the issues with appeal to uninformed masses, promise of rapid improvement in conditions, distrust of capitalist ideas and motives, appeal to chauvinism and national pride,* elevation to a position of undisputed authority, and ruthless extermination of opposition and rivals.

Now the monoculture appears to be developing cracks. Repression of religion and of the literature of dissent, however, still exists. The winds in genetics may shift again, but, at least there are many encouraging signs that the rulers of the Soviet Union have learned the lesson and are aware of the costs of tampering with the freedom of research and of the need to keep inquiry free from ideological and political interference. And it might be hoped that the western societies, including our own, will take heed from this lesson too. As Sir Julian Huxley, in discussing Lysenkoism, said: "The battle of Soviet genetics will not have been fought . . . in vain if over the great majority of the world the scientific movement will . . . have become fully conscious of itslef and its social functions, of the vital importance, but at the same time the limitations, of scientific method, of the equal importance of a proper degree of scientific autonomy, and of the rights and duties of science in relation to other higher activities of man, to the State, and to human society as a whole."

---

* To the extent of a claim that even though Mendel was wrong, he had really been first appreciated by a Russian; see Section 7.2.

22
ENVOI

22.1 THE SHAPE OF THINGS TO COME

Predictions about the future and normative descriptions of what human society should be like have been with us since Plato's *Republic* and *Laws* (fourth century B.C.), and through Thomas More's *Utopia* (1516), Edward Bellamy's *Looking Backward* (1888), Aldous Huxley's *Brave New World* (1932), H. G. Wells' *The Shape of Things to Come* (1933), George Orwell's *1984* (1949) and many other books. More recently, exploration of the future has become a widespread occupation of natural scientists, technologists, social engineers, and government bodies. A large number of reaserch groups, subsidized by both federal and private funds, are investigating what scientific and technological advances are likely to be made, time tables for their achievement, and the effects they will have on war and peace, on social structure, and on nearly all other aspects of human existence. Planning in our society is no longer a simple matter of looking ahead five years, and explorations of the future are being pursued with nearly the same vigor as the exploration of space. A spate of books and articles, both technical and popular, on human prospects is appearing in a steady stream.

Predictions and description of some genetic potentialities of man's future are scattered throughout the previous chapters of this book. Some more general possibilities that have biological bearing, gathered from a variety of sources, are presented here. Many of them have already been alluded to, albeit in oblique fashion.

The first question about the future of man is, of course, whether there even will be one. The biggest immediate threat to man's existence is the breaking out of another world war. Some experts compute the probability of a major war before the end of our century at 20 percent. Thermonuclear weapons would almost certainly be used in such a war. Opinions as to the consequences to mankind of an atomic war range through a wide spectrum. At one end of it lies the suggestion that mankind would be completely wiped out, and insects, which are more resistant to radiation and have tremendous reproductive potential, would take over the world. A less (or more?) pessimistic outlook is that a band of resistant human survivors would need to rebuild civilization from barbarism, while the human gene pool would have to be purged of numerous deleterious mutations. Development of a highly authoritarian state following a nuclear holocaust has also been predicted. More optimistic prognosticators hope that if nuclear weapons are actually ever used, the powers-that-be would be shocked into a full realization of the consequences of proliferation of an atomic war and would immediately then form an effective world organization and effect general disarmament. And these optimists even hope that the movement towards such an organization will win the race against chauvinism and nationalism before war breaks out. They believe that international politics and the tensions they cause will fade away in the face of a supergovernment, and the wonders that can ensue from the harnessing of atomic and biomolecular powers will be enjoyed by all humans, forever at peace with each other.

But even in a peaceful world, problems beyond those already mentioned must be solved. They include air and water pollution, the use of pesticides harmful to man, mutation from spontaneous causes, the role of the scientist, the philosopher, and the theologian in social decision making, and many others.

Of the many marvels of the near future foreseen by experts, we may list development of fully acceptable synthetic foods, individual worldwide telecommunication, transformation of ocean areas into marine-life farms, complete climate control, efficient desalinization of sea water, development of robots to do factory and housework, establishment of permanent manned artificial satellites and lunar and planetary installations, with intraplanetary travel, even if confined to the solar system, becoming commonplace.

To mention but a few of the predicted changes in the biological and psychological life of man: Successful methods of inducing human hibernation for short periods of time, or for years, are promised. So are euphenic techniques for changing one's sex in mid-life (which, in fact, are to some extent already available) and measures for overcoming forms of deafness and blindness that cannot be corrected now. The possibility of completely wiping out communicable disease is a debatable point, but there is little doubt that further and substantial increases in life expectancy, postponement of aging, advances in the technology of controlling human suffering, and limited rejuvenation are all certain achievements of the near future. In a less serious vein, it has been suggested that when barriers to organ transplantation have been removed, Olympic competitions will be held between organisms consisting of pooled athletic resources, with the best muscles, hearts, lungs, and kidneys from different human beings.

One of the biggest problems to be faced is how man will use the leisure time produced by a prolonged life-span, which prospects for the future promise. The expected removal of limitations on the expression of intelligence and creative ability could help to solve this. But it is also possible that man's future lies in a pleasure-oriented society, full of what has been called "wholesome degeneracy," in which people would devote most of their time to programmed dreams.

22.2 DIRECTIONS OF FUTURE RESEARCH

As is true of the preceding comments, much has already been said in the various chapters of this book on the topic of this section. This material will not be recapitulated here. Neither is it feasible or necessary to list here all that we do not know about genetics and evolution. Hence, only a partial listing of problems towards which genetic research is, or should be, directed is given. It must be emphasized that the listing does not contain all of the most important problems. Many of these have already been noted. Rather it is a supplement, presenting items that are somewhat neglected in the earlier chapters. It is based to some extent on committee reports to United States government agencies, but these committees are in no way responsible for the selection of items included here.

Many problems of genetic chemistry pertaining to structure and function of nucleic acids, proteins, and whole chromosomes remain to be solved. Even though the genetic code has been cracked, much is still unknown about replication, damage and repair of DNA and RNA, and the details of transcription and translation. Actual codon sequences of individual genes are yet to be worked out although this is already being done for some of the smaller yeast genes. Genetical engineering would have to have such information at its command. Determination of the structure of many proteins and of their amino acid sequences, so useful in the reconstruction of the evolutionary past and of taxonomic relations, is also an important need. Instrumentation and automation for the mass production of euphenic substitutes for natural substances is yet to be developed.

Moving from molecular to cellular studies, investigation of regulator mechanisms in higher organisms should have a high priority. All too little is known of the fine physiological details of mitosis and meiosis. Only a formal description of nondisjunction is now available: its causes and precise mechanics are still to be determined. Automation of procedures for screening and diagnosing of cytological abnormalities is still in its infancy.

Almost every aspect of developmental biology, and, in particular, the mechanisms of differentiation in individual development deserves intensive study. Investigation of metabolic pathways between immediate gene products and their phenotypic expression can be carried out for some parts of the process in tissue cultures. Autoimmune diseases should share the research stage with immunological tolerance. Studies on various gene-environment interactions and, especially, that between the genotype of the foetus and uterine environment, should be extended.

The causes of spontaneous mutation are very imperfectly understood. A search for antimutagens should be undertaken. Methods for more accurate estimation of human mutation rates are badly needed. In formal genetics, practically nothing is known about linkage systems in man. Biochemical identification of heterozygotes is possible only for a handful of human genes.

The extent of heterozygous advantage in human polymorphisms is still at issue, and only guesses can be hazarded in the majority of instances of the nature of selection between polymorphs. We are also ignorant of the equilibrium status at most loci in man. Accumulation of familial data, development of genetic registers for human diseases, adaptation of census material for genetic use, extension of studies on human phylogeny, and genetic investigations of rapidly disappearing isolates provide goals for human population genetics research.

Only a few methods of increasing genetic variability in plant and animal stocks have been exhaustively tested. Comparative biochemical studies combined with hybridization experiments may be able eventually to increase food supplies by producing new forms of plants and animals. It has even been suggested that extinct forms of life found in a frozen state, such as the Siberian mammoths, could be thawed out and propagated from single cultured cells to provide material for hybridization that might increase our sources of food.

Finally, the gaps in our knowledge of behavioral genetics of man and other animals and of the inheritance of psychological traits must be only too apparent. More studies of monozygotic twins reared apart are needed. An increased reciprocal understanding and cooperation between geneticists on the one hand, and psychologists and psychiatrists on the other is a prime desideratum. And beyond this mutual understanding, a real interpenetration of thought between geneticists and social scientists, virtually absent today, is needed.

22.3 GENETICS AND MANKIND'S CONCERNS

By now the inescapable involvement of genetics with medicine and public health, law and politics, agriculture and industry, nuclear warfare and space exploration, and with religion and social relations should be clear. As a coda, this section reemphasizes the serious impact of the explosion of scientific and technological advances on man's continuous search for a body of beliefs and values.

Long the province of theologians and philosophers, ethical systems and the bases of individual and group behavior more recently have become within bounds to social and behavioral scientists, and now to natural scientists. Here we will not discuss in detail either the history or the status of the ethical foundations of human mores, but rather express a personal viewpoint bearing on the purposes of this book.

In the past, some systems of ethics were based on the assumption that there are either supernatural sanctions or natural laws to which human beings must conform. Others were constructed from purely hedonistic justifications or based on criteria of personal happiness and well-being or of the maximum common good. Still others, alleged to have an objective basis, rested on such criteria of value as energy production per caput, or minimal psychological conflict within a society, or life expectancy, or even the second law of thermodynamics, that is, that increase in order is good. The dubiousness of the system based on the second law of thermodynamics was demonstrated by *reductio ad absurdum* by one critic who pointed out that since life has a degree of order so much higher than that of the inorganic world, it should be encouraged. Hence, we should breed Drosophila by the million. Further, since man is the highest form of life, we should promote human reproduction to the limit of its capacity. The first conclusion is ridiculous; the second is monstrous.

Among biologists the debate on the possibility of deriving objective ethics based on the evolutionary mode of thought is an unresolved one. In particular, Sir Julian Huxley and C. H. Waddington have proposed such systems; G. G. Simpson and Th. Dobzhansky do not share their belief that human values and wisdom are derivable from the principles of organic evolution. A summary of the various views on the matter may be found in Dobzhansky's book *Mankind Evolving*. Much of what follows is drawn from Dobzhansky and from the writings of Simpson.

It should be clarified that argumentation here is within the naturalistic framework of reference. This framework can be defined by quoting the late American anthropologist, Clyde Kluckhohn: "Philosophers tell us that there have been four main approaches to the problem of value: the Platonic view that values are 'eternal objects,' the position of subjectivism or of radical ethical relativity; the assumption held in common by certain Marxists, logical positivists, and 'linguistic' philosophers that judgments of value are merely 'emotional' or 'verbal' assertions altogether removed from the categories of truth and falsity; the naturalistic approach which holds that values are accessible to the same methods of enquiry and canons of validity applied to all forms of empirical knowledge."

The naturalistic approach is the valid one from the evolutionary viewpoint. Man, in Waddington's phrase, is *the ethical animal*, and the process of ethicizing is a biological adaptation necessary for his welfare. The other approaches seem to be nonadaptive. But the question whether an actual system of ethics is objectively derivable from biological evolution rather than from cultural evolution is still at issue.

A variety of evolutionary criteria have been proposed to provide the objective basis of ethics. They include, with and without attempts at precise definition, increased individual and gene-pool integration, complexity or homeostatic control, maximization of metabolism, minimization of effort, survival (of the species, since no individual ever survived), improvement or progress, however defined, and increased richness of experience. Yet since it is a reasonable assumption that protists lack ethical or moral values, we, with Simpson, must reject all of these as being irrelevant to the only ethics we know, human ethics. These human ethics involve not only the moral ideal of goodness, but the scientific ideal of perfect knowledge, the aesthetic ideal of beauty, and even the economic ideal of abundance, only the last of which can possibly be located in prehuman biological history.

This is not to say that ethics is solely a cultural phenomenon. There is a feedback between biology and culture, as has been already pointed out on several occasions, so the ethical beliefs have evolutionary consequences, just as ongoing human evolution has ethical sequelae. Indeed, ethical systems must undergo evolution themselves if they are to function. The new theological thought realizes it. Among Roman Catholics, Teilhard de Chardin, in a mystical and profoundly unscientific way, has seen the relevance of evolution to man's ideals and aspirations. Among Protestant theologians, the Lutheran Philip Hefner has recently discussed the new doctrine of man which emphasizes the two aspects of evolution that have been stressed in this book: change and diversity. The first refers to the historical dimension of man's biological existence, a dimension that has not been abolished, even if cultural evolution is now the more rapidly operating force. The emphasis on diversity abandons the view of man having been created after an archetypal image. Both ideas would have been totally unacceptable to last century's Christian theology.

Whatever the new ethics of our day are, Hefner calls "attention to the imperative that the life sciences seem to place before man to assume ever more intelligent and responsible control over . . . nature . . . , as well as over his own evolutionary process within it." The fruit of the tree of scientific knowledge that we have now tasted places an obligation on man to exercise his growing powers in distinguishing between good and evil, not as absolutes established by divine sanction, not as characteristics that can be derived from science itself, but as forces operating between people, forces whose meaning man has to define for himself.

The decision-making discussed in the introduction to this book is of an individual and more-or-less trivial sort. The collective decision of what man wants to do with his species is not. The development of an effective and just machinery for collective ethical decision-making has a high priority on mankind's agenda. Only an informed society can accomplish this task. That is why an understanding of genetics, of the new biology, and of the evolutionary outlook are indispensable ingredients in the cultural baggage of every person.

ADDITIONAL READING

There are many books that deal individually with the various issues which have been discussed. The following selected list of paperbacks includes those listed in print in the latest Paperbound Book Guide for Colleges. Most of them call for no more biological knowledge than is provided in this book and many have further bibliographical information.

In addition to the books there are several hundred offprints from the *Scientific American* which are available at 20 cents each from W. H. Freeman and Company, San Francisco. References to many of these are scattered throughout this book. Some of them have been collected into books of readings under the titles: *Psychobiology*, *The Living Cell*, *Thirty-nine Steps to Biology*, *From Cell to Organism*, and *Human Variation and Origins*.

Baker, W. K. *Genetic analysis*. Houghton-Mifflin.
Beadle, G. and M. *The language of life*. Doubleday.
Bonner, D. M. and S. Mills. *Heredity*. Prentice-Hall.
Brewbaker, J. L. *Agricultural genetics*. Prentice-Hall.
Brink, R. A. (ed.) *Heritage from Mendel*. Wisconsin Press.
Cain, A. J. *Animal species and their evolution*. Harper and Row.
Carson, H. L. *Heredity and human life*. Columbia U. Press.
Clark, W. E. LeGros. *Antecedents of man*. Harper and Row.

Darwin, C. *Origin of species*. Atheneum; Collier; New American Library; Washington Square Press.

Dobzhansky, Th. *Evolution, genetics, and man*. Wiley.

Dobzhansky, Th. *Heredity and the nature of man*. New American Library.

Dobzhansky, Th. *Mankind evolving*. Yale U. Press.

Dowdeswell, W. H. *Mechanism of evolution*. Harper and Row.

Dunn, L. C. *Heredity and evolution in human populations*. Atheneum.

Gottlieb, F. *Developmental genetics*. Reinhold.

Grosch, D. *Biological effects of radiations*. Blaisdell.

Haldane, J. B. S. *Causes of evolution*. Cornell U. Press.

Hardin, C. (ed.) *Population, evolution and birth control*. W. H. Freeman and Company.

Hamilton, T. H. *Process and pattern in evolution*. Macmillan.

Hartman, P. E. and S. R. Suskind. *Gene action*. Prentice-Hall.

Herskowitz, I. H. *Basic principles of molecular genetics*. Little, Brown.

Huxley, J. *Evolution: the modern synthesis*. Wiley.

Jinks, J. L. *Extrachromosomal inheritance*. Prentice-Hall.

Kalmus, H. *Genetics*. Doubleday.

Keosian, J. *Origin of life*. Reinhold.

Lack, D. *Darwin's finches*. Harper and Row.

Levine, R. P. *Genetics*. Holt, Rinehart and Winston.

Loewy, A. G. and P. Siekevitz. *Cell structure and function*. Holt, Rinehart and Winston.

Markert, C. *Developmental genetics*. Prentice-Hall.

McKusick, V. A. *Human genetics*. Prentice-Hall.

Moore, J. A. *Heredity and development*. Oxford U. Press.

Ovenden, M. W. *Life in the universe: a scientific discussion*. Doubleday.

Peters, J. A. (ed.) *Classic papers in genetics*. Prentice-Hall.

Rhodes, F. H. T. *Evolution of life*. Penguin.

Simpson, G. G. *Life of the past*. Yale U. Press.

Simpson, G. G. *The meaning of evolution*. Yale U. Press.

Smith, J. M. *Theory of evolution*. Penguin.

Solbrig, O. T. *Evolution and systematics*. Macmillan.

Sonneborn, T. M. *Control of human heredity and evolution*. Macmillan.

Srb, A. M. and B. Wallace. *Adaptation*. Prentice-Hall.

Stebbins, G. L. *Processes of organic evolution*. Prentice-Hall.

Steiner, R. F. and H. Edelhoch. *Molecules and life*. Van Nostrand.

Stern, C. and E. R. Sherwood (eds.) *The origin of genetics: a Mendel source book*. W. H. Freeman and Company.

Swanson, C. P. *Cytogenetics*. Prentice-Hall.

Waddington, C. H. *The nature of life*. Harper and Row.

Wallace, B. *Chromosomes, giant molecules and evolution*. Norton.

Watson, J. D. *Molecular biology of the gene*. Benjamin.

Wilson, G. B. *Cell division and the mitotic cycle*. Reinhold.

Woese, C. R. *The genetic code*. Harper and Row.

CREDITS

Many ideas and some data were presented in the various sections of this book without direct citation of sources. The following listing acknowledges the contributors whose work was so used. Any responsibility for misinterpretation or misrepresentation is mine. The Teacher's Manual for this book has bibliographic references to most of the names and to other sources of information.

1.3   G. W. Beadle, G. G. Simpson
2.4   C. H. Waddington
2.5   B. G. Campbell, B. S. Kraus, D. Mainardi, G. G. Simpson, L. B. Slobodkin
2.6   E. S. Barghoorn and J. W. Schopf, N. H. Horowitz, G. G. Simpson, M. J. D. White
2.7   S.-S. Huang, I. S. Shklovski and C. Sagan
3.1   Th. Dobzhansky, T. S. Kuhn, P. B. Medawar, G. G. Simpson
3.3   B. S. Blumberg
3.5   E. Margoliash, F. Sherman
3.6   R. A. Fisher, G. Wald
4.1   T-Y. Ho, A. Seilacher, S. Wright
4.2   R. B. Cowles, B. Kurten
4.3   M. Scriven
5.1   B. G. Campbell, J. T. Robinson, S. L. Washburn
5.2   Th. Dobzhansky

5.3 S. N. Agarawala, H. Brown, A. Champagnat, G. C. Darwin, K. Davis, P. Ehrlich, B. A. Hamburg, G. Hardin, G. Leach, J. Lederberg, C. Markert, O. E. Nelson *et al*, R. Revelle, W. Schockley

6.1 Sambrook, J. F. *et al*.

6.2 R. S. Edgar and W. B. Wood, E. B. Lewis

6.3 F. R. Babich *et al*., E. H. Davidson *et al*., J. W. Fristrom, A. L. Hartry *et al*., J. T. King and R. W. Briggs, M. Luttges *et al*., F. Rosenblatt *et al*., G. Ungar and L. N. Irwin

6.4 J. D. Cooper, C. Denniston, R. T. Jones *et al*., D. S. Kleinman, C. C. Mabry *et al*., M. Murayama, R. S. Stevenson and C.. C Huntley, C. J. Witkop, Jr.

6.5 H. J. Curtis, S. M. Gershenson, S. Rogers

7.2 V. A. McKusick

7.3 C. Stern

7.4 H. E. Sutton

8.1 W. E. Kerr

8.2 G. Pincus, C. Stern

8.3 H. Grüneberg, V. A. McKusick, L. B. Russell

8.4 M. D. Casey *et al*., E. H. Y. Chu, M. M. Cohen *et al*., A. de la Chapelle *et al*., C. E. Ford, P. A. Jacobs *et al*., L. Moor, H. E. Sutton, H. C. Thuline and D. E. Nordby

8.5 A. W. Edwards, R. G. Edwards, W. D. Hamilton, A. S. Parkes, C. Stern, J. A. Weir

8.6 G. Klein, M. W. Olsen and E. G. Buss

9.2 H. G. Baker, N. E. Morton, J. R. Platt, W. K. Silvers and R. E. Billingham, C. P. Swanson, J. D. Watson

9.3 Th. Dobzhansky, K, Kojima and K. M. Yarbrough, E. Mayr

9.4 H. Laven, R. Sager, T. M. Sonneborn

10.1 K. Pearson

10.3 L. S. Penrose

11.1 M. G. Bulmer, Th. Dobzhansky, H. P. Donald, L. Eisenberg, L. Erlenmeyer-Kimling and L. F. Jarvik, J. Gurdon, A. F. Guttmacher, M. M. Haller, J. Hirsch, R. C. Johnson, H. H. Newman *et al*., N. Pastore, J. Shields, C. Stern, J. S. Thompson and M. W. Thompson

11.2 C. J. Bajema, C. O. Carter, K. Davis, Th. Dobzhansky, B. K. Eckland, K. Hutton and C. Carter, D. M. Johnson, D. Krech and R. S. Crutchfield, L. S. Penrose, E. W. Reed and S. C. Reed, J. N. Spuhler and G. Lindzey

11.3 D. S. Falconer, I. I. Gottesman, L. L. Heston, J. S. Huxley *et al*., D. D. Jackson, F. J. Kallman, E. W. Reed and S. C. Reed

11.4 L. Erlenmeyer-Kimling and W. Paradowski, J. L. Fuller and W. R. Thompson, G. E. McClearn, J. R. Nichols and S. Hsiao, J. P. Scott and J. L. Fuller, W. C. Rothenbuhler, R. Shuter, C. Stern

12.3 Th. Dobzhansky, R. C. Lewontin, J. L. Lush, R. Milkman, J. Price, H. E. Sutton

13.1 W. C. Boyd, F. Fenner, E. R. Nye, J. N. Spuhler, T. E. Reed, C. Stern, F. Vogel and M. R. Chakravartti, T. Watanabe

13.2 J. F. Crow, R. H. Post

14.1 M. S. Al-Aish *et al*., M. Benazzi, L. S. Penrose, O. Smithies, H. E. Sutton

14.2 J. F. Crow, M. Kimura, E. T. Mørch, J. V. Neel, G. Schlager and M. M. Dickie, J. N. Spuhler

14.3 H. Harris and J. F. Watkins, C. B. Kerr, J. D. Watson, M. C. Weiss and H. Green

14.4 C. Auerbach, L. Ehrenberg *et al*., D. Grahn and J. Kratchman, H. Grüneberg, S. Mittler *et al*., A. Novick, R. B. Webb and M. M. Malina

15.1 J. F. Crow and S. Abrahamson

15.2   E. B. Lewis, K. Z. Morgan, J. V. Neel, H. B. Newcombe and J. F. McGregor, W. J. Schull *et al.*, C. H. Waddington, B. Wallace and Th. Dobzhansky

15.3   H. Abplanalp *et al.*, S. I. Alikhanian, B. L. Astaurov, R. D. Brock, Å. Gustafsson, E. F. Knipling, J. Monro, R. E. Scossiroli, Y. Tazima

15.4   F. J. Ayala, J. W. Crenshaw, J. F. Crow and S. Abrahamson, Th. Dobzhansky, L. S. Penrose

16.1   W. C. Boyd, G. de Beer, L. C. Dunn, S. M. Gartler, S. B. Holt, J. V. Neel and W. J. Schull

16.2   W. C. Boyd, M. Smith, S. Yada

16.3   H. F. Blum, Th. Dobzhansky and M. F. H. A. Montagu, W. F. Loomis

16.4   B. Glass and C. C. Li, B. E. Ginsburg and W. S. Laughlin, D. M. Heer, J. Lederberg, T. E. Reed, H. Slatis, C. Stern

17.1   V. A McKusick, A. G. Motulsky

17.2   A. C. Allison and K. G. McWhirter, J. W. Fristrom, G. Hardin, H. Kalmus, V. A. McKusick, C. R. Shaw, G. Skude

17.3   R. J. Berry, C. A. Clarke, G. Dean, V. A. McKusick

17.4   M. Alter, R. C. Juberg, A. G. Motulsky and F. Hecht, S. C. Reed

18.1   W. Bodmer, W. C. Boyd, C. S. Chang *et al.*, H. Levene and R. E. Rosenfield, J. Moor-Jankowski and A. S. Wiener, L. E. Schacht and H. Gershowitz

18.2   P. Parsons, O. Smithies

18.3   R. E. Billingham, G. J. V. Nossal and G. Ada, R. R. Porter, J. D. Watson

19.1   D. F. Aberle, *et al.*, M. Fortes, H. D. F. Kitto, J. Nada, S. C. Reed, L. D. Sanghvi, S. Sugiyama and W. J. Schull, S. L. Washburn and C. S. Lancaster

19.2   L. Beckmann, F. Cooke and F. G. Cooch, H. P. Donald, H. Heidger, E. H. Hess, H. Kalmus, H. Kalmus and S. M. Smith, D. Mainardi, P. O'Donald, M. B. Seiger, W. Sluckin, J. N. Spuhler

19.3   J. W. Eaton and R. J. Weil, B. Glass, V. A. McKusick *et al.*, A .Moroni

19.4   J. B. S. Haldane and S. D. Jayakar, F. S. Hulse, A. P. Mange, E. Matsunaga, S. Rayner

20.1   C. O. Carter, F. H. C. Crick, R. W. Day, L. C. Dunn, J. B. S. Haldane, C. W. Kline

20.2   B. L. Astaurov, R. Bellman, R. G. Edwards, J. Lyman, M. R. Rosenzweig *et al.*, J. M. Tanner

20.3   H. Hoagland, R. S. Morison

21.2   C. H. Waddington

22.1   B. Commoner, J. B. S. Haldane, H. Kahn and A. J. Wiener, J. Lederberg, "Time"

22.2   R. D. Owen *et al.*, O. Smithies *et al.*

22.3   R. L. Ackoff, A. Stander

INDEX

The appearance of a page number in **boldface** type indicates that the term or name is introduced on that page and is one that the student should remember.